Construction Project Management

A Managerial Approach

J F McCarthy

PARETO
PUBLISHING

Construction Project Management – A Managerial Approach

Second Printing 2011

Published by:
Pareto - Building Improvement
1220 Bristol
Westchester, IL 60154

Library of Congress Cataloging in Publication Data

McCarthy, J. F. (Joe F.)
        Construction project management -a managerial approach
        / J.F. McCarthy.
        p. cm.
        Includes index.
        ISBN-13: 978-0-9799969-1-7
        ISBN-10: 0-9799969-1-0

        1. Construction industry--Management. 2. Project
        management.   I. Title.

        HD9715.A2M33 2010
        690'.068
        Library of Congress Control Number 2010936324

Printed in United States of America

Table of Contents

Planning and Initiation

Project Scope Evaluation, Definition, Planning
Finding a feasible and worthwhile project

Costing — Finding Feasible and Needed Costs

Time Planning and Scheduling Integrates with Scope and Cost Planning

Project Delivery Methods and Bidding and "Buying the Job"

Part III

Building The Project 213

Introduction Part III

People - Their nature, Organization and Management

Communication and Documentation are Essential Management Tools

Monitoring and Controlling the Project for Quality and Profit

Risk Management is a Tool that Affects Project Planning and Execution

Project Completion and Closeout — A Key Last Step and a Crucial Next Step

Appendices

Acknowledgements

Academic reviewers of the in process manuscript

David Arditi Professor and Director Construction Engineering and Management Program Department of Civil Architectural and Environmental Engineering, Illinois Institute of Technology Chicago, IL

Salaman Azhar Assistant Professor McWhorter School of Building Science, Auburn University Auburn, Alabama

David L. Bilbo DEd, CPC Clark Endowed Professor of Construction Science Texas A&M University College Station, Texas

Rick W. Cherf Assistant Professor Construction Management College of Engineering Washington State University Pullman, Washington

Academic reviewers of the present text

Salaman Azhar Assistant Professor McWhorter School of Building Science, Auburn University Auburn, Alabama

Craig D. Capano Academic Department Head Civil, Construction and Environment Wentworth Institute of Technology Boston, Massachusetts

Dr. Joseph Dusek Professor and Director Construction Management Department Triton College River Grove, Illinois

Paul E Harmon Associate Professor Construction Management College of Engineering, University of Nebraska Lincoln, Nebraska

Industry and professional reviewers

Robert J. Hannigan CPA Bansley and Kiener LLP Chicago, Illinois
John L. Beata CPA, MST, CVA Beata and Associates Ltd. Hinsdale, Illinois
Robert J. Stolper President R.J. Stolper Insurance Agency Inc. Elmhurst, Illinois
William A Burke R.A. Senior Vice President, Director of Design and Construction CPC New York, New York
Sean Ehlke, Architect Ehlke Lonigro Architects Arlington Heights, Illinois.
Martin Varpa AIA Director of Facility Management Gateway Foundation Chicago, Illinois

Industry contributors

TEC (Carrier) Lansing, Illinois Scott McCollam LEED® AP Territory Manager
Harsco Infrastructure Paramus, New Jersey Cara Baillie
Hayward Baker Odenton, Maryland Marisa H. Schleter
Symons Elk Grove Village, Illinois Mary Callahan

Editorial Credit

Dr. E.J. McCarthy Michigan State University and author of *Basic Marketing a Managerial Approach,* provided substantial editorial assistance that helped shape the text's approach and increase its value to college instructors and students.

Photograph credits

Specific attribution for photographs provided by industry contributors appear in the text.

Richard Lanega Photography provided photographs, including the construction photos of the Wheaton Bible Church, not otherwise attributed in the text.

Permissions granted

AIA New York, New York Cassandra M Brown
Acord Lake Buena Vista, Florida Michael Carroll
AGC Arlington, Virginia Megan McGarvey copyright license number 0179
NCCI Boca Raton, Florida Gregory Quinn

Construction Project Management— a Changing Business

The construction business can and should be managed as well as any other business. The project manager must learn present practices unique to the construction industry to work effectively now. And project managers who recognize the similarities between construction and other businesses can manage more effectively and improve communication with the project owner—a large competitive advantage. This book provides these focused and broad tools and skills—both for the first job and for a career spanning 30–50 years.

Change Is Constant—Adaptability Is Essential

Change is constant and cumulatively profound. A feel for the pace and scope of changes can be seen by the changes that occurred during the author's career (1971 to present):

- Personal computers changed tools from pencil and paper, slide rules, and adding machines to word processing, spreadsheet, estimating, scheduling, document management, accounting, drawing (CAD), and building information modeling (BIM) software programs.

- More advanced business skills became expected from construction firms (MBAs were unheard of in 1971).

- Government regulation increased dramatically—adding agencies such as OSHA (Occupational Safety and Health Administration), the EPA (Environment Protection Agency), and storm water management agencies.

- Construction materials became more sophisticated with higher, but more complex, performance. For example, concrete strength that was formerly expressed in the number of bags of cement per cubic yard of concrete with the usual maximum strength of about 6,000 psi, was increased (with chemicals such as plasticizers) to 60,000 psi.

- Building codes changed from the Uniform Building Code in some areas of the country and regional BOCA (Building Officials Conference of America) codes in other areas to nationwide International Codes—followed by revisions about every 3 years.

- AIA (American Institute of Architects) fixed percentage design service fee rates were ruled unconstitutional, and the resulting lower fees distributed design responsibilities to many parties—including the construction manager and its subcontractors and vendors.

- Microprocessor-controlled building components, patented chemicals, and proprietary products and processes also distributed knowledge and specification control to subcontractors and vendors.

These changes completely changed building technology and construction management systems every 10–15 years. Construction management firms and construction managers who did not change at this pace failed.

Seeing Construction Management in a Broader Context Builds Leaders

Understanding present practices is essential to manage now, but understanding why things are done and how they came to be is necessary to adapt to continual change. To achieve this, the construction manager must understand the construction industry in the context of many other disciplines and businesses. Engineering draws from and adapts, but does not reinvent, chemistry, physics, and geology. Construction management similarly uses operations management, organizational behavior, and communication knowledge and techniques developed in other industries and academic disciplines. This interchange and borrowing is inevitable, beneficial, and can be exploited if recognized.

Construction management can and must draw from the experience of other industries because academic research in the construction industry is sometimes limited, and the best information may come from other industries. Information and illustrations from other industries are used in this text to place construction management in this broad context.

This text seeks to prepare the construction manager for the first job. But also seeks to provide knowledge and skills not just for this first job or for 10 years, but for an entire career. What exists now, how it came to be, and how it works is discussed so the construction manager can both work well now and become a leader.

The Business of Construction Must Be Understood to Manage Projects Well

Construction is a culture with established rules and traditions—some effective and efficient and others founded in traditions that may now need improvement. Understanding what exists now, how it came to be, and how strengths and weaknesses affect outcomes is essential for working in the construction industry.

Construction is also a business, and is run very much like other businesses. There are some unique features in construction, but there are more similarities than differences. Every customer is a business as well, and understanding their business improves communication—which is key for effective project management.

The business and regulatory framework influence all project decisions. All construction personnel—company executives, project managers, and superintendents—must have at least a basic understanding of this framework to operate effectively.

Accounting is a report card of a company's financial performance and capacity that is evaluated by project owners when awarding new projects, by bonding agents to provide bonds, by bankers to provide loans for equipment and also for income tax management and payments.

Finance—the time value of money—affects every contractor and subcontractor using all project delivery methods. The timing of receipts for work completed and of payment of project costs, as well as decisions to lease or buy equipment, affects the hard bid contractor and a service-oriented construction manager. Poor cash flow management—the misalignments of receipts and payments—is a frequent cause of construction firm failure. And this is not just an office activity—field operations (a missed milestone or test report) affect cash flow as well.

Although detailed discussion of construction and real estate finance is beyond the scope of this text, some understanding of these subjects can help the construction manager satisfy the owner's needs while protecting his own interests.

Insurance is desirable and legally and contractually required, but insurance costs are larger than project profit and highly variable. And this vital subject is extremely difficult to learn on the job—many parties have select parts of the knowledge, speak a different language, operate by different rules, and in different time frames.

The basic business understanding provided in this text is a foundation that will put the construction manager in the top 5% of the project team.

Winning the Job and Initiating the Project Starts the Process

All projects must be developed from initial concept through design development to provide instructions and documents needed for construction. Construction managers or general contractors in all project delivery systems—from hard bid to service-oriented construction management firms—are affected by the project development process. But the time and nature of involvement varies.

The hard bid contractors start when the documents are ready to bid and do not participate in early project development. But understanding the development process can assist these contractors select the most viable high-profit projects. If the contractor determines that a project is poorly conceived and poorly coordinated and the owner has limited financial resources, the project may be deemed too risky and avoided. However, if a different owner of this same project had sufficient financial resources, the project might be accepted anticipating many high-profit change orders. Understanding the project development process is like getting a copy of the other team's playbook—a huge competitive advantage.

Construction managers providing a range of services from preconstruction, value engineering, constructability analysis, and construction can add significant value during project development. Early service fees can be obtained, performance and outcomes managed, risk of project execution reduced, and development of a preference for the CM's services that reduces competition gained.

All contractors can benefit from knowledge of the development process—only how and when this information is used differs.

And construction managers also require the skills needed to "get the job": costing and estimating, time planning and scheduling, and bidding and buying the job. Both the theory and practical application are needed and presented by this text.

Building the Project Is a Continuation of Starting the Project

Although some may think that building the project is the "meat" of construction project management, it is really a continuation of all the previous activities. The essential knowledge and skills about people management, scheduling, risk management, communication, and monitoring and control for both quality and cost start in project planning and continue in execution. And project closeout is an essential last step.

Project execution must be seen in the context of construction rules, regulations, business practices, and the purposes and needs of the owner. Understanding construction management in this broader integrated context is the defining characteristic of professional project management and project leadership.

Introduction Part I
The Culture and Business of Construction Must Be Understood to Manage Projects Well

Construction is a culture with established rules and traditions—some effective and efficient, and others founded in traditions that may now need improvement. And tradition has produced roles and responsibilities that are puzzling until explained. Understanding what exists now and how it came to be—including the impact of forces that at first appear remote and unrelated—is essential.

Construction is a business, and must follow most of the same rules and regulations as any other business, and this business framework influences all project decisions. All construction personnel—company executives, project managers, and superintendents—must have at least a basic understanding of this framework to operate effectively. Every customer is a business as well, and understanding their business improves communication—which is key for effective project management.

Accounting is a report card of a company's financial performance and capacity that is evaluated by project owners when awarding new projects, by bonding agents to provide bonds, by bankers to provide loans for equipment, and also for income tax management and payments. And (financial) accounting in the office has different rules and time frames than compared with (job cost) accounting, which can produce misunderstandings and office–field conflicts if not explained. Every one in the construction firm plays a role in maintaining the best accounting picture. For example, field personnel's timing and method of equipment acquisition affects the balance sheet and income statement.

Finance—the time value of money—affects every contractor and subcontractor using every project delivery method. The timing of receipts for work completed and of payment of project costs, as well as decisions to lease or buy equipment, affects both the hard bid contractor and a service-oriented construction manager. Poor cash flow management—the misalignments of receipts and payments—is a frequent cause of construction firm failure. And this is not just an office activity—field operations (a missed milestone or test report) affect cash flow as well.

Although detailed discussion of construction project and real estate finance is beyond the scope of this text, some understanding of these subjects can help the construction manager satisfy the owner's needs while protecting his own interests.

Insurance is desirable and legally and contractually required, but insurance costs are larger than project profit and highly variable. And this vital subject is extremely difficult to learn on the job—many parties have select parts of the knowledge, speak a different language, and operate by different rules and in different time frames. The impact of insurance costs makes safe operations critical for the firm's survival.

Laws, regulations, codes, and standards conformance is the responsibility of both all: attorneys, architects, and engineers and those executing the work—project managers, project engineers, and superintendents. Laws and regulations affect relations between the parties including payment and dispute resolution. And codes and standards affect what can be built and how it can be built. And some idea of history and theory is needed to adapt to continual change.

The basic business understanding provided in this text is a foundation that will put the construction manager in the top 5% of the project team.

CHAPTER
1.1

The Personnel and Companies Required for Construction Projects

Concrete form work (a concrete cost line item) and access scaffolding (a general condition cost line item) must be planned together for maximum productivity and safety. STUDFORM® and JUMPFORM concrete wall form work along with 20K® shoring towers were supported by custom-designed support frames for construction of the air traffic control tower at Washington Dulles Airport, VA. *Photo courtesy of Harsco Infrastructure.*

The Personnel and Companies Required for Construction Projects

A simple organization chart cannot show the real and best type and timing of parties' contributions

The parties who assist and support builders' efforts are discussed in this chapter. The division of responsibility among these parties is shaped by customs, laws and regulations, and training. A surprising number of parties and sometimes puzzling specializations result.

This list is intended to guide recognition of the strengths, weaknesses, preferences, and capabilities of parties to structure optimal project delivery methods. Some types of buildings will never use all these players, and smaller firms may combine specialties. But larger firms performing more sophisticated work will require additional specialized parties.

This short narrative cannot do justice to any one specialty—each specialty represents a profession, business, and career. But this abbreviated construction industry analysis describes realties to assist construction project management—to select project delivery systems realistically.

Construction Represents about 10% of the U.S. Economy

The construction industry represents a large portion of the U.S. economy—about 10% as described below. And this only counts those directly involved with the building process and does not include designers, material suppliers, finance companies, and regulatory and testing agencies.

The value of all sales by all companies in the country is called the gross domestic product (GDP) and is calculated quarterly by the U.S. Department of Commerce's Bureau of Economic Analysis. The methods of calculation and reliability of the GDP figures are widely accepted.

The value of sales by construction companies is calculated by the U.S. Census Bureau and requires careful definition to produce understandable and believable figures. The U.S. Constitution requires the Census Bureau to do an actual count of the entire population every 10 years to determine each state's number of representatives in the U.S. House of Representatives. The census of economic data is similarly done at a slower pace—with annual estimates subject to revisions, so the finalized data may be 2 years old.

The U.S. Census Bureau for 2007 (released March 17, 2009—the most recent finalized data) found the annual construction put in place in 2007 by NAISC (North American Industry Standard Classification System) category codes was:

NAICS Code	Meaning of NAICS Code	Sales, Shipments, Receipts, Revenues, and Business Done ($1,000)
236	Construction of buildings	$701,719,130
237	Heavy and civil construction	$287,793,774
	Subtotal	$989,512,904

But also lists:

238	Specialty trade contractors	$792,265,781

Specialty trade contractors may work directly for the project owner that would then constitute additional construction sales or may work as a subcontractor. Since general contractors or construction managers would count their sales including subcontractor amounts, inclusion of the full specialty trade contractor sales in the construction total could result in a double counting—but how much is unknown.

And some companies not classified as construction companies may self-perform construction work:

312	Support activities for mining	$ 56,978,557
221	Utilities	$581,553,952
444	Building material and garden equipment and supplies dealers	$323,227,611
531	Real estate	$344,548,019

It is certain that some of these companies self-perform some construction, but the construction portion of their sales volume is unknown. Attempts to prorate the last five NAICS codes listed above can produce highly variable estimates of annual construction volume in the United States.

High and low order of magnitude estimates of construction volume and percentages of GDP of $13,795,600,000,000 for the first quarter of 2007 are:

Construction Sales/GDP		
236, 237	Building and heavy	7.2%
236, 237, 238	Building, heavy, specialty	12.9%

For the purposes of the professional construction managers, the owner's self-performed work may be disregarded. So an order of magnitude estimate of U.S. construction sales of about 10% of GDP is a reasonable approximation.

The breakdown of construction volumes (in $1,000,000s) by project type also for 2007 is:

Value of Private Construction Put in Place 2007

Type of Construction	Cost
New single family	$305,184
New multifamily	$48,209
Residential Improvements	$139,106
Lodging	$27,503
Office	$53,377
Commercial	$84,999
Automotive	$6,373
Food/beverage	$7,929
Multiretail	$34,249
Other commercial	$12,799
Warehouse	$16,368
Healthcare	$34,776
Educational	$17,071
Religious	$7,429
Public safety	$495
Amusement and recreation	$10,352
Transportation	$9,444
Communication	$26,947
Power	$41,481
Sewage and waste disposal	$383
Water supply	$460
Manufacturing	$42,229
Subtotal	$927,163

Value of State and Local Government Construction Put in Place 2007

Type of Construction		Cost
Residential		$5,092
Multifamily		$4,500
Office		$7,112
Commercial		$1,744
Health care		$6,975
Educational		$77,604
Public Safety		$8,429
Amusement and recreation		$11,015
Transportation		$21,197
Power		$11,411
Highway and street		$74,779
Sewage and waste disposal		$23,123
Water supply		$14,880
Conservation and development		$2,179
	Subtotal	$270,040
	Total	$1,197,203

Design: Architects and Engineers Have a Legally Required Project Role

Credentialed professionals complete a specified 4 to 6-year college education and pass an examination developed by their professional organization, such as the American Institute of Architects, and approved by the government licensing agency granting the credential. Professionals also establish and enforce their own industry wide ethics and practice standards. A professional license is granted by each state, with mechanisms for interstate transferability.

Use of credentialed professionals for design services is customary—and legally required for some building tasks.

These designers are concerned with the building concept, layout, and artistic features

Building programming (transforming the owner's needs and preferences into a building concept), planning, functional layout, artistic features, and integration of structural, civil, mechanical, and electrical work performed by others are performed by building designers, as explained below.

Architects once (up to the middle of the 20th century) designed all building components, including mechanical and electrical, and performed site supervision and project administration. This diverse responsibility is now usually found only on single-family homes. Architects now focus on the design and employ outside consultants for all other tasks such as civil, structural, and mechanical electrical design. Administrative management is found on a small and decreasing portion of projects. The services of an architect are legally required for most commercial buildings, but for only some residential, industrial, and civil projects.

Interior designers at one time focused on colors and finish materials but now design lighting and plan space layouts for interior renovation projects. Although the interior design credential is seldom legally mandated, substitution for an architect's credential for some commercial interior and residential projects is permitted in some states. (An interior designer is distinct from an interior decorator who is not credentialed and typically still focuses on colors, finish materials, and furniture.)

Landscape architects can design the plantings for a building designed by an architect. The landscape architect can also work independently and design entire regional parkway systems, including roads, significant land reshaping, streams, ponds, and related accessory buildings. (The design of the building itself may still require design by an architect.)

Engineers Lay Out, Calculate, and Specify Building Systems and Components
Engineers may be consultants to architects, or lead project designers

Architects establish floor plans and the requirements for a building. Engineers, as consultants to the architects, perform the calculation, sizing, and equipment specification for exterior pavement and storm water drainage, and mechanical electrical systems. For nonbuilding projects such as roads, locks and dams, and refineries, engineers assume the lead design role and architects, if needed, will be a consultant to the engineer.

Civil engineers are concerned with slopes, grades, and structures
Civil engineering is typically a single university department and credential, but the practice is diversified and specialized. Civil engineers could, but seldom, perform all types of civil work. (Structural engineering is an exception and frequently has a specialized credential.)

Civil engineers for land development and roads focus on soils, paving materials, drainage piping and structures, optimal slopes and grades for erosion control, and vehicle and pedestrian circulation. Their work includes extensive surveying to determine the initial conditions, the conditions of the work in progress, and certification that the design contours have been achieved. Land development work can also involve ongoing and extensive interaction with government agencies.

Civil environmental engineers add a focus on environmentally undesirable chemical containment with pond liners and landfill caps, drainage structures, and permeabilities of the soil, which requires a slightly different focus and some additional knowledge.

Structural engineers for permanent buildings perform the structural design for all but the simplest structures. (Architect credentials frequently permit structural design, but in practice, architects' structural design is usually limited to wood-framed single-family residential and some light commercial.) Structural engineers design the buildings in their completed form. Design of structural measures needed to maintain the safety and stability of the building in its partially completed form, "the construction means and methods," is the responsibility of the installing contractor. This temporary stability control is a critical project management task.

Structural engineers for temporary measures and construction, such as foundations for tower cranes, earth retention systems, and temporary structures, such as scaffolding, perform a specialized subset of structural engineering. These specialists are comfortable with incomplete and moving structures and can provide the needed design to the CM or their subcontractors. These engineers are rare and in demand, so adequate lead time must be scheduled.

Mechanical engineers are concerned with flow and heat transfer of fluids and gases
Mechanical engineers design the heating, air-conditioning, ventilating, and refrigeration systems for all commercial/industrial buildings. These design engineers may be on the staff of a consulting engineering firm or increasingly on the staff of the installing HVAC contractor. The architect frequently designs the plumbing (the provision, circulation, and waste removal of potable water systems) engineering for residential and light commercial projects. (Water lines can be sized with tables, and code-required minimum waste pipe sizes exceed the size needed for projects of this scope.) Consulting engineers design plumbing systems for larger buildings.

Process piping, fire protection systems, and control engineering may be provided by consulting engineers, engineers on staff of the installing contractor, or for some components, large supply vendors. The design needs of smaller projects may be insignificant—gas piping to a single HVAC rooftop unit or hot-water heater, or a single thermostat—and are usually handled by rules of thumb, charts and tables. But this "experience" will be grossly inadequate for a manufacturing facility with multiple process chemicals, some of which are flammable or explosive.

Similarly, fire protection for small projects can be adequately handled by the fire protection contractors' staff, and is typically not designed by a consulting engineer. However, more complex buildings with very different occupancy types, such as a convention center with hotels, meeting rooms, restaurants, and retail with high atriums, require consulting engineering.

Electrical engineers are concerned with power and light, and sometimes telecommunication

A single consulting engineer usually designs the power and lighting for commercial buildings. A specialized engineer usually designs projects that are primarily or exclusively power, such as power-generating plants and related distribution networks.

Design responsibility of the telecommunication infrastructure is confused, inconsistent, and frequently produces mediocre or poor results. Vendors, contractors, and consulting engineers may all execute portions of the design with little leadership and insufficient coordination.

These Designers Need and Seek Technical Assistance
Specialty consultants can add depth and precision but can also change scope and add cost and time

Specialty consultants provide highly specific knowledge and skills that can confirm, alter, or substantially influence project design. If this input is not completed at the required time, needed changes can be significant and cost and schedule control may be compromised or lost. These consultants can be, but usually do not have to be, professionally credentialed.

Traffic consultants are first concerned with safe and efficient flow of traffic, but they can also seek to optimize the desired result of this traffic, such as traffic speeds that promote patronage of retail establishments. In the reverse, the anticipated additional traffic flow generated by a new development can be calculated. This calculation can be used to demand that the developer make improvements, such as new public roads, at their expense—to accommodate this new traffic.

Retail consultants advise on the number, type, size, and location of stores in a large retail center, as well as desirable center amenities. Since what is thought to be "hot" in retail changes, late project scope changes might result.

IT (information technology) consultants specify the types of equipment needed in that location and configuration and distribution networks. Signal strength degrades with the distance of distribution, so planning of data rooms, and the distribution networks must be included in early project planning. Cooling, fire protection, and emergency or critical power requirements for equipment must be included early in mechanical electrical design. If a significant battery backup system is required, structural accommodation must be included in project planning as well.

Security consultants are used when security from multiple perils is a great concern—retail theft, criminal trespass, industrial espionage, and telecommunications breaches. Solutions to these concerns can include both surveillance and access control but can also alter floor plan layouts and site improvement features.

Specific consultants for churches, theaters, golf courses, zoos, swimming pools, commercial kitchens, and manufacturing facilities can provide advice and critiques of plans and process, substantial design input, or full design. The timing and results of this consulting input can challenge the scope, time, and cost.

Lighting, elevator, and acoustic consultants are seldom used on smaller projects but can provide essential advice for larger or more complex projects. A power and light consulting engineer may design functional light levels but may not optimize the light qualities critical for sports facilities or museums.

Elevators for highly variable occupancy loads may benefit from more careful consulting analysis. And acoustical consultants are essential when rigorous acoustical performance is essential, such as concert halls or auditoriums.

Testing and analysis firms provide needed information to designers and builders

Surveyor is a professional engineer who works for the development, building, and design communities. (The consulting civil engineers described above may also be registered surveyors but perform surveying work only in conjunction with their own designs.) The surveyor establishes boundaries and grades at the time of property acquisition and start of development activities. This activity involves analysis of property legal descriptions and determination of monuments distant from the site. The builders should not attempt this activity. (The builder lays out the building—line and grade work—using the monuments the surveyor established.) Surveyor's confirmation of as-built lines and grades is frequently legally required.

Geotechnical engineers are civil engineers, frequently with a supplemental geology background. Geotechnical engineers will perform soil borings, analyze soil and water condition, and determine a required drainage system, if any, and the allowable bearing capacity of the soil. The structural engineer will then use this information to design the foundation. Testing and analysis of uncertain soil conditions encountered during construction is also common.

Environmental engineers—in the building business—usually refer to those who do the testing and analysis of structures and materials to determine the presence and needed removal of environmentally objectionable materials. Such testing, presently called phase I (determination if environmentally hazardous material probably exist) and phase II (confirmation of existence and guidelines for remediation), is required for sale, financing, and demolition of commercial–industrial properties. (In manufacturing, environmental engineers monitor and analyze environmental conditions that affect the health and safety of the occupants.)

Independent testing laboratories test and analyze construction materials in accordance with established, usually ASTM, standards. Concrete cylinder breaks (to determine the specified concrete strength achieved), testing of welds, plastic compositions, and fluid discharges are common uses.

Utility Companies Have Monopolies and Can Impact Cost and Schedule

Unavoidable and difficult to control—proper scheduling must be included

The utilities required for a project usually are:

Water and sanitary sewer are typically provided by the municipality. Although the capabilities and attitudes vary by city, the decision makers are available, so sewer and water connections are seldom a schedule problem if started sufficiently early. However, the cost of impact fees for connection varies hugely, over 10,000%, by municipality, which can impact cost planning.

Storm water management connections are also typically handled first by the municipality, but the permitting and fees may be by the regional storm water management agency. This regional agency can require substantial engineering, review, and permitting, which can have both a significant cost and a schedule impact.

Natural gas service is typically provided by an area-wide utility monopoly. The connection application and engineering can range from a neighborly chat at the front desk to an administrative bureaucratic mess that lasts a year. Each district will have a personality and a reputation. Connection to locally available infrastructure is usually free, and there are usually no impact fees. Projects requiring natural gas service where no local delivery infrastructure exists may be required to contribute to the cost of the infrastructure installation.

Electrical service area-wide distribution is provided by an area-wide utility company (a monopoly), but local distribution is provided either by the utility company or by the city. Electrical service installation encounters the same range of cost service and schedule difficulties described for water and gas above.

Telecommunications area-wide distribution is also provided by a utility monopoly. Installation requires nominal charges but no impact fees. Installation time can range from a few weeks, if infrastructure exists in the area, to 6–24 months.

Other impact fees, such as curb cuts, or general fees for unspecified reasons may also have a cost impact for the fees and the schedule impact for the review process necessary to determine the fees.

(It should also be noted that it is becoming increasingly common for utility services to involve a reseller for natural gas, electrical power, and telecommunications. This may impact the owners' contractual relationship for the completed building but does not alter the CM's relationship with utility companies described above.)

Associations Influence Standards and Industry Practices and Players
An indirect but powerful effect

Associations have a lobbying, industry promotion, and networking function but may also set standards and provide the best or only source for technical information and model construction contracts. Use of this information and these contracts is voluntary, but the superior product quality and widespread— sometimes nearly universal—use of the output of these organizations make them an important force.

Design associations establish model contracts for designer led project delivery

The *AIA* (American Institute of Architects) provides model contract suites (integrated documents for owner–architect, owner–contractor, and contractor–subcontractor, including change order and start-up and closeout documents). These documents view the architect as the project delivery central authority and driving force. The AIA also establishes standards of professional conduct and lobbies for the interests of the profession.

The *ASCE* (American Society of Civil Engineers) acts in the same manner as the AIA but is a smaller and less publicly prominent organization.

Construction associations establish model contracts for integrated project delivery

The *AGC (*Association of General Contractors) provides model contract suites that provide the same function as the AIA suites but places the general contractors as the project delivery central authority and driving force. These contract suites have recognized and used integrated project delivery for decades, but the AIA model contracts are only now attempting this integration. The AGC represents unionized contractors in union labor contract negotiations and lobbies for the maintenance of the unionized workplace such as maintenance of Davis–Bacon prevailing wage requirements. The AGC performs some management training, but the union performs craft training. In some areas of the country, the AGC membership includes both union and nonunion construction management firms.

The *ABC* (Associated Builders and Contractors) is similar to the AGC but represents exclusively nonunion (open shop, merit shop, right to work) contractors. The ABC provides craft and has recently started management training.

CMAA (Construction Management Association of America) provides standards of practice for the construction management delivery system and offers training and certification for construction managers.

The *Design Build Institute* promotes model contracts and lobbies for and promotes the design build process.

NAHB (National Association of Home Builders) is a large and powerful lobbying group promoting the interests of the home building industry. The organization also provides real estate sales brokerage and technical and educational assistance.

AIC (American Institute of Constructors) promotes industry standards, training, and certification. Constructor certification is valued in some areas of the country and unknown in others.

CII (Construction Industry Institute) seeks to improve the safety, productivity, information flow, project delivery methods, and other "best practices" of the construction industry. It is an academic institution–industry partnership that seeks methods of improvement and disseminates their findings to industry members.

Standard setting bodies may be the best or only source for some information
Incorporation by specification reference may be as powerful as the specifications themselves

CSI (Construction Specification Institute) provides three functions. (1) The master format system, which establishes an accepted organizational structure for the work breakdown structure. This structure is nearly universally accepted and recognized throughout the commercial building industry. (2) The CSI also has a similar organization format for the layering of CAD drawings. (3) The CSI supports the efforts of construction specifiers.

PMI (Project Management Institute) establishes a very detailed organizational format and processes for project management in general—with a heavy emphasis in the information technology industry. There is a supplement for the construction industry, but PMI deals only with organization and processes and strictly avoids any technical information or industry-specific conditions. Although the PMI project management system provides significant benefits, acceptance by the construction industry has been limited.

ASTM (American Society of Testing Materials) establishes detailed material testing procedures and protocols but does not perform the tests. ASTM test numbers may be referenced on the drawings and specification, but a new or untried material must be tested. These test standards only require the daily attention of the construction manager when ongoing field or laboratory testing is needed, or untested materials are used.

ANSI (American National Standards Institute) establishes product standards similar to the ASTM testing standards. Some ANSI standards are short and dry technical specifications, but others such as "Providing Accessibility and Usability for Physically Handicapped People" are an excellent guide that became the standard of the industry and was adopted by reference into building codes.

USGBC (U.S. Green Building Council) establishes product standards and educational materials related to "Green Buildings." It is also involved with LEED (Leadership in Energy and Environmental Design) certification of buildings.

ACI (American Concrete Institute) provides technical standards for the complete concrete installation, including form work, reinforcing, curing, and related chemicals. These standards are highly detailed and address many unusual special conditions, such as when a possibly deficient condition can be considered conforming. Documents are detailed and highly demanding so will be only used on larger projects with more sophisticated personnel.

AISC (American Institute of Steel Construction) provides detailed technical standards for structural steel fabrication and erection. This information is considered authoritative standards and is frequently included in architects' and engineers' specification without alteration.

American Iron and Steel Institute promotes the interest of the steel industries and produces technical material such as load tables for light-gauge steel framing, which are essential for design. The information in these tables is found nowhere else.

AWI (Architectural Woodwork Institute) publishes the material, fabrication, and installation design standards that govern the cabinet and woodworking industry. Specifications may reference these standards but seldom provide any useful additional information.

USG (U.S. Gypsum) promotes correct use of USG products but also defines installation standards that govern the drywall and plaster finishing industry—similar to the AWI standards for millwork.

NFPA (National Fire Protection Association) wears many hats. It produces the National Electric Code but also produces installation standards for fire protection and fire alarm installations. This combination of codes and installation standards by single organization is unique.

The installation standards are necessary and highly useful for construction installations. At one time, the standards were readable and were understood by design professionals and installing tradesman, but have suffered from bureaucratic bloat in recent years that compromises usefulness.

ISO (International Organization for Standardization) establishes standards and certification protocols for company-wide management capabilities. Management structure, quality control capabilities, and documentation of continuous feedback, control, and process improvement are assessed. ISO certification of products is required for some products in some industries—which requires purchasing the material and components for these products from ISO certified facilities. Certification of construction project sites is not sought.

SMACNA (Sheet Metal and Air Conditioning Contractors' National Association) provides technical standards and installation details for sheet metal. The standards are geared toward the practical needs of fabricating and installing firms. These are the most complete, useful, and authoritative sheet metal standards and are frequently referenced and incorporated into the architects' and engineers' specifications.

MCA (Mechanical Contractors Association), among other functions, provides very detailed cost-estimating data that can be used as the basis of contract cost negotiation and resolution for fast-track construction management projects. This level of detail of high-quality mechanical cost information is unique.

ASHRE (American Society of Heating and Refrigeration Engineers) documents uniquely combine the standards of acceptable levels of human comfort, engineering values, and standards for calculation, as well as accepted industry practices. This information is the essential source of record for design engineers and installing contractors.

IES (Illuminating Engineering Society of North America) provides lightning information similar in character and use to the ASHRE for heating and air-conditioning. Highly technical documents are provided for sophisticated professionals and more accessible documents for construction managers.

Other Sources of Guidance and Essential Technical Support

The *Asphalt Institute, Portland Cement Association, Masonry Institute, National Association of Roofing Contractors, and* principal HVAC equipment vendors all provide highly detailed and widely recognized standards, installation details, and, in some cases, free consulting. The standards and publications of these industries are intended to promote their industry and products but are also recognized as frequently the best, and sometimes the sole source, of definitive product information.

Testing agencies

UL (Underwriters Laboratories) is a recognized independent testing laboratory that reviews and establishes fire rating standards for construction assemblies that utilize products from multiple manufacturers—such as an entire wall section. Once established and published, the standard remains valid for decades. UL design numbers are frequently found in specifications, and detailed information about these tested assemblies can be obtained from UL publications. Single proprietary products can be tested and a UL certification label attached, but this process can take months or years, so is seldom done for a construction project. UL-certified fabricators may certify products and apply UL labels in their own facility. Warnock Hersey is a certifying organization for wood doors.

Other independent testing laboratories can also perform similar tests that provide certifications of conformance but do not fix labels to the product. Common uses include concrete cylinder breaks to confirm strength, and fluid tests to confirm purity.

Summary

The construction industry represents about 10% of the entire U.S. economy. The surprising number of different types of construction project players segregate by knowledge possessed, work performed, project type and size, capacity for analysis and communication, and project delivery methods favored.

This reality must be recognized when evaluating and selecting project delivery methods and must also be included in project planning. Recognition of the realities of the construction industry, and the nature and preferences and capability of the firms and their personnel, is essential to achieve the triple constraint of scope, cost, and schedule.

Review Questions (True or False)

1. The contract values of the designer, construction managers, subcontractors, material suppliers, finance companies, and testing agencies together equals about 10% of U.S. economy.
2. The architect, who is a credentialed design professional, is legally required to provide the planning, functional layout, artistic features, and integration of structural, mechanical, and electrical work for most commercial projects.
3. Interior designers always perform work under the direct supervision of a registered architect.
4. One civil engineer is typically involved with all the disciplines of land development, environmental and structural engineering.
5. Mechanical engineers are concerned with the flow and heat transfer of fluids and gases, and electrical engineers are concerned with power and light and sometimes telecommunication.
6. Engineers may legally design some industrial buildings without the input of a registered architect. The architect can, but does not have to, perform work as a consultant to the engineer.
7. Additional consultants such as retail, IT, security, elevator, and acoustical may work for the architect or the project owner.
8. Utility companies have an obligation for public service and must perform at the time the construction manager requires.
9. Some associations developed model contracts that have become accepted industry standards.
10. Standard setting bodies can be the best or only source for technical specification and design guidance for some products or systems.
11. Testing agencies such as UL must be employed to test materials on site for each project.

Test Your Understanding

1. Visit a small construction project in your area, even if only viewed from the curb, and identify and count the probable parties involved, even infrequently and remotely. Include consideration of:
Government agencies
Utility companies
Architects
Engineers
Landscape architects
Specialty consultants
Testing and surveying companies

2. For an elevator installation in a commercial building, identify and list the number of parties affecting or performing the design, installation, and quality review. Draw from the list above but also consider water removal from the elevator pit, structural support for the elevator rails and machine, architectural enclosure of the shaft, and ventilation, power, and control wiring.

3. What are the levels of education and types of credentials required for the following?
   Architects
   Civil engineers
   Structural engineers
   Registered surveyors

CHAPTER
1.2

The Builders: Construction Managers, General Contractors, Subcontractors, and Vendors

The Max-A-Form® forming system can support concrete loads over long spans without supplemental shoring. It can be used for gang-forming walls, large columns, and bridge piers. Large productivity increases over hand forming are possible, but needed workroom must be available and required hoisting equipment planned. *Photo courtesy: Symons.*

The Builders: Construction Managers, General Contractors, Subcontractors, and Vendors

Required skills and capabilities, regulations, and customs produce specialization

Last chapter discussed all parties needed for a project, and this chapter refines the focus on the parties who build or who supply and support builders. The division of responsibility and knowledge, strengths, weaknesses, preferences, and capabilities of parties is again discussed to structure optimal work packages by assigning tasks to the most capable parties and avoiding expectation or demands for performances from the unwilling or incapable.

Construction Managers Specialize by Project Type and Delivery System

Construction firms specialize by residential, commercial, industrial, and heavy and highway construction

The construction industry is segregated into types of work performed. Skills, temperament, and financial capacity tend to keep firms and individuals focused on certain project types. Industry, the media, and governments also maintain statistics with these subdivisions. These established categories are listed below.

Residential construction is divided into three categories. (1) A *developer* owns and improves (clearing and land grading, and installation of sewers, water, and roads) raw land and later constructs homes—typically with repetitive designs. Land ownership and marketing are the focus, and construction is a secondary priority. (2) *Home builders* may own land or build on land owned by others. Sales, design, and construction are balanced priorities. (3) *Home improvement, remodeling, and repair* consist of kitchens and bathrooms, additions, reroofing, flooring and decorating, and decks. Firms in the underground cash economy, as well as owner's self-performing work, make measurement of the size of this segment difficult.

Commercial construction includes all nonresidential buildings for the primary purpose of human occupancy—offices, retail, some industrial, schools, hospitals, and churches. Smaller firms who prefer to work locally may seek and perform multiple project types. Construction for retail chains typically requires national coverage. Owner demands for specific project experience generally force firms to specialize in a few project types.

Industrial construction includes buildings whose primary purpose is manufacturing, chemical processing, food processing, and refineries. Large specialized firms perform this work.

Heavy and highway consists of roads, bridges, locks and dams, and sewage treatment plants. This is most frequently, but not exclusively, publicly bid work requiring an established track record and appropriate bonding capabilities.

Project construction management leadership differs by owner, industry, and project size and type

The terms *general contractor* and *construction manager* describe project leaders but are used loosely without consistently accepted definition. In the early 20th century, a high-rise building might be constructed with an electrical, piping, and general contractor. The general contractor performed all work that was not piping or electrical with his own trade forces—so the term *general* had clear meaning. Specialization and the increased number of required subcontractors evolved to the point where some "paper generals" employ no trade labor, besides a few cleanup laborers.

At the same time, increasing need for preconstruction consulting on constructability, cost, schedule, and materials and methods added new management tasks, which increased the amount of communication, analysis, and documentation in the construction process. Not all project delivery systems benefit from this increased communication, and not all construction personnel are capable of providing it. So, the degree of open communication and knowledge and analysis separate general contractors from construction managers. Construction mangers analyze and communicate more.

General contractors bid and perform work in the public sector and for project type where sufficient initial project definition for the owner's purposes is possible and ease of administration is sought, such as multifamily residential. In the middle are "paper generals" who get and show three bids to the owner but are incapable of providing any analytical depth of knowledge. Construction managers can provide this depth of knowledge with early constructability, cost, and schedule input into the design that carries through to project execution. This is a simplified continuum that varies principally by any amount of management skill and sophistication of communication sought and provided for the project. Some, but not all, firms can effectively perform as a general contractor and as the construction manager.

One other type of construction manager is really a paperwork processing and public relations shield for large public owners. For projects such as roads, a construction manger can process the massive amounts of testing and payment documentation required. The construction manager is also the owner's spokesperson for public relations difficulties about accidents or cost or schedule over-runs, shielding owner's personnel from adverse notice. These "construction mangers" manage paperwork and public relations but not projects.

Project management firms, who are not at risk, have no authority, and perform no trade work, have emerged as advisers to an owner. This additional layer of management over the construction manager or general contractor begins to introduce a matrix management structure with dual—to the PM firm and to the owner—lines of reporting and responsibility. The potential to subtract value and slow the process is clear, but the benefits are not.

Owner's agent (sometimes called owner's rep) is similar in authority and responsibility to the project management firm but focuses more on prequalifications, contracts, change orders, insurance, pay requests, and meticulous documentation. Again a matrix structure is introduced, which confuses lines of authority and slows communication.

The Builders' Office and Field Staff Divide Project Responsibilities

Larger construction firms typically have staff primarily in the home office and staff almost exclusively at project locations. Very large projects may temporarily shift some office staff to the project location, and very small projects may require the office and field staff to assume multiple duties and float between multiple locations. Although office staff frequently have college or graduate education and field staff usually have trade training, this is not a division of brains and brawn—knowledge and management skills are needed and found throughout the organization.

Office staff are concerned with cost estimating, scheduling, purchasing, contracts, and insurance

Project executives, sometimes called the officers in charge, must have a strategic view of the firm's work volume and new or diminishing sales prospects for multiple industries and project types. Project executives will also oversee specific project manager's performance but perform little or no project-specific work. Public relations and sales functions are also important tasks.

Project managers are responsible for developing and executing the project in accordance with the triple constraint of scope, cost, and time. This includes preconstruction consulting, solicitation, analysis, and award of proposals from principal subcontractors and vendors, and developing and maintaining budgets and schedules. Administrative duties include permissions, pay requests processing, insurance, and ensuring that necessary job site controls and facilities are adequately planned and maintained.

Project engineers are responsible for securing, processing, and reviewing technical documents, such as shop drawings, test documentation, and processing and reviewing requests for information or requests for changes. Feedback and control to monitor job site productivity and schedule maintenance are also required. The output of their job is technical in nature, but extensive administrative work and documentation are required.

Estimators perform cost estimates for both initial project scope and changes. For small and midsize projects, the project manager is also the estimator. Project managers estimate projects until one is won and then proceed to manage it. For very large projects that involve significant on-site investigation, the estimator must be dedicated solely to new projects estimating. Civil projects may require the estimators' time at the proposed project location for weeks or months to determine soil and water conditions, evaluate principal subcontractors and vendors, and assess local customs and practices and economic conditions.

Scheduling and purchasing are also combined with project managers' responsibilities on small and midsize projects. Larger projects that demand and support extensive scheduling activities can afford highly skilled scheduling specialists. Larger firms that require more internal controls may find addition of purchasing agents beneficial.

Field staff are concerned with trade labor, materials, and equipment

General (project) superintendents manage men, material, and equipment to execute the planned project, but the job is far larger than just following instructions. Advice or even selection of significant equipment such as tower cranes, personnel hoists, and construction means and methods, such as type of concrete forming, are significant superintendent decisions affecting productivity and schedule. The superintendent must ensure that reporting of trade hours worked is accurate (the first step in cost accounting and control). And the superintendent's tone and management style can have significant impact as well. Superintendent is a defined term and requirement in most model contracts.

Other superintendents, assistants, and discipline. Larger projects will have multiple superintendents reporting to the general superintendent, which may also be supplemented by assistant superintendents. A project involving multiple buildings on one project site may have a superintendent assigned to each building. Or, superintendents may be assigned by discipline such as mechanical, electrical, site development, large commercial kitchen, or concrete.

General foremen supervise sublayers of foreman, who supervises trade labor. Supervision to obtain the required levels of productivity and quality is the focus. Management of tools, equipment, safety, and records of expended material and labor is also required.

Layout sometimes called *field engineering* works from the control lines established by the surveyor to establish control lines and grades for columns, walls, and floors. As construction continues, these controls will be reestablished on every floor. Then, control lines for following trades such as interior walls, shafts, and curtain walls will be established. This layout both provides necessary information and has a quality control and management decision dimension—where to place control lines to minimize trade damage and assist observation of deviations in installed work.

Other job site functions consist of the following. *Safety engineer* posts required notifications, conducts meetings and training, and site surveys to monitor conformance. *Quality control* and *cost engineers* will only be found on the largest demanding projects. On all other projects, these tests will be performed by the existing office or field personnel. *Oilers* and *mechanics* provide the fuel, lubricants, and parts and repairs for heavy trucks and equipment. *Drivers* perform trucking but can also be the eyes and ears of the superintendent and provide feedback, which is difficult to obtain in other ways.

Subcontractors and Vendors—Specialization Produces Many Players

A subcontractor is a vendor performing substantial on-site trade labor, assembly, and fabrication. A supplier is a vendor fabricating off site and performs little or no on-site labor. Subcontractors are required to provide specified insurance and are typically paid monthly, less 10% retention. Vendors who deliver material to the site by common carrier may have fewer or no insurance requirements, and are typically paid in full with no retention.

The specialization and therefore number of subcontractors and vendors continues to increase. Understanding the capabilities and nature of subcontractors is critical, so items in the work breakdown structure can be effectively combined into work packages that the available subcontract and vendor pool can execute well. Including unfamiliar or uncomfortable tasks in the work package will tend to produce inferior results at higher cost.

Some of the most common subcontracting classifications, and relevant notation about capabilities or peculiarity of this classification, are listed below. Some firms may attempt to perform several classifications, but a single classification is more common. This is by no means an exhaustive list but is comprehensive and provides an indication of the diversity and complexity of building construction, subcontractors, and vendors. (The division numbers listed below conform to the CSI (Construction Specification Institute) Master Format system for organizing work tasks. This system is the most widely recognized organizational structure in the construction industry.)

Division 2 Site construction

Demolition tends to segregate into the interior demolition, demolition of commercial structures, and demolition of industrial structures for which the scrap value of the debris may be a significant pricing factor. (The value of scrap metal, particularly steel, fluctuates wildly and can produce some supplemental income for the demolition contractor, or in other cases sufficient income so the contractor will actually pay the owner to perform the demolition.) Demolition contractors employ laborers, drivers, and operators.

Earthwork tends to be driven by equipment possessed and related skilled operators, as well as project size and type. Earthwork contractors employ laborers, drivers, and equipment operators.

Foundations include the temporary earth retention systems such as sheeting, and slurry walls necessary to permit installation of the permanent foundation, and foundation structures such as piles and caissons. Foundation contractors employ laborers, operators, carpenters (for concrete forms and sheeting and pile driving), drivers, and operators.

Asphalt paving firms tend to segregate into (1) residential and commercial parking lots and drives and (2) highway paving.

Division 3 Concrete

Concrete construction segregates into the areas of general building, structural concrete (building framework), high-volume flat work such as warehouse floors or toppings, highway paving, curb and gutter and sidewalk, and architectural concrete with specialized finishes or patterns.

Concrete reinforcing steel firms provide installation labor only for concrete steel reinforcing furnished by others. These firms typically work only on larger commercial–industrial projects requiring continuous reinforcing steel installation. Installation on smaller projects is typically performed by the general contractor or concrete subcontractor with their own trade labor.

Precast concrete material fabrication for civil structures such as pipes, catch basins, and manholes are fabricated and sold in a similar manner to lumber—stock components are manufactured and stockpiled, but project-specific engineering or installation is not performed. Structural precast concrete used for bridges and structures such as parking garages is engineered by professional engineers on the precast firm's staff. This engineering is in addition to the architect or engineer of record's engineering.

Precast concrete with a decorative finish such as the facing of buildings and tilt-up panels typically used in warehouses is engineered in the same manner as structural concrete but usually by a different firm. Installation of the precast structure and building cladding is typically performed by the fabricator. Other types of precast, such as flat planks for mezzanines, are typically installed by the construction management managers or their subcontractors. Traditionally, precast concrete is erected by ironworkers.

Division 4 Masonry

Masonry firms tend to favor either high-production work, such as warehouses, or more detailed ornamental work, including complicated coursing patterns and cut stone. Few firms can achieve both the required installation quality and the needed market price for both types of work. Large scale masonry restoration, such as entire high-rise facades, is a specialty of the third type of firm.

Division 5 Metals

Structural steel and miscellaneous metals erection. Structural steel forms the building framework. Miscellaneous steel encompasses a wide range of components including support structures for masonry, curtain walls, wall shafts, and elevators, complete stair assemblies and ladders, and protective devices such as angles embedded in concrete and bollards and guard rails. Steel angles, channels, tubes, or beams not part of the structure are probably miscellaneous steel.

Structural and miscellaneous steel is frequently, but not always, performed by a single firm. But firms will favor either structural or miscellaneous work, so allocation of these tasks to different firms may be needed for some projects. These firms will typically subcontract the installation.

Ornamental gates, doors, and church furnishings constructed of materials other than carbon steel, such a stainless steel, brass, bronze, or aluminum, are fabricated by multiple specialty firms. These firms typically perform their own installation.

Division 6 Wood and plastics

Carpentry is one of the most diverse trades, performing job site layout (line and grade work), pile driving, concrete form work, wood-framed construction, light-gauge (less than 10 gauge) steel erection, millwork, store fixtures and wood trim, drywall, acoustical tile, flooring, specialties such as corner guards, and equipment tracks constructed of aluminum and plastic, to name just a few. Installation firms may select one specialty or a couple of specialties—favoring lighter, more detailed work, or heavy work requiring larger equipment. No firm does all carpentry well.

Division 7 Thermal and moisture protection

Roofing contractors specialize by the type of roofing system and favor certain manufactured products. Sloped roofs (3/12 or steeper pitch) are specialized by the materials of asphalt shingles, wood shingles, slate, tile, and metal. Flat roofs are specialized by the type of roofing material and the manufacturer. "Green" landscaped roofs may be an additional flat and sloped roof specialty.

Sloped roof contractors will typically fabricate and install their own sheet metal flashings. Flat roof contractors typically fabricate in house and install with their own trade labor but occasionally subcontract the work, which can produce scheduling delays. Each roofing contractor will have trade labor familiar with a few systems and products, and firms receive significant discounts and technical support to favor one product line or manufacturer. Roofing contractors may say that "they can do it all," but in fact they can only execute a few systems at a high level of quality, prompt scheduling, and market rate costs.

The soil nailing installation sequence shown below was installed by Hayward Baker for the Dallas Cowboys stadium in Arlington, Texas.

Excavate 3 to 6 feet of soil.   *Soil nailing operations photo 1 of 6*

Waterproofing (subgrade) is performed in the same manner as roofing, with specialization in fluid or mastic-applied membranes, bentonite panels, or proprietary products. Above-grade waterproofing for plazas, curtain wall, or masonry claddings are usually installed by the contractor installing the related materials—unless the installation has large enough available work areas to justify a waterproofing subcontractor.

Division 8 Doors and windows

Aluminum glass and glazing includes the categories of (1) ornamental, such as mirrors, and etched and cut glass; (2) structural glass used for ceilings, floors, and stairs; (3) storefront (smaller openings supported by the immediately surrounding wall structures) used for single-story "punched" openings in midrise buildings; and (4) curtain wall (supported by the structure, and includes interior water drainage systems) used for taller openings and structures. Some firms, such as producers of curtain walls and structural glass, perform only one type of work. Other firms may attempt to perform two types of work, but favor one and perform the second at a less than optimal level. The engineering, installation, materials, tools, and methods are completely different for these glazing types—rules of thumb and trade knowledge alone can produce costly failures. No firm does it all—specialization is needed.

Division 9 Finishes

Painting firms tend to specialize by construction type, such as single-family residential, multifamily residential, commercial, industrial, and historical restoration and artistic work. Painting firms utilize different crews to perform more than one specialty well, but no firm performs all specialties at a professional level.

Flooring consists of carpet, vinyl, composition tile, sheet flooring, wood flooring, ceramic tile, and fluid-applied coatings. A tradesman will typically install one or two materials well. Some firms claim to perform multiple categories but actually subcontract portions of the work. In the extreme, broker contractors can purchase the material and subcontract all labor—acting as a flooring general contractor. This arrangement can work well, but frequently the multiple layers of management produce costly additional markups and scheduling difficulties. Flooring contractors may have strong ties to a particular manufacturer and receive incentives to push a material, which can prejudice their advice on appropriate materials.

Division 14 Conveying systems

Vertical transportation firms are divided into firms moving material and people. Material handling and vehicle movement such as dock levelers, material hoists, and vehicle turnstiles are all separate subspecialties with very narrow performance capabilities. Product design, fabrication, and usually installation are included.

Vertical transportation for people consists of walkways, escalators, and elevators. Elevators of less than about six stories are provided by many local or regional firms. Higher and larger elevator installations are performed by only five firms in the world. These large firms may also seek smaller elevator installations and may provide escalators and walkways. Product design, fabrication, and installation are included.

With this restricted competition, the firms will have substantial or complete influence over specifications, and will perform project specific engineering that can cause some cost and very severe scheduling problems.

Division 15 Mechanical

Fire protection contractors (small and midsize) may specialize in wet fire protection systems for residential and light commercial applications. Larger contractors will also perform dry pipe and deluge systems. Kitchen hoods, Halon and foam systems, and lightening protection will usually be performed by specialty firms. Virtual all fire protection engineering is performed by the installing subcontractor (the engineer of record may provide a concept only). Fire protection contractors will cut and thread their pipe, but purchase all other equipment and material, and perform the installation.

Plumbing and storm drainage consisting of storm and sanitary sewers, and water installations outside the building are typically performed by sewer and water contractors. Curiously, in some municipalities, the sewer and water contractor is not a licensed plumber or may have a less-rigorous license, but plumbing work within the building must be performed by a fully licensed plumber.

The licensed plumbing contractor performs the plumbing work inside the building consisting of potable water, sanitary, and storm drainage. Plumbing contractors will specialize by building type such as multifamily residential, medical, and new or renovation work. High-production new work, such as multifamily residential, demands high-production, low-cost repetitive work. Renovation work requires

If all earthwork operations are off road, higher capacity equipment may be selected.

thinking and adapting to existing conditions as well as working well around the existing conditions and occupied spaces—lower production and higher cost results. The renovation plumber will be unable to achieve the productivity and therefore needed costs, and the high-production, new-work plumber will find the normal and customary work of the renovation plumber impossible.

HVAC contractors segregate into sheet metal and piping specialties, and project types hugely favor one trade. For example, strip shopping centers are almost exclusively sheet metal work with limited gas piping. Multifamily residential projects are predominantly piping with more limited sheet metal work. Many firms that perform both sheet metal and piping favor, and possibly even subcontract, the less favored specialty.

Subbing out some or all sheet metal fabrication is increasingly common. In-house fabrication typically uses sheet stock, which produces significant waste. Production fabricators use coil stock and computerize the cutting patterns, which reduces cost to the extent that subbed out fabricated cost is sometimes less than the in-house raw material cost alone. To realize these savings, the sheet metal contractor must prepare shop drawings and provide cutting diagrams—and the duration of this activity must be included in the schedule.

Process piping for delivery of chemicals, fluids, and gases other than potable water is performed by pipe fitting contractors. A limited amount of waste piping, such as condensate piping, may be performed by the process piping contractor, but the balance of waste piping is performed by the plumbing contractor. Process piping materials include plastic, glass, copper, steel, and stainless steel of varying gauges, and fastening methods include soldering, brazing, welding, and clamping. Process piping contractors have diverse capabilities but tend to segregate by building type.

Control contractors provide the temperature and process control for the building HVAC and industrial processes. The HVAC contractors perform control work for small and medium-sized projects but may subcontract the work on some medium and most larger projects. The control subcontractor performs his independent engineering, specification, and installation. These contractors typically start submittals and engineering after most mechanical equipment is installed. The engineering time and the late installation start must be managed and included in the project schedule.

Division 16 Electrical

Electrical contractors perform the power, lighting, and sometimes telecommunication and low-voltage work within the building. Different electrical contractors perform power line and substation work. Segregation by project type and size, and new or renovation work for electrical contractors is similar to the plumbers' segregation described above.

The Large Number of Principal Vendors Affects Design, Cost, and Schedule

Vendors who custom fabricate materials require shop drawings, technical submittals, and samples, and these tasks must be included in the work breakdown structure and project schedule.

A midsize commercial project might have the following critical vendors: reinforcing steel, precast concrete, masonry shapes (cut stone), miscellaneous steel, structural steel, wood trusses, laminated wood, millwork, roofing, curtain wall, storefront, doors frames and hardware consisting of hollow metal and wood doors, aluminum doors, overhead doors, monumental doors, door operators, and light-gauge wall framing, finishes consisting of vinyl wall covering, carpet, ceramic tile, resilient flooring, wood flooring, specialties, dock equipment, elevators, plumbing fixtures and pumps, HVAC rooftop units, exhaust fans and grilles, electrical service gear, and lights—33 items—all requiring technical information that must be reviewed and lead times verified. All these items will require sub-vendors, and if any one of the parties in the chain does not perform, the schedule may be impaired.

Mega vendors control product features, cost, and delivery—an impact to include in project planning

Over the last 30 years, many industries have consolidated so that there may only be a few firms in the world providing certain goods or services. These few giant vendors influence possibilities for even the largest construction managers in the world. For example, Ingersoll Rand, a manufacturer of door closers, is worth five times more (measured by market capitalization—the value of all stock) than the largest publicly traded construction manager.

During this same time, products have become more sophisticated, including patented processes and proprietary designs. This has led to vendors controlling the design and product specifications, and even writing the specifications for the design architect or engineer—including electronic files in the appropriate CSI format so that no further knowledge or effort of any kind is required.

A few examples of mega vendors include the following: in construction chemicals surface coatings and caulking—BASF, Sonneborn, GE, and Dow; finish hardware—Assa Abloy and Ingersoll Rand; elevators—Kone, Schindler, Thyssen Krupp, Otis, and Fujitec; HVAC equipment such as rooftop units: Carrier, York, Trane, and sometimes Lennox.

Control of both supply and design turns the normal design and construction process on its head. Instead of deciding what is best and then seeking a firm to provide this good or service, the available products from the mega firms must be reviewed and their normal and customary offerings included in the design. This reality must now be recognized in project planning, costing, and scheduling for building construction.

The impact of mega vendors is now less pronounced for heavy and highway construction that heavily involves soils, concrete, asphalt, and steel—materials that are available from many small and large vendors. But this too is changing. Patented chemicals such as concrete additives and surface treatments, geotextile fabrics, and mechanical equipment (e.g., for sewage treatment plants) and controls (e.g., for highway lighting and signals) are increasingly engineered and sold by mega multinational vendors. The design and management dimensions that are now realties in building construction will continue to transfer to heavy and highway construction.

Summary

The surprising number of different types of construction project players segregate by knowledge possessed, work performed, project type and size, capacity for analysis and communication, and project delivery methods favored. This reality must be recognized when developing a project work breakdown structure and work packages to assign tasks to the most capable, efficient, and willing parties.

And the builders', subcontractors', and vendors' possession of needed knowledge or control of proprietary materials or processes must also be recognized to include this valued input starting in project planning. This recognition of the realities of the construction industry, and the nature and preferences and capability of the firms and their personnel, is essential to achieve the triple constraint of scope, cost, and schedule.

Review Questions (True or False)

1. A skilled construction manager effectively performs residential, commercial, industrial, and heavy and highway construction equally well.
2. The terms *general contractor* and *construction manager* may be used interchangeably without difference or distinction.
3. Construction managers will typically provide more preconstruction services and consulting during the project than a general contractor.

4. Project management firm and owner's agents typically self-perform significant portion of the trade work.

5. For very large construction projects, a project manager and engineers will usually, estimators and scheduling personnel will frequently, but project executives never will work full time on site.

6. A general superintendent may be assisted and supplemented by discipline superintendents on larger or more complex projects.

7. OSHA requires safety engineers on all projects.

8. A subcontractor can effectively execute a very wide range of the work items without regard to trade specialty, or type or size of the project.

9. Poured-in-place and precast concrete are usually installed by the same subcontractor.

10. A single door subcontractor is preferred for most projects to avoid coordination difficulties.

11. The decision to award HVAC ductwork piping and controls to a single or multiple subcontractors is governed by the complexity of the project and the capabilities of subcontractors in the project area.

12. Mega vendors may control the design specifications of products or systems, so their impact must be included early in project planning.

Test Your Understanding

1. Visit a construction project in your area, even if only viewed from the curb, and identify and count the probable parties that have, are, or will work on site. Include consideration of the following contractors:
Earthwork contractor
Concrete contractor
Reinforcing steel installation contractor
Masonry contractor
Carpentry contractor
Roofing contractor
Exterior door and window contractor
Drywall contractor
Painting contractor
Site utility contractor
Plumbing contractor
HVAC contractor
Electrical contractor

2. For a large publicly bid road construction project, discuss which of the following project management leaders would probably be and which would probably not be involved, and why:
Construction manager
Project management firm
Owner's agent
General contractor

3. A speculative office building (no tenants have yet been secured), an outpatient surgery center, a warehouse, an apartment building, and a pharmaceutical manufacturing plant all have a project value of $20 million and a construction time of 2 years. Which of the following discipline superintendents would be most beneficial for each of these projects?
Concrete
HVAC focusing on ventilation
Process piping
Manufacturing and building automation controls
Electrical

CHAPTER
1.3

Project Management, Project Life Cycle and Chronology

This Space-Lift™ concrete jump forming system integrates the forming system and work platforms. The workers do not need to be on the platform when the forms are being jumped, which increases safety. *Photo courtesy: Symons.*

Project Management, Project Life Cycle and Chronology

A discipline and structure to achieve one purpose, and then disband

Project management is a new field with ancient roots. Production and general management seeks to be continuous—long production runs of great profitable products are desirable. In contrast, projects by definition have a start and end—always temporary and short is usually best. Because the project is temporary and short, project management focuses on processes and tools (that are employed less or not at all in general management) to initiate a project, define scope, cost, and time in early planning, execute and control, and close the project as planned.

Project management is less focused on the long-term global impact of strategic planning and finance. The project must help achieve a previously established business purpose—a strategic objective within financial constraints—but these objectives and constraints were established before the project start. (Understanding established strategy and constraints is needed to make the project responsive.) And financial analysis of the project's execution and control remains an important and time consuming project management task.

Large, innovative, and complicated projects were built before project management

Some say project management was developed because of the demands of big and complicated projects, but this is not correct. There were many large and complicated projects thousands of years before project management. For example, the Great Wall of China is a structure so extensive that it can be seen from space. The Appian Way is a road constructed by the ancient Romans for thousands of miles throughout Europe. The Palace of Versailles in France was constructed on a swamp, used the finest decorative techniques of the time, and employed 35,000 workmen on site. The Great Pyramids of Egypt are massive structures with probable astronomical significance. Some of the great cathedrals of Europe took 300 years to construct. More recently, the Panama Canal was both large and had unique engineering challenges. The Brooklyn Bridge also used pioneering techniques, such as marine caissons. All these projects were constructed before project management was developed, and all of them are standing now.

How Project Management Evolved from "General and Operations Management"

Management has been studied and documented for thousands of years. Books on running farms, monasteries, and military organizations have been available for many years. For example, *The Art of War*, written about 500 BC, describes the management of military enterprises. *The Rule of St. Benedict*, written about 1,500 years ago, describes the management of a monastery. In these cases, the person actually doing the work described the management techniques. St. Benedict was the founder of the Benedictine order and the abbot of a monastery. The authors of *The Art of War* were working generals. These books are still in print today.

The study of management by a person not doing the work arose in the early 20th century. Taylor, with his time and motion studies, developed "management" as a separate topic. The man with a clipboard and a stopwatch was not actually doing the factory's line production work. The separate field of "project management" is frequently said to have started with the construction of a nuclear submarine in the late 1940s in America. Although project management did begin at this time, it did not begin just because of the complexities of building a nuclear submarine.

The factors that gave rise to project management are as follows.

The first was the growing wealth and expansion of America following victory in World War II. Europe and Japan were both devastated and required years to rebuild. There was a huge domestic expansion in the United States—booming production and little competition—so there was less pressure to compete.

Included in this boom in America was the GI Bill, which permitted many more people to complete a college education. If not for college, many would have worked in factory production or the trades. This helped produce the notion of people spending more time in the office and less time on the shop floor or job site because thinking and talking is more important than actually making and doing. In the building and engineering areas, similar trends existed for architects and engineers. They began to spend less and less time at the job site, with most of their time spent in the office. This trend continued through the second half of the 20th century until many younger architects and engineers seldom went to a job site and were unable to execute any task on a professional level once there.

Another development was the tendency for people to view themselves as more important than they formerly did. These perceived elevated values of the individual (theoretical book learning and assumed intelligence) produce a situation where everyone wants to be the manager, but nobody wants to do the work. Lack of field knowledge can divorce these people from common sense and the real physical world.

Finally, within large or cumbersome organizations populated by these new managers where quick execution of new tasks is counter to the organization's nature and culture, rapid project execution was unfeasible. A way to divorce from this management structure was to make project management a "special temporary exception" to the rules and procedures of the organization. Nothing is as permanent as a temporary exception—especially when it works.

PMI (Project Management Institute) added standardized structure

PMI was founded in 1969 to document project management practices common to all industries—as diverse as pharmaceuticals and construction. In 1981, PMI began developing a standard body of knowledge, certification, and ethics for the profession. The PMBOK® (*Project Management Body of Knowledge*) book (and books on other specialized project management topics) documented the results of these efforts. The PMBOK addresses only processes and knowledge applicable to all industries, and specifically avoids any business environmental factors specific to any one industry.

The PMI awards the PMP (Project Management Professional) credential to those who have a proscribed combination of relevant experience (usually 7 or more years), education (at least a 4-year postsecondary degree but can be reduced by additional experience), and successful completion of the PMP exam. There are also entry-level certifications (CAPM, Certified Associate of Project Management) and additional specialized certifications in the area of scheduling (PMI-SP,PMI Scheduling Professional) and risk management (PMI-RMP, PMI Risk Management Professional). All certifications require continuing involvement in the industry and a specified amount of continuing education to maintain the certification.

PMI standards are widely accepted in many industries worldwide. Many construction management firms in Latin America, Middle East, and Southeast Asia increasingly require the PMP certification. Adoption of this standard for construction management firms in the United States has lagged, but the GSA (General Services Administration), the federal government agency that builds and manages much of the U.S. Federal government civilian buildings, has recently specified that the PMP credential is a relevant qualifying factor for award of new work to construction managers.

The PMBOK structure uses the processes of:
>   Initiating
>   Planning
>   Executing
>   Monitoring and controlling
>   Closing

And the knowledge areas of:

      Project integration management (coordinating the processes and knowledge areas)

      Project scope management

      Project time management

      Project cost management

      Project quality management

      Project human resource management

      Project communication management

      Project risk management

      Project procurement management

And the PMBOK construction extension adds the knowledge areas of:

      Project safety management

      Project environmental management

      Project financial management

      Project claim management

This discipline of this process structure and content of these knowledge areas are fully covered in this text, but the sequence of knowledge areas has been reordered to conform to the expectations of traditional construction management texts—subjects are presented in the approximate order of usual construction project execution. The reordering of this text's table of contents into the PMBOK knowledge area sequence is shown in an appendix.

The CMAA uses a more limited construction focused structure

Construction Management Association of America (CMAA) defines seven core construction management competencies:

1. CM professional practice
2. CM project management
3. Cost management
4. Time management
5. Quality management
6. Contract administration
7. Safety management

Four of these competencies—cost, time, quality, and safety management—are identical to the PMI knowledge areas, and CM project management and contract administration are addressed, but differently, by CMAA. However, CMAA does not address the PMI knowledge areas of human resources, communication, risk, financial and environmental management—all of which can add managerial competence and value to the project. Finally, the CMAA's omission of project initiation and scope management limits the construction managers' very early project involvement (which can add significant value) and reduces the construction managers' input to a reaction and execution of a partially or substantially defined scope and completed construction documents.

Some engineering and industry knowledge must be added to these structures

Although the rigorous PMI structure can provide great benefits for the construction industry, environmental factors needed to manage a project are compelling as well. Much of construction is part of the physical world and is governed by the rules of science and nature. The impact of water on the strength of soil, concrete, the integrity of the weather envelope, and HVAC cooling and heating efficiency and effectiveness is compelling and further influenced by weather—influencing both cost and schedule planning. Most construction managers are vastly smaller than many global suppliers, who control proprietary knowledge, equipment, and materials—which limits the CM's ability to dictate project delivery and procurement methods. And regulations and industry standards further restrict project planning and management possibilities.

A construction project manager must have a working knowledge of this environment—learning from others on the project is too large a task to learn for a new project. This text uses much of the PMI structure integrated with construction industry-specific knowledge to provide a managerial approach.

Both the hard side and the soft side of construction management must be integrated and balanced. Quantitative analytical tools for control and schedule management are essential and powerful project management tools, but can only be effective if balanced with the softer side of qualitative understanding of the nature of people, business standards and structures, and industry environmental factors.

What Project Management Is Not—General Management with Parts Missing

Because project management focuses on a single temporary purpose with a defined cost and time, many aspects of management that are needed in a company as a whole are not needed in a focused project and are minimized or omitted.

First, strategic planning is absent. Since the project has been authorized, the portion of strategic planning that determines that a project is a good idea has been done and is not open for further discussion. Understanding the strategic purpose is still needed to plan the project to achieve this strategic goal.

Second, strategic finance is minimized for the same reason—the financial analysis was performed to authorize the project, including the cost. Cash flow management of the project is a critical project management task, but the main focus is usually to finish as quickly as possible while getting paid as promptly as possible to minimize finance (interest) costs.

Third, inventory cost (which can be a major large general management task, particularly in manufacturing and retail) is not a concern because the project scope is fixed and the needed components are known. The only concern is getting these necessary components, and no more, to the project as needed. No inventory is kept for future stock.

Finally, promotion and advertising are substantially eliminated. There may be some promotion for the company performing the project—using the project as an example of their capabilities—but because the project will stand alone and will not be repeated, ongoing advertising to promote the project is omitted.

What Project Management Is—for a Specific Purpose with a Defined End

Project management is a system to execute a single purpose within a specified time and cost. The project management structure is different from the rest of a company's management burden, rules, and structures. The project management structure is extremely flat, with the project manager usually authorized to make decisions within agreed broad limits. Unless there is a deviation from the agreed planned scope, cost, or time, no outside approval of decisions is required. The project is a stand-alone profit center with its own cost and record-keeping systems. Accounting and financial knowledge and systems (as taught in 4-year business schools and employed in general business) is used in a slimmed-down focused version as described above.

Because of the intense focus on cost and speed for a single purpose, four tools and techniques, though not unique to construction, are more heavily used and highly developed. These are as follows: (1) the cost estimate and the related development of the workable approach, (2) information systems to track the procurement of the building blocks (permissions, materials, and equipment), (3) job costing with intense focus on labor productivity, and (4) scheduling tools to check that the relationships of the building blocks suggested in the workable approach will probably work before starting, and continue to work while executing the project. The focus on these four activities and the reduction in many general management functions define much of the difference between general management and project management.

The Project Life Cycle Limits Management Possibilities over Time

A project has a defined start and end, and must balance the triple constraint of scope, time, and cost. Time is always passing, work preformed, and costs continuously expended, so the ability to manage the triple constraint declines over the life of the project.

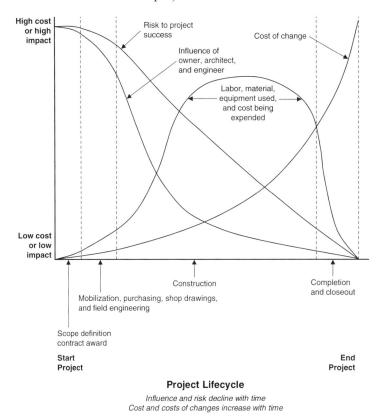

Project Lifecycle

Influence and risk decline with time
Cost and costs of changes increase with time

This graph indicates that the project owner's, architect's, and engineer's influence and project risk decline, and cost and cost of changes increase over time. The direction of these changes will exist on all projects, but the slope of the lines will change significantly by project type, delivery method, and style of management.

This graph depicts a construction management delivery system with the construction manager assisting the owner, architect, and engineer in the early stages of project development—CM influence is sought and expected in these early project stages. The owner's, architect's, and engineer's influence line for a lump sum hard bid delivery system, which attempts complete definitive initial construction documents that require little or no additional CM input, would shift to the left. And the cost of changes line for a building project where interior finishes may be specified late in the project will have a lower slope, but a road project for which changes require demolition and replacement of completed work would have a very steep cost-of-change slope.

The project life cycle relationships highlight the critical importance of early scope definition—late scope changes increase the risk and the cost of the project. But the project life cycle makes the importance of time in the triple constraint crystal clear, influencing both scope and cost. And communication of the importance of time to project owners, architects, and engineers remains one of the most challenging and critical project management tasks. Scope and cost are readily understood, but understanding of the impact of time remains elusive.

The Construction Project Chronology

The generic project life cycle described above emphasizes the impact of time on management of the triple constraint. The application of this life cycle in construction, which is influenced by traditions, customs, and regulations, is described below. The construction managers' beneficial involvement in the development process and possibilities for improvement are then identified.

Project development steps are as follows:

Initiation
The project owner identifies a need, and parameters for satisfying that need.

Feasibility analysis
The project owner identifies market conditions and the cost and rate of return needed to make the project viable. The cost and time impact of government requirements, such as infrastructure improvements and zoning approvals, and site-specific conditions, such as unsuitable soils, are assessed.

Project Financing
Financing commitment or determination that financing can be obtained in the form of bank loans, bonds, government or corporate fund allocation, or a capital fund-raising campaign (for not-for-profits) is obtained.

Design
Design is performed in four steps (which may or may not later include architect and engineer construction administration).

Programming
Programming converts the owner's needs and goals into a written statement of the building's requirements. The process may be as simple as a few interviews with key owner personnel or as extensive as structured exercises with many groups both in and outside the organization, consultations with experts, and review of other facilities. The output may include diagrams of functional relationships but not building plans. The desired project time and cost may be loosely identified.

Schematic design
Schematic design takes the programming information and develops massings, shapes, circulation patterns, and orientations. Concepts of mechanical electrical systems are identified, but no engineering is performed on this step. The output may be two or three possible schemes.

Design development
One of the schematic designs is chosen, and materials, equipment, and systems are researched and selected. At this point, drawings are sufficiently complete for some preliminary market pricing. (Since drawings are only partially complete, competent estimates can only be performed by sophisticated contractors with significant estimating capability.)

Construction documents

Detailed drawings and specifications that can be bid in the open market are then produced.

Procurement

In a design-then-bid delivery system, the completed construction documents are competitively bid by general contractors. In a construction management delivery system, the sub-trades are bid to the construction manager.

Permissions

Permits must be obtained from the authorities having jurisdiction. These can include the local city building department, highway departments, regional planning departments, environmental and storm water management agencies. Project-type-specific permissions such as department of public health (hospitals and restaurants), departments for children and aging (day-care centers and nursing homes), and fire marshals (fuel-handling facilities) are also needed. Although many of these permissions require construction documents, some, such as the regional planning departments, can be slow and controversial and may be started in the feasibility analysis step.

Construction

The project is built by the general contractor or construction manager.

Commissioning, turnover, and closeout

This involves punch lists, final cleaning, testing, adjusting, certifying, and furnishing as-built documents and operating and maintenance manuals. It also involves removal of temporary facilities and restoration at the removed areas. And it finally involves owner acceptance of the project and should involve documentation of lessons learned for future process improvement, as well as building a relationship with the owner for future work.

Drill near horizontal holes into the exposed face, typically on 3- to 6-foot centers.

Soil nailing operations photo 2 of 6

Commissioning has traditionally been solely the province of the general contractor or construction manager, but recently a commissioning consultant has sometimes been injected into this process.

Operation of the facility

Some callbacks and warranty work may be required during the first year of operation, but other construction opportunities exist as well. Commercial and medical office buildings may initially include the shell and core only with build out of the individual offices, which can exceed the cost of the original shell and core, following turnover. Some owners frequently renovate or need building additions.

Disposal of the facility

At the end of the building's useful life, it will be either demolished or completely renovated.

Project Life Cycle Time Frames

The timing of typical project development is listed below. Some small tenant work or retail projects may be designed, permitted, and built in less than 2 months, and some controversial regional projects may languish for over 50 years.

Construction Life Cycle Times (months)						
	Commercial		Commercial		Commercial	
	Multi-family		Industrial		Industrial	
	Residential		Institutional		Civil	
	Small		Medium		Large	
	Low	High	Low	High	Low	High
Initiation	2	6	2	6	2	12
Feasibility analysis	1	6	1	12	12	60
Project financing	1	3	3	12	6	48
Design						
Programming	1	4	3	8	6	18
Schematic design	1	2	3	6	6	18
Design development	1	3	3	8	8	24
Construction documents	1	4	4	10	10	18
Procurement	1	2	2	4	4	6
Permissions	1	8	2	12	1	12
Construction	6	18	18	36	36	60
Commissioning, turnover, closeout	1	2	2	4	4	6
Months	17	58	43	118	95	282
Years	1.4	4.8	3.6	9.8	7.9	23.5
Operation of facility						
Exterior improvements	15–25 years					
Building	30–60 years					
Civil	60–80 years					
Disposal of facility						

The approximate useful lives of facilities are: exterior improvements such as parking lots 15–25 years, buildings 30–60 years, and civil improvements such as dams and bridges 60–80 years.

The Construction Managers' Beneficial Involvement in Project Development

The discussion of the project life cycle above indicated that the ability to influence project outcomes declines over time. Therefore, the earliest possible construction managers' involvement will be most beneficial. The types of customary feasible involvement are described below.

Initiation and feasibility

The construction manager can add little or no value to project initiation. The construction manager can assist feasibility evaluation for constructability and market conditions for the following:
- Trade labor availability
- Customary and cost-effective construction approach at the project location
- Regulatory conditions
- The difficulty and cost of utility infrastructure improvements
- Soil borrow pits and disposal sites

Project financing

The construction manager will place the financing in the design-build-transfer delivery system. The construction manager who has relationships with many banks favoring construction and permanent real estate loans may provide some assistance to the one project owner, but involvement for larger projects may be minimal or nonexistent.

Smaller commercial projects' loan commitment now frequently requires hard construction costs and even a construction contract—before construction documents have been developed. A construction manager with sophisticated estimating capability can fulfill this requirement.

Design

As the architect and engineer develop the *desired* scope in programming and schematic design, the construction manager can contribute by supplementing with the *required* scope to ensure that initial cost estimates are comprehensive. These required activities include heavy site development activities, parking structures, utility infrastructure, and permissions that the architect usually does not address in detail until the design development and the construction documents.

The construction manager provides guidance on constructability, value engineering, present market realities, and cost alternates during the design development phase. Long lead materials can be ordered, and contractor-engineered design documents for fire alarm, fire protection sprinklers, elevators, and building automation systems can be developed in the construction document phase. This both assists the completeness and accuracy of the contract documents and accelerates the schedule.

Throughout the entire development process, the construction manager must guide time planning. Both the owner and the architect will be very concerned about scope, fairly concerned about cost, but usually much less concerned about time. Yet, time influences scope possibilities and costs. The construction manager can add great value by structuring and managing the time of project development.

The Project Manager's Skills and Knowledge

A project must have a defined purpose, a workable approach, a count of all components, and an itemization of all affected parties. A project manager must have a theoretical knowledge of the tasks being executed and must have a workable knowledge of how they are actually done. The project manager must have all information about the building blocks, cost, availability, sequence, and time to obtain and install.

This means, without exception, the project manager must have one or two areas of expertise, including some field exposure. Some have come up through the trades. Some have come up with education in subjects such as civil engineering, and then some field experience. Others have related architectural engineering training plus field experience. A 1-year field experience minimum, if diverse and well supervised, is required. Three years is more realistic since a new hire will be given repetitive low level tasks. Whatever career path is followed, a project manager must have a time horizon that is at least a little longer than the project duration.

Finally, a project manager must have at least some authority to hire, fire, and purchase, or he is just a coordinator or expeditor, not a manager. And the project manager must be able to communicate effectively verbally and in writing.

If all these conditions are not met, the project manager will not achieve the purpose. Printing up business cards saying "Project Manager" without the knowledge and authority to actually manage anything will produce nothing.

Summary

Project management is a subset of general management, which reflects the project focus on rapid execution of a single task with a fixed duration. Many areas of general management such as strategic planning, finance, and advertising are minimized or eliminated. Use of the tools of cost estimating to develop the workable approach and information systems to track the procurement of the building blocks is emphasized. Job costing, particularly labor productivity, and scheduling are emphasized. Properly executed project management minimizes mid-project change and value engineering.

Review Questions (True or False)

1. General management of production operations seeks to be continuous with the long production runs. But construction project management is temporary with a definite start and end date, and shorter durations are usually best.
2. All large projects have always required the tools and techniques of project management.
3. The PMI has established five processes and nine knowledge areas applicable to most industries.
4. The CMAA defines seven core construction management competencies.
5. Both the PMI and the CMAA include detailed civil and mechanical engineering information in their knowledge areas and competencies.
6. Strategic planning and finance for the firm, inventory management, promotion, and advertising are key elements of general management but not project management.
7. The project owner's, architect's, and engineer's influence and project risks decline, and cost and cost of changes increase over the life of the project.
8. Contractors for lump sum hard bid delivery system have significant input into scope definition.
9. Early scope definition can reduce project risk and cost.
10. A construction project manager with excellent command of analytical tools can successfully manage by delegating all technical engineering matters to subordinates.
11. A project manager must have authority to hire and fire and authorize expenditures, or he is a coordinator or expediter but not a project manager.

Test Your Understanding

1. Compare the characteristics of a project (temporary, for a defined purpose, with a definite start and end date, to achieve measurable results) with the characteristics of a one-semester college class.

2. The project life cycle diagram shown earlier in this chapter depicts a project with construction project management delivery. Redraw the cost of changes and project risk line for a lump sum hard bid delivery for which the general contractor has no scope definition input.

3. If the construction manager is able to define the scope early and then freeze the scope (allow no changes) and accelerate the schedule, what is the impact of owner's influence, project risk, and cost of change?

CHAPTER
1.4

Accounting (Financial)—a Management Tool and Required Report Card

Custom-designed forms were required for these piers. The number of sets of forms purchased is a critical decision that balances the cost of the forms against increased productivity and shortened schedule that reduces general condition costs. *Photo courtesy Symons.*

Accounting (Financial)—a Management Tool and Required Report Card

Financial accounting first, then tax and job cost accounting

Financial accounting both provides a picture of the financial state of a company—for others such as investors, bankers making loans, bonding companies, and taxing authorities—and assists company-wide management improvements. But project managers use cost accounting (discussed in a later chapter), not financial accounting, to monitor and control projects. Since the construction manager's home office uses financial accounting to determine the status of the entire company including all of the company's projects, basic understanding of this report card can produce a higher score and enhance communication.

Accounting can seem a dull subject—not central to construction project management. And accounting works within the rules and systems of others—with different purposes and time frames—so accounting systems and reports (if not understood) will frequently appear puzzling and contrary to common sense. But the results of accounting are required by law and common practice, so need to be understood—not avoided. The understanding provided below will change accounting from a problem to a tool—and move the project manager to the top couple percent of the building team. Since most project owners are focused on financial accounting, tax accounting, and finance, the project manager who can "speak their language" has a sales and management advantage.

Integration of the construction firm's financial accounting (used by management) and job cost accounting (used by project managers) is explained below. The project owners' accounting systems and needs are also explained to show how they think and what they find most important—to improve customer service and sales. Project managers seek accounting for project control and improvement but can only realize this goal by understanding the entire system of financial, tax, and job cost accounting together.

Accounting Records for a Purpose

The three accounting systems start with financial accounting, which records the completed or committed exchanges of payments for goods and services. It also records changes in asset values. The amount, purpose, and timing of these records are noted and structured to provide cash flow management and useful strategic management information. The results of financial accounting are later integrated into tax and job cost accounting.

Financial Accounting Started with Lists, Then Moved to Systems

Lists record only one type of transaction

Lists of expenditures for goods and services are as old as written history; 6,000-year-old stone tablets and parchments recorded grain and livestock production. But single-purpose lists showed no relation to a larger system. These lists quantified production but not the impact of this production on the farm's profit.

Double entries recorded transactions twice—which started and promoted systems thinking

Double-entry bookkeeping first appeared in Genoa, Italy, in about 1340 and was formally documented by the Franciscan monk Fra Luca Paciolo in his book *Arithmetic, Geometry, and Proportion* in 1494. In this system, each entry was entered in two accounts to show cause and effect. For example, if a good was purchased with cash, the purchase cost would be subtracted from the cash account and also added to an asset (good) account. These two transactions would in turn affect other accounts. In this way, every transaction became part of the accounting system for the entire enterprise. This system is still in use.

This accounting system mirrors project management systems thinking—which manages the relations between scope, cost, and schedule. Each action produces many reactions.

This system then became standardized and regulated

Financial accounting is governed by established rules. In the United States, these rules were developed following the stock market crash of 1929. The (SEC) Security and Exchange Commission was established to regulate standardized preparation and presentation of accounting information to permit investor evaluation and to avoid deception. In 1973, the SEC established the (FASB) Financial Accounting Standards Board an organization of distinguished senior accountants to set the rules other accountants must follow. The rules are called (GAAP) Generally Accepted Accounting Principles. These rules, updated slowly in small steps, are in use today. The rules were originally reasonable and tended to be compatible with common sense. However, accounting rules soon became influenced by the demands of politics and tax regulation, and common sense was compromised.

The United States uses GAAP—other countries have different systems

The GAAP accounting system was developed and used in the United States as described above, and enjoys worldwide recognition. The European area and Japan developed and use the (IFRS) International Financial Reporting Standards. This causes difficulties in comparing international business—and multiple-country stock exchange listings.

Although the merits of each system continued to be discussed, few strongly argue that one system is clearly deficient or superior—they are just different. Moves to reconcile these systems have been underway for decades—with little progress. These differences must be understood for international construction operations.

Payroll Deductions—Bookkeeping for the Government, Insurance Companies, and Unions

Before World War II, workers received their gross pay, frequently in cash, and paid their own taxes. During World War II, to accelerate the collection of taxes to fund the war effort, the government mandated deduction of income taxes from gross pay as a "temporary measure." The government also mandated freezing wages. Employers began offering health insurance—then a low-cost service—to compensate for the unattractively low wages.

Not only did these temporary measures become permanent but everybody else piled on. Although payroll accounting is fully part of financial accounting, the multiple political and administrative rules and methods of calculations merit a separate discussion. A sampling of the thieves market of deductions from payroll includes the following:

- The employees' state and federal income taxes and Social Security and Medicare contributions are deducted from weekly pay. These federal deductions, plus an employer-matching Social Security and Medicare payment, are paid to a bank acting as a Treasury agent or directly to the Treasury. "Small" companies that incur less than $200,000 per year in tax liabilities must deposit this payment by the 15th day of the month following withholding. Larger employees must deposit by electronic transfer weekly.

- State and federal unemployment taxes are generally paid quarterly (some states require more frequent payment) with a cap per employee, but the contribution rates are tiered and altered by the company's quarterly gross payroll. Further, there can be annual retroactive surcharges if the government needs more to make ends meet.

- Workers compensation and liability insurance are paid as a percentage of payroll. The company must estimate annual payroll at the beginning of the year and pay a premium deposit and the balance in monthly or quarterly installments. In addition, liability insurance can have flat rates for the year, regardless of payroll volume.

- Union dues and benefit contribution rates are based on hours worked—with some caps and alterations—and are usually paid monthly.

- Other benefits, health, and vacation costs can be paid either with yearly deposits and monthly installments, or lump sum.

- Court mandated payroll deductions, such as child support and wage garnishment for the employee's unpaid bills, are deducted from employee's pay and paid to the court or its agent.

There has been a long-term trend to increase the number and amounts of payroll burdens, until total burden now centers around 50% of gross payroll, but can run as high as 80% for safe well-run construction companies—much higher for others. (For every $1.00 of a tradesmen's take-home pay, more than $2.70 can be paid to someone else.)

Failure to make the required tax deposits on time triggers additional (loan shark brutal) government imposed interest and penalties. And if the company does not pay these sums, the "responsible person" (broadly defined by the IRS to include officers, partners, sole proprietors, employees, directors, trustees, and accountants) becomes personally liable.

"Real-time" hourly labor costs must use estimates

The complication of the different methods and timing of payments and the retroactive imposition of additional fees make the question, "what does a worker cost per hour?", a troublesome and uncertain calculation. The real answer will not be known until about 15 months after the start of the financial year—a time frame that has no relation to a project's scheduled progress.

But job costing requires real-time hourly labor costs. Hourly rates must be identified to the owner, for time and material work, and when a contract requires stated labor rates for change orders. And the complexity and uncertainty of payroll cost calculation is beyond the comprehension of all but the most diligent and knowledgeable owner's representatives. So, establishing and agreeing on carefully calculated hourly labor costs—and a time and method of needed change of these rates at the start of the project—is essential for job costing and good owner relations.

Different Purposes and Timing Lead to Three Accounting Systems

Accounting systems seek to answer three questions: (1) what occurred in the last period, (2) what is the present situation, and (3) what can we expect next. Although accounting data deal with facts, the purposes and timing of inputs and uses are so radically different that three separate accounting systems are used: (1) financial accounting, (2) tax accounting, and (3) managerial, also called cost or job cost, accounting.

Financial accounting—helping management and others evaluate a business

For management, investors, bankers, and bonding companies

Financial accounting builds a picture of a business conforming to GAAP to satisfy outsiders but not for project process improvement. This system shows wealth at a point in time, the income for a period of time, usually 1 year, as well as information to assist understanding.

These financial statements are prepared for a yearly period—a few months after period end. Larger companies will prepare quarterly statements. Monthly statements may be prepared for internal use or to satisfy bank loan covenants but not for outside publication.

There are three levels of financial statement rigor and scrutiny. A compilation places management's accounting data into an accepted organized format without attempting analysis and verification. A review then adds analysis by ratios and established benchmarks to determine that the compilation is reasonable. An audit further adds verification of assets and project completion status. With an audit, the company's assets and liabilities are verified through third-party confirmation or direct CPA (Certified Public Accountant) observation. Creditors are contacted to determine that all bills received are accurate and complete. Large equipment may be physically viewed to confirm existence, and projects toured to determine that claimed completion is reasonable.

Investors use this accounting information to increase, maintain, or decrease company stock holdings, and to evaluate existing management performance. Bankers use the information to consider granting loans by assessing the probability of sufficient future profitability to service the loan, and identifying assets that can be seized and sold if the loan payments are not made as agreed.

Bonding companies providing payment and performance bonds require the same profitability and asset documentation that the banker demands. The bonding company also seeks a deeper understanding of the construction business as a going concern and evaluates the character and capacity of the owners.

Project owners seek to confirm that the construction company is solvent and has the necessary equipment, cash, or lines of credit to complete the project. CM company owners get outside verification of what they should have already known about their firm.

Tax accounting—reprocesses this information but with new or slightly different rules
Record keeping for the government

The legislators make laws, and the IRS produces regulations that can be long-term and consistent or short-term and politically expedient. Change is continual. These rules are applied to the financial accounting data and organization described above to determine the amount of tax to be paid. This results in two different profit figures: one for book (financial accounting—the way management understands it) and one for tax (the way tax laws and regulations require). Conformance to rules and regulations is required—but management of the amount and timing of tax payments is the goal.

For all but the smallest enterprises, successful preparation of these tax documents requires a CPA doing tax work full time. Tax returns are prepared annually, but tax payments are frequently paid quarterly.

Managerial, cost, and job cost accounting seek real-time information
Record keeping for process, productivity, and profit improvement

Managerial accounting seeks to manage and improve productivity and profit of processes in progress—so information as close to real time as possible is sought. Trade labor is paid weekly, so weekly information is achievable with this accounting data. More frequent analysis can be performed—but only with more management time and effort than is usually available.

The finance, tax, and cost accounting systems use the same information—the same deck of cards. But just as the deck of cards can be used to play simple childhood games, such as slapjack or old maid, or adult thinking games such as bridge, the accounting systems can have different purposes and results. It is most practical to view these three related systems as separate. Reconciliation is more confusing than informative.

Established Customs and Ideas Are Not Obvious

A little different from common sense, but unavoidable. Workable—if explained and understood

Timing—irregularly timed inputs are managed to provide a consistent realistic picture

As discussed above, financial statements are prepared yearly. Assets or obligations (such as a lease but not a project) that last longer than 1 year are classified as long-term assets or liabilities. This distinction frequently defines what may be expensed in the current year or must be capitalized (entered as an asset on the balance sheet), which has large tax consequences.

A cash transaction is easy to understand—an asset or service is received and a bill is paid and recorded. An accrual is an agreement to pay or receive cash or other assets in the future. Even though cash is not yet received or paid, the accrual is recorded as income or expense. This is required to accurately document current positions and agreements.

Although easy to understand, the significance of cash and accruals is frequently overlooked by those new to management and accounting. It is possible and common to have lots of cash and be losing money, or to have very little cash and be highly profitable. Spending current cash without recognizing that an accrual will soon require this same cash has produced many company failures. Cash may be king—but only cash not already spoken for counts.

Asset valuation—tricky and confusing with huge accounting effects

A long-term asset will exist 1 year or more from the current balance sheet date. If an expenditure (asset) has value beyond the balance sheet date, the portion of the expenditure that has value will be recorded as an asset and the remainder will be taken as an expense. The remaining value of an asset that become worthless, such as equipment that is stolen, will be taken as an expense. Short-term assets and the depreciation of the asset will both appear on the balance sheet and cancel—showing no increase in company wealth. For assets on the borderline of 1-year useful life, management opinions and purchasing decisions can alter income, taxes, and the appearance of wealth. Expense the asset to reduce current taxes—capitalize to increase wealth.

Fixed assets (property, plant, and equipment) are valued at acquisition cost less accumulated depreciation. If asset values are stable, this is a conservative and accurate representation of the assets' current value. If asset values fluctuate, this system becomes less accurate, and its credibility becomes questionable.

In the last part of the 20th century, when the stock markets experienced rapid valuation increases, some pension funds were allowed to "mark to market" (adjust asset values to present market values) pension fund assets and "prove" overfunding. With this new valuation, additional contributions to the pension funds were suspended or previous contributions withdrawn.

In this same period, Enron—an energy trading company—found the current market value of its assets far less than acquisition cost and collapsed. This produced a call for a yearly updating of the assets to reflect current value. Easier said than done.

Yearly valuation is always costly and is difficult in times of stagnation because no similar assets change hands—to establish current prices. But the larger problem is that recognizing a change in asset value also increases or decreases current period income. (The asset value change is booked as a gain or loss on the yearly income statement.) This can produce wild income swings that mask the performance of continuing operations. Partial inclusion of mark-to-market asset valuation produced chaos and wealth destruction, particularly in banking.

Income and Taxes Can Be Managed

Management's opinions change short-run results with long-term consequences
Accounting is not just facts—judgment also changes results

Accountants can record all transactions and accruals based on information provided, but management opinion is required to complete the accounting analysis. Management must first provide its opinion of percentages of project completion. This must be reasonably consistent with received accounting data, but there is a subjective element as well. Current-period income and taxes can be altered by this subjective judgment. Management's judgment of completion is the single most powerful tool for current income and tax management.

Management can also choose when to write off an asset. For example, when management decides a long overdue bill is uncollectible, the bill will be written off in the current period. Deduction of this loss on the income statement reduces current income, but deduction from the balance sheet also reduces wealth. Management can also claim or establish long-running disputes, sometimes supplemented with litigation, to establish that current income should not be recognized in the current period. This again affects current period income and taxes. And litigation can delay recognition of income until the litigation is finalized, which can take years to decades.

Depreciation—an asset value adjustment and an investment tool

Depreciation for businesses (depreciation is not recognized for individuals) documents an asset's declining value over its useful life. Although the asset may still be in use, it may be worn out, functionally obsolete, or uneconomical to operate and maintain. A portion of this depreciation is subtracted each year from the asset's balance sheet value to reflect this reality—and as an expense from the income statement as well.

Legislation can also allow or mandate depreciation schedules unrelated to reality to induce favored behavior. In the mid-1960s, depreciation of the full value of low-income multifamily housing projects was allowed within the first few years of construction, rather than a more reasonable 30-year life of the building. This caused those seeking tax shelters to finance projects they would not otherwise have considered.

This depreciation is prized by real estate investors because it is an accounting, but not a cash, transaction. This permits the investor to receive cash from a project but shelter (receive paper tax deductions that wipe out taxable income) all of the project income, and maybe more.

Understanding this dimension of a project owner's needs can increase the project manager's ability to serve these needs.

Standardized Formats Aid Analysis and Comparison

The financial statement—a standardized, widely recognized report format

Financial accounting reports a company's present position and last year's activities. Accountants need a piece of paper (or electronic equivalent) to confirm and believe that an accounting event is real—and therefore look only at historical data.

Financial accounting (for all industries) produces three elements: (1) a balance sheet that states the position at a point in time—the end of the period, (2) an income statement that documents the transactions for a period of time—a year or quarter, and (3) notes and assumptions. The notes and assumptions describe the accounting methods used in, management-provided assumptions, and explanation of extraordinary events. Without these notes, meaningful evaluation is impossible.

Construction company's financial statements provide a clearer picture if two additional elements are added: (1) statement of cash flows that describe where cash came from and where it was spent and (2) schedule of fixed overhead that describes the home office costs that are independent of project-specific costs. Since the portions of equipment, tools, vehicles, home office management, and insurance costed to the project can vary hugely by company, defining the components of home office overhead defines the components of job cost.

These elements of the financial statement can be illustrated with a simple construction company example, using unrealistically small round numbers for clarity.

The company is founded on the last day of the preceding year and starts and completes one project in the current year. The company owners contribute a piece of equipment, with a 10-year life acquired for $10,000 and loan $20,000 in cash. The opening balance sheet is

Balance Sheet For Sample Company
As of 12-31-preceding year

Assets		Liabilities		
Cash	$20,000	Loan (officer)	$20,000	
Equipment	$10,000	*Total liabilities*		$20,000
		Equity		
		Stock	$10,000	
		Total equity		$10,000
Total assets	$30,000	*Total liability and equity*		$30,000

The left asset column equals (balances with—hence the name balance sheet) the right column that combines liability and equity. The book value of the company is $10,000 (the equity—the $10,000 stock). Note that the balance sheet is at a point in time, but the income statement described below is for a period of time.

On the first day of the year, the company starts a project with the following cost components:

Project contract value	$100,000
Estimated labor	$10,000
Estimated material	$10,000
Subcontract cost	$60,000
Estimated gross profit	$20,000

The project is half complete on June 1, and $50,000 is immediately invoiced and paid. The subcontractor is also immediately paid $30,000.

The project is finally complete on 12-31-sample year and $45,000 is immediately billed and paid. The contract balance of $5,000 was billed but not paid. All materials and labor have been paid as the work progressed, but the final subcontract payment of $30,000 has not yet been made. The home office yearly overhead of $15,000 has been fully paid. The piece of equipment depreciated 1/10 of its use for life during the year, for a depreciation cost of $1,000.

The income statement at the end of the year becomes:

Income Statement For Sample Company
For the period 1-1-sample year to 12-31-sample year

Revenues		
Project revenue	$95,000	
Project accounts receivable	$5,000	
Total receipts		$100,000
Expenses		

Material	($10,000)	
Labor	($10,000)	
Subcontractor payments	($30,000)	
Subcontractor accounts payable	($30,000)	
Expenses from operations		($80,000)
Gross operating margin		$20,000
General and administrative expense		
Office overhead	($15,000)	
Depreciation (equipment)	($1,000)	
Total general and administrative expense		($16,000)
Profit		$4,000

The profit then increases the year-end company equity, and the year-end balance sheet becomes:

Balance Sheet For Sample Company
As of 12-31-sample year

Assets			Liabilities		
Cash		$50,000	Accounts payable	$30,000	
Accounts receivable		$5,000	Loan (officer)	$20,000	
Equipment	$10,000		*Total liability*		$50,000
Less accumulated depreciation	($1,000)	$9,000	*Equity*		
			Stock	$10,000	
			Retained earnings	$4,000	
			Total equity		$14,000
Total Assets		$64,000	*Total equity and liability*		$64,000

In this example, the statement of cash flows would look very similar to the income statement, except the accumulated depreciation, a noncash transaction, would be absent.

The schedule of administrative overhead would be in the form:

Schedule of Administrative Overhead
For Sample Company
For the year ending 12-31-sample year

Officers' salary	$4,000
Administrative salary	$2,000
Payroll taxes	$1,500
Insurance	$1,000
Office services	$500
Office supplies	$500
Professional fees	$500
Rent	$2,000
Vehicle expense	$2,000
Communication expense	$1,000
Total	$15,000

This documents the costs of home office overhead—the yearly costs that will be incurred even if no projects are won and built—the yearly "nut." And since all other expenses will be costed to the projects, it establishes the dividing line between fixed overhead and job cost.

Financial Statement Formats Influence Management Thinking and Decision

Definition of fixed overhead influences competitive pricing attitudes

The dividing line between office and project costs is specific for the nature of each construction firm and the type of projects performed. For example, a road builder who wins projects by public bid has no need to communicate all accounting data to the project owner, which makes accounting simpler and less rigorous. Long-term owned equipment is a competitive bidding advantage and might best be considered overhead—greatly increasing office overhead expense. This encourages taking projects at low-project overhead and profit when work is scarce "just to make the (office) overhead," but seek high-project overhead and profit when work is abundant.

A construction management firm that shares cost information with the owner must seek to show the lowest possible office overhead by shifting, to the extent possible, overhead costs to direct job costs so that the maximum costs may be expensed to the job and reimbursed by the owner. And project overhead must be consistent over time—the wild fluctuations of the road builder above will not be tolerated. A very different dividing line between overhead and job costs is needed for the construction manager and the road builder.

The "personality" and the project types of the construction company define the appropriate accounting format. And this format—a report card—shapes evaluation of projects and company employees. This can be troublesome for employees moving between firms and for firms attempting two very different project types—missed productivity clues, confused communication, and major mistakes may result.

In the real world, there may be many noncash transactions, accruals, different accounting methods, management estimates, and tens of thousands of additional entries. The form and methods remain the same, but the supplemental reports such as statements of cash flows, schedules of fixed overhead, and notes have greater relevance and usefulness.

Financial and Tax Accounting Results Are Modified by Management Opinion

Timing, management opinions, and purchasing methods are the tools

High income and low taxes are always desirable. A strong balance sheet to obtain loans and bonds is also desirable. But these two goals conflict, so priorities must be set and a balance sought. Accounting facts are persistent and limit management possibilities to achieve this balance to the techniques listed below.

Careful timing and management opinions can reduce current taxes

Accelerating purchase (with credit) of equipment near year-end will not reduce cash but will increase depreciation that reduces income tax. Declaring a project incomplete near year-end can also reduce current-period taxable income, but a credible explanation consistent with accounting data must be offered to the accountant. It is not easy, at least legally, to stretch the truth and classify a substantially complete project as incomplete just to gain a tax advantage. Convincing evidence from disinterested third parties can help support the case. Bankruptcy of the project owner, which reduces prospects for payment, is one possible explanation. And litigation is another—so some will start meritless litigation to extend declared completion for years after construction completion. But even in these cases, convincing accounting entries must reflect these changed conditions, and delayed recognition only applies to the disputed portion of the project value.

Management estimates of project completion can have a huge impact on current income. For example, if the project is 50% complete and accumulated costs have been documented, management's estimate of 25% complete would show a large loss, but an estimate of 75% complete would show a large profit. A failing company can mask deteriorating conditions for a few years by inflating estimates of completion.

A firm may provide management estimates that are true and accurate, or a little fudged to manage taxes, or outright fabrications to hide failing operations. Anyone can hide a lie for 1 year, but accounting facts will catch up with the lie within 3 years. So, a 3-year evaluation of potential vendor or subcontractor financial statements to assess their financial capability may be needed.

Larger accounting firms auditing larger contractors will attempt field verification of project completion to prevent this distortion. But a skilled project manager can influence the opinion of an accountant unschooled in construction.

Management can decide, within reasonable limits, when to declare a formerly valid receivable uncollectible. Such a transaction will reduce both current income and balance sheet equity.

Purchasing methods can be structured for tax efficiency

Large equipment may be purchased for cash (affects cash but not the net balance sheet or income statement) or purchased with financing (does not affect cash, small effect on income, no net effect on the balance statement—the new asset value balances with the new loan). Accounting treats a "capital lease" as a disguised purchase.

A capital lease is one where the lessor assumes the risk and enjoys the benefit of ownership and is really a contract for purchase not a lease. Both the FASB and the IRS have rules to determine if the lease is a capital or operating lease, but as a practical matter, the lease will usually be a capital lease if there is an option to purchase the equipment at the end of the lease for amount that is substantially below fair market value—often as little as $1.00 or 1% of the original purchase price.

A capital lease is entered on the balance sheet as the sum of the present value of lease payments and the present value of the cost to exercise the purchase option. A corresponding entry is made to reflect the liability. Each lease payment is applied to principal and interest expense, and the asset is depreciated.

In contrast, accounting treats an "operating lease" (where the lessor transfers only the right to use the property to the lessee, and at the end of the lease period, the property is returned to the lessor; some operating leases have the option to buy, at fair market value, at the end of the lease) as an operating cost that does not affect cash, and has a small effect on the income statement. The equipment is not owned so is not entered as an asset. Using "off balance sheet" accounting, the lease payment expenses are deducted from the income statement and the terms of the lease are disclosed in the footnotes of the financial statement. But this omission of lease liabilities from the balance sheet can conceal "company killing" obligations from those who do not carefully scrutinize the entire balance sheet.

Knowledge of these rules and their benefits can use accounting and tax considerations to increase equipment purchasing cost efficiency. For example, two leases with only a few altered words can obtain identical assets while presenting radically different financial pictures of the wealth of the company, as well as different cash flows and income tax liability. Although this subject is somewhat dry and technical, it is not just for home office accountants—project managers and superintendents can employ this knowledge to gain significant project benefits.

Project Owners Have Different Priorities—a Service and Sales Opportunity

Not-for-profit organizations—hospitals, schools, churches, and social service organizations—find it far easier to raise capital than continually obtain required operating costs. Wealthy donors may contribute—seeking building naming rights but are unwilling to endow the janitor. And nonprofits are not concerned with depreciation or taxes. This means nonprofits may be very willing to consider and seek higher initial construction cost to achieve lower operating costs. Selling them a more efficient, but expensive, building may be what they want and need.

| Insert nail and grout. | *Soil nailing operations photo 3 of 6* |

Multifamily residential is more balanced. Modest capital cost that produces low operating costs and modest depreciation is the goal. Construction solutions to strike this balance are needed.

Commercial rental real estate, such as office buildings and shopping centers, frequently lease on a triple net basis (in addition to the rent, the tenant pays the real estate taxes, insurance and common area maintenance, and a portion of building repair). Here, extremely low capital construction cost is sought and high operating costs (since the tenant pays) are acceptable. A building with good curb appeal but low quality and high maintenance and operating cost may be sought. These operating costs must remain close to the normal standard for the area, or the real estate owner's reputation may be damaged, and occupancy rates and profit decreased.

Understanding these owners' very different accounting methods and needs helps the construction manager provide the right building solution, and increase sales.

Audits—Were the Rules Followed?

Required, sometimes a management tool but not intended to catch a crook

Auditors from the construction companies' accounting firm, insurance companies, unions, and occasionally government agencies will audit the company's accounting information.

Larger companies will audit internally to diagnose irregularities in operations. If both the internal auditor and the personnel in the departments audited have the right attitude, internal audits can be a valuable management tool to assist process improvement. This cooperation does not regularly occur—internal auditors are usually viewed as snoops and tattletales.

For all audit types, the auditor tries to determine if rules were followed but does not attempt to improve project performance or detect malfeasance, such as employee theft. All project performance management remains the project manager's responsibility.

Summary

Accounting is structured record keeping for a purpose. The construction companies' purpose will vary by type of work performed and the portion of the accounting data that must be shared with the project owner. The accounting structure must reflect the company's "personality" and usual project type.

The project owners' accounting system will be influenced by their capital, tax, and depreciation structure. Understanding these owner needs can help provide the building most appropriate for their requirements. And tailoring your project accounting presentation to their familiar methods can aid communication and understanding—and increase value added and sales.

Accounting can provide tax and income benefits for the construction company as well, but the major project management focus is job cost accounting—which seeks to understand current project status and methods of improvement.

Review Questions (True or False)

1. Financial, tax, and job cost accounting are all required for construction companies and projects.
2. Financial accounting is started first, then tax and job cost accounting.
3. Financial accounting must follow established rules and formats. In the United States, GAAP rules are followed, but in other countries, other systems such IFRS are followed, which can complicate accounting for international construction projects.
4. The employer must pay many additional costs (burdens) for each hour of employee wages. The question "what does a worker cost per hour" can be precisely calculated each week.
5. "Real-time" hourly labor costs based on carefully calculated estimates are used for job costing and for established labor rates in time and material contracts.
6. Tax accounting uses the financial accounting format and timing without alteration to calculate taxes due.
7. Fixed assets (property, plant, and equipment) are valued at acquisition cost less accumulated depreciation. Only assets with a useful life of 1 year or more appear on the balance sheet.
8. Income and taxes are hard facts that cannot be influenced or altered by management's opinions.
9. The balance sheet states the position of a construction firm at a point in time and the income statement states the transactions for a period of time.
10. The schedule of administrative overhead identifies fixed costs that must be paid every year—even if no projects are performed. The profit realized from construction projects must exceed the administrative overhead before the firm will realize a profit for the year.
11. Obtaining equipment by purchase or lease has identical effects on the balance sheet and income taxes.

Test Your Understanding

1. Reconstruct the sample company's opening balance sheet in the text using the following figures: Cash $40,000; equipment $20,000; loan (officer) $10,000.
2. Construct your personal balance sheet identifying cash, assets such as real estate, vehicles, or other properties with an individual value over $1000, and liabilities such as loans. (Large student loans can produce a negative equity.)
3. Obtain the pay stub from a weekly payroll check and calculate the percentage of gross wages for each category of deductions (e.g., federal taxes, FICA). Then, list five other types of payments your employer made for the wages paid.

4. Most of your construction work volume requires payment and performance bonds. You wish to increase your work volume which requires acquisition of additional equipment, but your bonding agent insists that you maintain your present balance sheet cash position for working capital. Does leasing or purchasing (with a loan requiring a 10% down payment) the equipment best satisfy your bonding agent's requirement?

CHAPTER
1.5

Finance—the Time Value of Money Affects Many Project Decisions

This soldier pile and lagging retention system was installed by Hayward Baker for construction of the Ernie Davis Hall at Syracuse University in Syracuse, New York. The steel H-sections are driven into the unexcavated earth along the planned excavation limits. Timber lagging is placed between the piles as the excavation progresses. Steel tiebacks through the H-sections into the earth are installed at planned intervals to resist the pressure of the retained earth. The open work area permits rapid excavation and installation of the structure that can produce both cost savings and schedule acceleration. This type of retention system can be installed in many soil types. *Photo courtesy of Hayward Baker Inc.*

Finance—the Time Value of Money Affects Many Project Decisions

One of the largest project costs and an important project management task

Money stores value to purchase goods or services. Money stuffed in a mattress produces nothing, and time is always passing—money not in use is an opportunity lost. Money can and should earn at all times. Finance manages this continual earning power—time value—of money. And the time value cost magnifies the impact of the relationship in the project management triple constraint of scope, time, and cost—making the time value of money a driving force in project management decisions.

Some transactions seem too small or fast—such as the money in your pocket right now—to justify financial analysis. Yet construction management consists of a vast number of small transactions, which together have large impacts. Similar to the banking practice of sweeping (temporarily moving cash from noninterest-bearing accounts to interest-bearing accounts) at the end of the business day and investing the money overnight, even for a few hours, is an example that can be imitated in construction.

Project management decisions from initial planning, contract term negotiations, delivery of materials, and project scheduling all have a financial dimension. Finance is not just something for the bookkeeper, accountant, or comptroller—it is a necessary project management task. Construction has large contract values, small profit margins, and sometimes late payment for work performed. So the construction manager's finance cost of progress payments can exceed the project's profit—if not recognized and managed. Poor cash flow management and the resulting high finance costs is a common cause of construction firm bankruptcy and failure.

Determining the Cost Impact of the Time Value of Money

Financial analysis requires a start and end date, just like a project. The rate of return (interest rate), and amount and timing of each payment are also required.

The Type and Purpose of Calculation Methods

Future value of a single transaction
The future value finds the value at the end of the period, including accumulated interest, of a single receipt or payment made at the start of a period. Uses include finding the value of a certificate of deposit at maturity and calculating escalated costs due to project delay.

Future value of repeated payments (an annuity)
This is similar to the future value of a single transaction described above except multiple identical payments are made at identical intervals, such as daily, monthly, or yearly. Uses include calculating the amount and number of payments necessary to accumulate a sum of money for purposes such as a car purchase, school tuition, house down payment, or retirement. Calculating the financing cost of retention withheld from progress payments is another use.

Present value of a single transaction
The present value is the inverse (reciprocal) of the future value and can determine either the implied interest rate for early receipt or payment, or the resulting value at a stated interest rate of an early receipt or payment. Calculating the implied interest rate for vendor offered discounts for prompt payment and evaluating the financial impact of contract payment terms are other uses.

Present value of repeated payments (an annuity)

Determining the present value of the stream of future payments, sometimes called the capitalization rate, is one of the owner's financial workhorses. This determines the building cost justified by a future stream of income such as rent payments and is a key determinant of project feasibility. It can also be used for the financial analysis necessary to support proposed value engineering—such as an equipment upgrade offering a future stream of energy savings.

Common financial conventions

Most industries calculate interest at the end of the period. All calculations in this chapter and most calculations in the construction workplace use this method. Interest rates can be calculated from the period middle or beginning. The project manager needs to be aware of, but need not master, these other calculation methods.

Financial calculations frequently use 360 rather than 365 days for annual calculation. This convention—used in financial tables and some computer software—may be used without correction for the missing 5 days.

Three Calculation Methods All Get the Same Answer

Different purposes use different calculation methods to obtain the same result
Comfort level and number of calculations needed influence choice of method

Tables—Labor-Saving Precalculation

Before computers, slide rules were used for rapid, but not highly, precise calculation. Greater precision required time consuming hand calculation. One table, such as the required monthly principal and interests payments for a 30-year mortgage (360 payments) for 10 interest rate possibilities, required 3,600 hand calculations. To avoid repetition of this labor, the calculated values were placed in tables that were included in finance and engineering books.

Widely available computers and handheld calculators provide alternatives to tables. Older engineering books using tables still have substantial engineering value, so familiarity with calculation by tables is useful. Tables can also be helpful for at glance go-no-go decisions of project feasibility. Finally, since tables only require multiplication of two numbers, those not confident of their mathematical abilities may be more comfortable with this method.

Four examples of calculation by tables are shown below.

Tables Used for Calculation						
Future value at period end of a single $1 transaction (extracted from larger tables)						
Period	*5%*	*6%*	*7%*	*8%*	*9%*	*10%*
10	1.6289	1.7908	1.9672	2.1589	2.3674	**2.5937**
Future value at period end of repeated payments (an annuity) of $1 for 10 periods						
Period	*5%*	*6%*	*7%*	*8%*	*9%*	*10%*
10	12.578	13.181	13.816	14.487	15.193	**15.937**
Present value of a single $1 transaction						
Period	*5%*	*6%*	*7%*	*8%*	*9%*	*10%*
10	0.6139	0.5584	0.5083	0.4632	0.4224	**0.3855**
Present value of repeated payments (an annuity) of $1 for 10 periods						
Period	*5%*	*6%*	*7%*	*8%*	*9%*	*10%*
10	7.7217	7.3601	7.0236	6.7101	6.4177	**6.1446**

Since $1 was used for each of these examples, the table value becomes the calculated value. For example, the future value of a single transaction at period 10 with a 6% interest rate is $1.79. If the initial value was $10 instead of $1, the value would be 10 × 1.79 or $17.90.

Algebraic Calculation May be Used for Those Comfortable With this Method

Memorized formulas are always available, so those accustomed to mathematical calculation, such as engineers, may prefer this method. Handheld financial calculators purchased for 1 to 2 hour's wages will speed calculation. If many repeated similar calculations are needed, algebraic calculation may prove less desirable.

Four examples of algebraic calculation are shown below.

Algebra Used for Calculation

Future value at period end of a single $1 transaction

$$FV = R(1 + k)^n$$

R = amount of the payment
k = interest rate
n = number of periods

Future value at period end of repeated payments (an annuity) of $1 for 10 periods

$$FV = R \sum_{t=1}^{'n} (1 + k)^{n-t}$$

Present value of a single $1 transaction

$$PV = \frac{1}{(1 + k)^n} = \left[\frac{1}{(1 + k)}\right] n$$

Present value of repeated payments (an annuity) of $1 for 10 periods

$$PV = R \sum_{t=1}^{n} \left(\frac{1}{1 + k}\right) t$$

Financial Functions on Computers

Software spreadsheet programs such as Microsoft Excel can also be used. (The program must have installed and activated financial functions.) The method only requires typing 4–6 values, and the answer is calculated—no mathematical skill or knowledge is required. And these functions can be arranged on a spreadsheet to instantly perform thousands of calculations to evaluate multiple scenarios.

Examples of calculation by financial functions are shown below.

Financial functions on a computer software program

Future value at period end of a single $1 transaction

FV (rate, nper, pmt, pv, type)
Rate = interest rate per period
Nper = number of payments

Pmt = payment made each period

Pv = value of the initial payment (can be 0)

Type = time payment is due (0 = end of period, 1 = beginning of period)

FV (.10,1,1,1,0)

Here the number of payments is 1

Future value at period end of repeated payments (an annuity) of $1 for 10 periods

FV (rate, nper, pmt, pv, type)

FV (.10,10,1,1,0)

Here the number of payments is 10

Present value of a single $1 transaction

PV (rate, nper, pmt, fv, type)

PV (.10,1,1,1,0)

Present value of repeated payments (an annuity) of $1 for 10 periods

PV (rate, nper, pmt, fv, type)

PV (.10,10,1,1,0)

One additional useful calculation method is the loan payment calculator shown below.

Calculation of the amount of loan payments

PMT(rate, nper, pmt, pv, fv, type)

Modifying Considerations May Be Ignored or May Have Large Impacts

Changing rates and times can add calculation complexity

Calculation of interest rates for the beginning or middle of the period was discussed above. Also, real-world interest rates and the amount and regularity of payments may vary throughout the project. These changes can be calculated meticulously at each change. And there are more complex financial calculations for many of the common situations. But this level of calculation complexity and precision is rarely needed for construction project management. Project managers usually use financial calculations to make a decision. Once the decision is made, more precise financial and tax calculations are done by accountants.

Depreciation and income tax impacts

For projects constructed solely for investment return, the impact of depreciation and income tax advantages can dwarf time value of money considerations. Such analysis occupies much of the attention of project developers and owners. The construction project manager should understand the owners' tax needs, but seldom actively participate in tax-related analysis and decision. But this understanding can add value by recasting construction cost information for the owner's tax needs.

Construction Company Financial Structure

All assets including cash should earn an acceptable rate of return. Short-term safe assets earn a lower rate of return and long-term risky assets command a higher return.

Equity to book value—a measure of leverage

The stockholders vote, make key decisions, and control the company, and expect a high rate of return—maybe 15%. If the company is financially troubled and all obligations cannot be paid, the order of payment usually is as follows: taxes, payroll labor, secured creditors, unsecured creditors, and then stockholders. Some or all of the stockholders' equity can be lost.

Sale of stock is a taxable event that discourages frequent changes in stock ownership. And stockholder's sale of shares can alter the voting rights and control of the firm, which further discourages ownership changes.

A higher rate of return is needed to compensate for these factors. One way to increase the return is to maintain low equity in relation to income, which can be accomplished by selectively borrowing needed capital. The capital structure of the firm—the relationship between income, debt, and equity—must be managed to maximize value as discussed below.

A loan to the company may have fixed terms and attractive interest rates

The loan has a principal amount, interest rate, and start and end date, and is both less patient and less risky than equity. So loans command a lower rate of return. And the repayment of the loan is not a taxable event—making it easier for owners to get their money out of the company. So, a company owner may act as both a lender and an equity contributor to manage both the firm's capital efficiency and the tax consequences of withdrawing money from the firm.

So if capital can be obtained on favorable terms by adding debt (getting a loan) or equity (selling stock), the debt will be more efficient and preferred. Less equity for the same income produces higher return on that equity—an efficient capital structure. There are, of course, prudent and appropriate limits to the amount of debt that can be assumed as described below.

The median balance sheet and income values for 643 construction firms are shown below.

COMMERCIAL CONSTRUCTION CONTRACTORS
Balance Statement Median Values

CONTRACT REVENUE SIZE	UNDER $1MM	$1MM & LESS THAN $10MM	$10MM & LESS THAN $50MM	$50MM & OVER	ALL SIZES
NUMBER OF STATEMENTS	86	398	126	33	643
	%	%	%	%	%
ASSETS					
Cash	18.5	17.5	13.0	8.5	16.3
A/R-Progress Billings	31.0	41.9	42.1	34.0	40.1
A/R-Current Retainage	5.4	8.4	14.5	13.0	9.4
Unbilled Work in Progress	7.9	4.6	2.1	9.0	4.8
Costs in Excess of Billings	3.0	4.0	3.8	3.6	3.8
Other Current Assets	6.0	4.9	4.8	5.5	5.1
Total Current	71.8	81.3	80.4	73.7	79.5
Equipment	13.4	9.3	8.2	9.3	9.7
Real Estate	6.1	2.7	3.6	5.8	3.5
Joint Ventures	0.3	0.6	0.9	1.7	0.6
Other Non-Current	8.4	6.0	6.8	9.5	6.7
Total Current	100.0	100.0	100.0	100.0	100.0
LIABILITIES					
Notes Payable-Bank	10.7	4.1	3.6	2.7	4.8
Accounts Payable-Trade	23.2	30.9	34.1	29.0	30.4
Accounts Payable-Retainage	1.3	3.9	7.4	8.2	4.5
Federal Income Tax Payable	1.6	1.8	2.2	3.4	1.9
Billings in Excess of Costs	3.1	7.1	7.9	7.1	6.7
Contract Advances	0.9	1.5	0.6	2.6	1.3
Prov. For Loss on Contr. In Progress	0.5	0.1	0.0	0.0	0.1
Current Maturities LT Debt	3.2	1.8	1.0	1.7	1.8
Other Current Liabilities	7.8	7.9	7.8	7.7	7.8
Total Current	52.3	59.1	64.6	62.5	59.4
LT Liabilities, Unsub.	8.3	7.9	8.5	11.5	8.3
Total Unsubordinated Debt	60.7	67.0	73.2	74.1	67.7
Subordinated Debt	0.3	0.8	0.5	1.5	0.7

Total Liabilities	61.0	67.8	73.7	75.6	68.4
EQUITY					
Tangible Net Worth	39.0	32.2	26.3	24.4	31.6
Total	100.0	100.0	100.0	100.0	100.0

Income Statement Median Values

	%	%	%	%	%
Contract Revenues	100.0	100.0	100.0	100.0	100.0
Cost of Work Performed	78.5	87.0	91.5	91.3	87.0
Gross Profit	21.5	13.0	8.5	8.7	13.0
All Other Expense Net	18.4	9.8	6.1	5.5	10.0
Profit Before Taxes	3.1	3.2	2.4	3.2	3.0

Note that the smaller firms have more equity and less debt than larger firms. Also note that the profit margins center around 3% for all firm sizes. These figures may seem low but include all costs including depreciation and possibly large salaries, perks, and bonuses for the owners.

Financial Ratios Suggest Appropriate Boundaries

Financial ratios seek to determine that current obligations can be safely met and that the capital structure will assist long-term viability and stability.

Current ratio

The current ratio compares current assets (that are expected to change within 30–365 days) to current liabilities. The ratio must be greater than 1 to meet current obligations without borrowing. To compensate for payment variablities, a cushion of up to 50% may be sought. Larger firms that have ready access to short-term borrowing may have a ratio less than 1.

Debt to equity (debt to net worth)

This ratio describes the capital structure efficiency. Larger firms with greater capacity to borrow have higher ratios. But the income must support the interest payments—with coverage of 1½ to 3 times earnings considered prudent.

Revenues to receivables

This ratio measures speed of project payments—a higher number means faster payment—and faster payment decreases required working capital.

Revenues to working capital

This ratio gives some guide to the working capital (current asset–current liabilities) required for a given work volume, which influences the firm's speed of growth. Larger firms with the ability to borrow will have a higher ratio.

The median ratios for the same 643 construction firms are shown below.

COMMERCIAL CONSTRUCTION CONTRACTORS
Financial Ratios Median Values

Quick	1.2	1.2	1.1	0.9	1.4
Current	1.5	1.4	1.2	1.1	1.3
Debt/Worth	1.7	2.1	3.0	3.4	2.3
Revenues/Receivables	7.7	6.3	6.1	6.0	6.3
Revenues/Working Capital	15.6	15.1	24.5	41.0	16.9

Project Cash Flow Management Is Vital for Owners and CMs

The interest carrying cost of project payments can equal project profit

Project cash flow projections for the project owner's use

Project owners seldom have all project funds on hand for disbursement when required or requested. The owner's loan requirements may dictate time consuming progress payment procedures. And all idle cash will have a cost. The CM prepares cash flow projections to assist the owners' planning and management.

The most common method uses a spreadsheet with the work items and total values from the contractor's sworn statement down the left column and months for column headings. Monthly costs for each line item are simple to enter and easy to explain. And manual adjustments for agreements such as prepayment of stored materials can be made.

Assigning costs to activity resources in the scheduling program software can also generate cash flow projections. This approach is accurate and automatic but difficult to explain to those not familiar with scheduling programs.

For all methods, the owner, CM, and principal subcontractors and vendors must have a clear understanding about the timing of eligible payments. Payment for items such as off-site fabrication and materials stored in remote warehouses, and upfront payment for reusable components, such as concrete forms, must be identified to make the cash flow projection accurate.

Cash flow management for the CM's fixed company overhead unrelated to project overhead

Projecting the CM firm's own cash flow requirements can be estimated by dividing the annual fixed overhead into 12 monthly payments. This is an order of magnitude estimate of probable cash flow needs and captures accruals for an invoice that is not yet received. Weekly tabulations of invoices due for payment within the next month, with addition of known accruals, will add greater short-term accuracy.

Timing of payment of ongoing expenses can be managed. Taking advantage of vendor offered discounts for prompt payment (e.g., 2%) has an imputed interest rate of about 18% a year. Any payment that can be legitimately delayed produces savings. Payment at the agreed time, which, if not stated, is commonly 30 days, should be made rather than the stated terms on the invoice that may be as prompt as "due upon receipt." Managing the timing of payment for these small amounts can contribute significantly to overall firm profitability.

Aging of accounts receivable and payable

The aging of accounts receivable and payable indicates if the speed of cash flows in and out of the company matches agreements and expectations. This report should also indicate the source and magnitude of problems to assist needed correction. The open accounts, with supporting line item detail, are segregated into 30, 60, 90, and 120 days and over 120 days columns. The source of unacceptable variation becomes immediately apparent, and qualitative judgment about corrective action can be made. For construction projects, payment under 30 days would seldom be a concern but over 120 days almost always need corrective action. Needed corrective action for the 60, 90, and 120 day accounts varies by project and subcontractors' size. Smaller projects and parties need and expect faster payment.

Average age of accounts receivable and payable is also sometimes calculated, but this figure can be deceptive and does not permit management judgment. One large item in the 30 day column could skew the impact of many smaller items in the over 120 day column. And an average figure provides no supporting line item data, which prevents qualitative judgment needed for appropriate corrective action.

Project Payments and the High Cost of Retention

Retention, a temporary 10% deduction from current payments, has a huge financial cost

Commercial and industrial construction payment terms typically have no deposits and are invoiced at the end of each month—and temporarily retain 10% from each monthly progress payment. This custom is found in few other industries. Initial payment of 90% of a washing machine price with the 10% balance due after the machine has been placed in use and satisfactory performance determined seems a puzzling idea. Accountants, architects, engineers, and attorneys all invoice monthly with no retention, well before the needed outcome is achieved. Yet retention in construction is a tradition that must be managed.

The cost of this retention and of any delay in progress payments amounts to a de facto loan to the project owner. The carrying cost of this loan can easily escalate to equal the total project profit, so timing of payments and minimization of retention must be managed.

The impact of prompt 30-day pay and 90-day pay is shown below.

Time value of project payments paid in 30 days

Project value	$1,000,000	
Project duration	10	months
Retention	10%	
Retention paid	11	months
Payment	30	days
Interest Rate	10	%

Month completed	Work net	Invoice withheld	Retention invoice	Interest on retention	Interest on
1	$100,000.00	$90,000.00	$10,000.00	$750.00	$954.19
2	$100,000.00	$90,000.00	$10,000.00	$750.00	$863.95
3	$100,000.00	$90,000.00	$10,000.00	$750.00	$774.42
4	$100,000.00	$90,000.00	$10,000.00	$750.00	$685.61
5	$100,000.00	$90,000.00	$10,000.00	$750.00	$597.50
6	$100,000.00	$90,000.00	$10,000.00	$750.00	$510.09
7	$100,000.00	$90,000.00	$10,000.00	$750.00	$423.37
8	$100,000.00	$90,000.00	$10,000.00	$750.00	$337.34
9	$100,000.00	$90,000.00	$10,000.00	$750.00	$252.00
10	$100,000.00	$90,000.00	$10,000.00	$750.00	$167.33
11					$83.33
	$1,000,000.00	$900,000.00	$100,000.00	$7,500.00	$5,565.78
Total interest cost of delayed payment					$13,065.78

Time value of project payments paid in 90 days

Project value	$1,000,000	
Project Duration	10	months
Retention	10%	
Retention paid	13	months
Payment	90	days
Interest rate	10	%

Month completed	Work net	Invoice withheld	Retention invoice	Interest on retention	Interest on
1	$100,000.00	$90,000.00	$10,000.00	$2,268.05	$1,136.84
2	$100,000.00	$90,000.00	$10,000.00	$2,268.05	$1,045.15
3	$100,000.00	$90,000.00	$10,000.00	$2,268.05	$954.19
4	$100,000.00	$90,000.00	$10,000.00	$2,268.05	$863.95
5	$100,000.00	$90,000.00	$10,000.00	$2,268.05	$774.42
6	$100,000.00	$90,000.00	$10,000.00	$2,268.05	$685.61
7	$100,000.00	$90,000.00	$10,000.00	$2,268.05	$597.50
8	$100,000.00	$90,000.00	$10,000.00	$2,268.05	$510.09
9	$100,000.00	$90,000.00	$10,000.00	$2,268.05	$423.37
10	$100,000.00	$90,000.00	$10,000.00	$2,268.05	$337.34

11				$252.00
12				$167.33
13				$83.33
$1,000,000.00	$900,000.00	$100,000.00	$22,680.48	$7,328.46
Total interest cost of delayed payment				$30,008.94

This second 90-day payment example indicates the carrying cost of approximately $30,000.00 that would also be the project profit at a 3% margin.

The human and schedule management value of prompt payment is huge
Payment timing can improve or poison project relations and performance

If the project or CM is known to be a "good pay," subcontractors and vendors respond well and move quickly. And subcontractors can smell money. If the CM receives a progress payment and does not promptly pay subcontractors their corresponding amount, bad blood quickly develops. Subcontractors will seldom identify the real reason for their dissatisfaction but will find reasons why the production was delayed or why they cannot come to the job at the appropriate time. If the subcontractors are forced to borrow to cover their operating costs, this dissatisfaction will increase. The CM can gain more financially from excellent subcontractor performance than a little bank interest on withheld payments.

Managing Payments and Retention to Minimize Financial Impact

Substantial beneficial deviations from the standard 10% retention can be negotiated. Possibilities include the following: agreements to pay for stored material including materials stored in bonded warehouses, payment for down payments on select equipment, and direct project owner payment of government fees such as building permit and impact fees. Agreements to waive retention on fees for services such as preconstruction work and consulting are commonly accepted. And agreements to waive retention on change orders and to reduce retention to 5% when the project is 50% complete can be sought.

Always try to negotiate something. Once the elephant has its toe in the tent and the project owner has agreed to the principle of less than 10% retention, incremental benefits are easier to obtain.

Finally, CMs have a "pay when paid" agreement with subcontractors. Classifying as many vendors, such as material fabricators (who do no work on site and therefore are not truly subcontractors) as subcontractors, allows withholding retention from their payments, which improves the CM's cash flow.

Contractor Financing Methods and Sources

Bank loans offer satisfactory terms for the adequately capitalized and well managed
Bank loans may be obtained for marketable real estate such as the CM's home office and identifiable (usually by serial number) higher value equipment. These items are viewed as marketable collateral that could be seized in the event of a loan default. 20% equity input (down payment) is frequently required.

Credit lines for working capital for ongoing operations secured by collateral (the project receivables) that are continually changing are more difficult to quantify and evaluate. These lines are secured by the worth of the entire enterprise. For all types of loans, the bank seeks a performing loan (with payments made as agreed) and does not want to seize collateral—and will spend great effort and expense to avoid repossessing hard assets.

Specialized finance companies and internal financing may offer better—or much worse—terms

Vendors of large equipment will frequently offer financing with the sale, but the cost-effectiveness of their offerings is not uniform. Lease rates below reasonable cost can offer a disguised discount to close the sale but avoid the appearance of discounting that cheapens the product image. Other firms use unreasonably high lease costs as an additional profit center. Each case must be evaluated on its merits.

Factoring—purchase of the company's receivables at a steep discount to provide urgently needed cash—does exist in the construction industry but is seldom used. The factors know less about the projects than the project CM, collect a lower portion of the receivables, and usually give up in 3–5 months. Discounts are so steep that use of a factor usually means the CM is severely troubled or on the verge of going out of business.

Small and midsize firms also turn to the private resources of the business owners. Borrowing against home equity and whole life insurance policies is common. Sale of stock or bonds to finance ongoing operations is not customary.

Lease or Buy Financial Calculations Involve both Nonfinancial and Financial Factors

Nonfinancial considerations must be considered first

The decision to lease or purchase equipment has operational and financial impacts. The estimated committed service time—the portion of the equipment's useful life—is the first consideration. If the equipment will be in service for a substantial portion of its useful life and can then be promptly sold for an acceptable price, purchase might be considered. If the estimated equipment use is in days or weeks, leasing is probably the preferable option.

Another consideration that favors leasing is that some leased equipment comes with maintenance and service that has a significant value that is difficult to economically reproduce. For example, cranes require trained operators and maintenance personnel who may require periodic retraining and certification. And crane rental companies will have access to discounted parts and supplies for needed maintenance and repair. In this case, the lease is really for crane services rather than for just the use of a crane.

Some vendors have also taken this service concept to the extreme of offering all equipment and small expendables for the entire job site—everything from chalk lines to cranes from a single source. Purchasing, equipment tracking, billing, and maintenance are all outsourced to these firms that can eliminate personnel at the CM firm and make invoicing of reimbursable project cost more comprehensible and acceptable to some owners. Equipment is only leased for the project duration, reducing equipment finance and disposal costs. This service is only available for larger job sites.

Financial considerations may, or may not, drive the decision

After nonfinancial considerations have determined that either leasing or purchasing equipment may be considered, the next consideration is the actual financial cost. The total cost of the acquisition for the life of the asset can be calculated and compared for the lease and purchase options.

The impact of the lease-buy decision on the financial and income statement is a large deciding factor. The lease may be classified as an operating or capital lease as described in Chapter 1.4 on financial accounting. Choice of leasing methods allows management to produce a stronger balance sheet, which increases borrowing capacity, or increase current period expenses, which can increase tax deductions and current cash flow.

Purchased equipment is entered on the asset side of the balance sheet. If the equipment is purchased for cash, the decrease in the cash will exactly balance new equipment value. If the equipment is financed, the loan equipment value on the asset side will exactly balance the loan value on the liabilities

| Install drainage system on exposed face. | *Soil nailing operations photo 4 of 6* |

side of the balance sheet. The equity of the firm will remain unchanged, and the balance sheet clearly identifies the new hard collateral. This presentation pleases banks and bonding companies.

A portion of purchased equipment value will be depreciated every year, which both reduces the balance sheet value and is also expensed on the income statement. (This reduced income could prove a disadvantage if the company is to be sold in the near future since one measure of appropriate sale price is related to revenue.)

Since depreciation on the income statement is a noncash transaction, it reduces income and therefore income taxes, without a cash outlay. The amount of depreciation that can be charged each year is determined by tax regulation and is intended to correspond to the useful life of the equipment. However, politicians seeking to stimulate the economy may mandate a more aggressive depreciation schedule—up to 100% of acquisition cost—that can hugely skew the lease-buy evaluation.

Owner Project Financing Methods and Sources

Well capitalized building owners constructing new facilities for their operations have a wide range of project financing possibilities—internal cash, bank financing, public financial markets, and specialized companies related to public financial markets. Developers building speculative real estate have fewer choices and harsher terms.

Obtaining project funds from internal resources is still financing

Large, well-capitalized firms may be able to pay for a significant construction project with available cash on hand. Companies of this size will have sophisticated and competent financial personnel who will analyze the opportunity cost of this cash. The internal rate of return determines the interest rate this cash could have earned if used for other purposes. Although the construction managers will not make this opportunity cost calculation, they should be aware that the owner views these project funds in this manner. Even well-capitalized owners financially analyze every project on its own merits—just like the CM—and there is no acceptable piggy bank for cost over-runs.

Project Specific Bank Financing Requires a "Business Plan"

The nature of the business and the loan, anticipated income, character, and credit quality all matter

Credit quality and the business plan

The bank will analyze the financial statements, including the balance and income statements of the firm, usually for the last 3 years, to determine assets and the demonstrated ability of these assets to generate income and cash. The bank will also analyze the character of the potential borrowers and the industry—is it cyclical, declining, or growing. The borrower must also present a case showing how the new activity this loan will facilitate will enhance and improve the firm's financial structure. Speculative real estate will require a very detailed business plan with performance milestones and severe penalties for noncompliance. (It is common for three or more developers to fail on a project before project completion.)

Banks not only want a convincing business plan but also want collateral that can be seized in the event of default. Large publicly traded firms seeking relatively small loans may not be required to pledge individual collateral. Smaller firms may be required to pledge all of the firm's collateral. And very often, the small firm owners must sign personally—pledging everything they own—and could be wiped out in a default. In addition, small commercial loans might only cover 80% of the value of the asset or activity—effectively requiring a 20% down payment, which can be in the form of land or other hard assets. Larger projects may require lower down payments but may have more sensitive performance triggers that can terminate the loan at very short notice.

Construction loans are for a specific project and for a specific time

Construction loans, as the name implies, are only for the funds needed for the preconstruction services and construction of the project and cannot be used for long-term financing. The borrower agrees to a completion time and then pays off the construction loan with a "permanent" real estate loan within this time. Construction managers should be aware that this constraint makes schedule maintenance critical. Even small schedule slippage past the construction loan end date can mean construction payments will not be made as agreed, or possibly at all.

Real estate loans are longer than construction loans but less than the life of the asset

Once the project is completed and becomes marketable real estate, a conventional real estate loan may be obtained. Since the completed project can generate income and has economic value, the loan terms are less restrictive and longer.

Unlike residential real estate, where a mortgage is structured to pay for the entire cost of the building over time, commercial real estate loans are for terms shorter than needed for full principal repayment. This required periodic refinancing can be a significant difficulty for the building owner in times of tight credit.

Most commercial real estate loans have floating interest rates tied to either the prime rate (a benchmark interest rate established by American banks for their most creditworthy customers) or LIBOR (London Interbank Offering Rate—a similar European benchmark). The loan interest rate will be initially set as a number of percentage points over a benchmark, and the loan interest rate will change (after an agreed time lag) when the benchmark changes. The number of percentage points over a benchmark can also be altered by project performance. For example, 3 points over prime for 90% rental occupancy, 5 points over prime for 80% occupancy, and "give me the keys" (the bank owns the building) for 70% occupancy. The construction manager who understands these owner pressures can recast cost and revise schedules to avoid problems for both the owner and the construction manager.

Industry-specialized loans offer additional possibilities

Some banks will have or will sponsor specialized lending arms with significant knowledge of and comfort with specific industries. Examples include dental offices, veterinary hospitals, day care centers, laundromats, restaurants, and some franchise operations. This specialized knowledge can allow lower collateral requirements, higher credit limits, and favorable interest rates, and facilitate rapid approval with less documentation.

Mezzanine financing—a high-priced last resort

Speculative real estate developments not quite able to meet the performance milestones required by the construction loan may obtain an additional second loan called mezzanine financing. The rates are high, sometimes several times bank rates, and the terms are harsh and brutally enforced. Unlike banks that do not want to seize collateral, mezzanine financiers may be primarily interested in obtaining collateral and use the mezzanine financing to obtain a building at a steep discount.

SBA (Small Business Administration) loans help small or new businesses

SBA is an agency of U.S. federal government, that guarantees bank loans to new or very small businesses. A bank actually makes the loan, but the SBA guarantees typically 70%–90% of the loan against default, and a 10%, rather than customary 20%, down payment is accepted. Loans up to $2–$4 million are common, with loans several times this amount possible in specialized circumstances. If a bank is unfamiliar with the SBA's large volume of unusual and specialized requirements, the application process can be time consuming, slow, and painful—but processing by experienced banks can remain fast and trouble free.

Public Markets Can Offer Lower Costs and Better Terms to Larger Firms

The SEC (Security and Exchange Commission) regulates public markets for stocks, bonds, commercial paper, and other financial instruments. Larger and more sophisticated firms may obtain lower cost, more patient funds from these markets.

Commercial paper provides general operating funds but not project-specific financing

Commercial paper is an unsecured loan (through financial markets) from investors to a firm for general unspecified purposes—a construction project will not be named. The terms are typically 2–270 days. And firms may constantly pay off maturing and issue new commercial paper. Although larger firms may use commercial paper for project financing, the project will not be identified and funds will appear to come from internal cash. This can impact project payments in times of extreme credit volatility when interest rates rise and the demand for commercial paper declines—an apparently large and well-capitalized project owner may be temporarily unable to sell commercial paper needed to make timely project payments.

Bonds are long-term debt for a specific purpose or project

State and city governments frequently finance their construction projects with bonds. Other quasi-government agencies may issue bonds for certain types of projects (without naming specific projects) and then use the funds to finance specific projects that are too small to access the bond markets. This practice is most prevalent for low-income housing and facilities providing social services.

A bond may be a general revenue bond that is backed by the full faith and credit of the agency, or a project specific bond only backed by the anticipated project revenue stream. The interest from state and city bonds is exempt from federal income tax and can be exempt from state income taxes as well. This tax benefit keeps the bond's lower interest rates competitive.

Another type of bond that uses tax advantages is tax increment financing. This type of financing is used in areas with little or no economic activity. Buildings funded are anticipated to increase economic activity and therefore taxes (the tax increment). The anticipated stream of additional taxes provides the collateral for the bonds.

Stock are rarely used for project funding

Issuance of new publicly traded stock once commonly financed real estate projects. Development of the railroads from the 1850s and early 1900s is one prominent example. But project specific stock issuance is seldom used now. REITs (real estate investment trusts) where wealthy investors pool their money to buy or build an agreed type of real estate is the closest present equivalent.

When the CM provides temporary project financing, the results are not good

The CM can "buy a job" by providing initial "temporary" financing to get a project started for an undercapitalized developer. Agreeing to delay payment for preconstruction services for 6–12 months attempts to lock in the construction of the project for the CM. But it does not.

The CM does not have the instincts, skills, and values of a lender, and views the transaction not as a contractual exchange but rather as a gigantic favor. Repayment of this favor escalates both the preconstruction and the construction costs.

The undercapitalized owner seeks a market rate return so cannot afford above market construction costs—and the CM may be terminated. Further, developers promote the project using "best case" rosy projections. When the needed and assumed conditions are not realized—a permission is not obtained or acceptable financing is not secured when needed—the owner's project involvement ends. The CM may not be paid in full or at all. CMs who have tried this "financing" method realize the risks are large and uncontrollable, the probable return on capital unacceptable.

Owners are affected by both financial and administrative constraints

Time has a cost for project owners—all money has a cost or opportunity cost every minute it is in use. The project owners also have administrative constraints as well. Even funds committed to the project will not sit idly in a checkbook—effort is needed to provide funds when needed.

To obtain funds in the public market, the total requested amount must be sufficiently large to justify the administrative expense needed to interest investment bankers. Although commitment to borrow the entire amount is required, a lesser amount may be initially needed. The agreement to withdraw the money in "tranches" may be used. For example, the borrower may agree to borrow $100 million but obtain the money in 10 tranches of $10 million. The decision to withdraw a tranche has both costs and administrative effort.

This owner's effort impacts progress payment processing time. Possibly a slightly lower payment would avoid withdrawal of an additional tranche, or an excellent cash flow projection would permit more efficient owner planning. The construction manager who understands these requirements can benefit the owner and gain a competitive advantage.

CM Understanding of Finance Can Help Sell More Projects
Understand and serve the project owner's needs

Cost–benefit analysis for more costly equipment

Construction managers involved in the preconstruction services and design review can identify either initial cost savings or equipment that will provide long-term benefits, such as lower operating costs. Lower initial cost for identical outcomes is easy to understand and sell. More expensive equipment that provides long-term benefits must address a problem the owner knows and understands well. One example is energy efficiency improvements for building owners, such as hospitals and universities, who pay all their own utility bills (no operating costs are reimbursed by tenants). Another example is increasing the useful life of parking lots and roofs.

Presentations Must Be Simple and Targeted to the Decision Maker
If you have to try too hard, your case appears weak

Time—short owner time frames limit saving possibilities

Time horizons are seldom long enough to take advantage of all possibilities. Owners will almost always accept an idea with a payback of less than 3 months. Many will accept an idea with a payback of less than a year, but a payback over 3 years requires a sophisticated owner with analytical skills.

Keep it as simple as possible

Cash expenditures that produce cash savings are always understood. Although the time value of money is very real and relevant, many unsophisticated owners do not instinctively understand this cost. And trying to communicate income tax benefits is lost on most. Sophisticated owners who are acutely aware of both the time value of money and the income tax implications will have complicated internal company affairs and will redo any presented time value or tax-saving calculation for their own purposes. So it is good for the construction manager to understand and calculate the financial impact of a cost saving suggestion but present this cost benefit to the owner—maybe lightly or just in passing—"this is the initial cost impact and does not include the additional tax savings that will be realized and the financing cost that will be avoided."

And selling savings in maintenance cost, though very real, is received with skepticism. Unless a project component will truly be maintenance free, selling savings in maintenance cost is difficult to present convincingly. The owner's construction and maintenance departments may have different goals and financial controls that further complicate coordinated decisions.

Cost thresholds owners perceive as worthwhile

Owners may welcome cost savings suggestions, but tire of evaluating a long laundry list of small items of puzzling merit. $35,000–$80,000 is a frequent threshold for complex cost–benefit analysis suggestions for smaller private projects—$250,000 for public projects where the decision-makers are not playing with their own money. These cost thresholds have been remarkably constant for decades, apparently ignoring the impact of inflation, and appear psychological not rational in nature.

Summary

The time value of money affects all aspects of project management—both for the construction manager and for the project owner. The construction manager must plan and negotiate contract terms that tie the time of receipts as closely as possible to the time of payments—and minimize the finance cost of retention. The construction manager can realize further savings by careful consideration of the lease-buy decision, including tax advantages.

The construction manager can also add value for owners by understanding their financing and cash flow needs. Presenting costs in needed formats, scheduling to conform to target financing requirements, and making reliable cash flow projections can greatly assist the efficiency of owners' operations and their ability to make prompt payments.

Benefits of financing can be only realized when applied comprehensively from project concept to completion—the "we know what we want, now how can we pay for it" approach can only produce limited results. But comprehensive financial management of all aspects of the project can more than double the construction managers' profit at no cost to the owner—a win-win solution.

Review Questions (True or False)

1. The construction manager's cash flow and financing cost of this cash flow can exceed project profit.
2. The future value finds the value at the end of the period including accumulated interest. The present value, which is the inverse of future value, can determine the implied interest rate for early receipt or payment.
3. Tables, algebraic formulas, and computer software can all be used to perform present and future value calculations.
4. For projects constructed solely for investment return, the financial impact of depreciation and income taxes are identical for the project owner and construction project manager.
5. An efficient capital structure for a construction management firm seeks to balance debt with lower financing costs, and equity with a higher expected rate of return.
6. A construction management firm's return on equity and profit before taxes are both about 15%.
7. For commercial construction contractors, the median ratios for debt to net worth range from 1.7 to 3.4.
8. Preparation of monthly cash flow projections (the amount to be billed by the construction manager to the owner each month) can assist the owner's financial management and make prompt payments more likely.
9. The cost of late progress payments and retention amounts to a de facto loan by the construction manager to the owner.
10. The amount and timing of retention and payment to subcontractors are facts that cannot be altered.
11. When the construction manager is evaluating lease or purchase of major equipment, the cost of financing is usually the only consideration.
12. Construction loans are for a specific project at a specific time and must be later converted to real estate loans that have a longer time period (but usually a period less than the life of the building).
13. Commercial paper, bonds, and stocks are all commonly used financing methods for construction projects.
14. The construction manager's effective administration of contracts and pay requests can, by understanding the owner's administrative and financing needs, add value for the owner and reduce the construction manager's financing costs through receipt of more prompt payment from the owner.

Test Your Understanding

1. Using the tables, algebraic formulas, and financial functions found on Microsoft Excel programs, calculate the future value of $150,000 with one payment in 10 years and an interest rate of 7%.
2. The table of the time value of project payments paid in 30 and 90 days shown earlier in the chapter shows a total interest cost of delayed payment of $13,065.78 and $30,008.94. What is the construction management firm's percentage reduction in net profit of 3% before taxes for the 30- and 90-day payments if the $1 million project was the only project for the year?
3. The commercial construction contractors' financial ratio median value for firms with $1–$10 million in sales shows a revenue to working capital ratio of 15.1. What is the working capital required by this ratio for a $10 million annual revenue (work volume)?
4. Using the PMT function on Microsoft Excel, calculate the monthly payment needed to fully pay for equipment within acquisition cost of $100,000 in 5 years at an 8% interest rate?

CHAPTER
1.6

Insurance—a Legal Requirement, a Huge Project Cost, and a Risk Management Tool

Typically, a poured in-place reinforced concrete structure requires reshores remain in place until the concrete floor has cured to design strength (usually 28 days). The installation and removal of reshores is both a labor and material cost and a schedule constraint. At the Hilton Hotel Disneyland, Orlando, Florida, the need for reshores was eliminated using a combination of 30″ deep castellated steel beams and aluminum J–400 joists that transferred all the load onto the columns and walls of the structure. Also, note that the form is being placed with the exterior safety rail in place to increase safety and productivity. *Photo courtesy of Harsco Infrastructure.*

Insurance—a Legal Requirement, a Huge Project Cost, and a Risk Management Tool

Confusing terms, practices, and time frames must be understood—learning on the job may be difficult

Insurance is a larger portion of project cost than profit. Insurance cost may be 15%–20% of project cost for safe projects and safe contractors—far more for riskier ones. The project cannot succeed unless insurance is understood and managed.

This large insurance cost is variable and can preclude contractors from securing needed projects, or even force them out of business. Some insurance is legally required, and other insurance is demanded by owners and desired by contractors. The actions of both field and office personnel can influence the cost of insurance—and the success of projects—so some insurance knowledge is needed.

The insurance industry has an unusual business structure, regulatory environment, and terminology, so common sense intuitive understanding of insurance is a struggle. And since insurance personnel do not understand the construction business very well, communication is imperfect and access to quality information rare. This chapter works to close this gap.

What is the purpose of insurance?

Frequent regular premiums cover infrequent irregular losses

Insurance trades responsibility for a specified portion of the consequences of an event for a premium payment. Determination of the present cost of unknown future events enhances business financial planning and avoids unbearable costs.

Insurance at best restores the insured to the position enjoyed before the loss, but does not provide for position improvement or a profit. Because of deductibles, inconvenience, and additional unreimbursed cost, full compensation is rare. And insurance is not a safety valve for bad or reckless behavior—"We don't have to worry, we have insurance to cover that"—is never an acceptable attitude.

Insurance and Construction Businesses Think and Act Differently

Long time frames and regulation produce puzzling behavior

Annual insurer operations are marginally profitable—long-term investments make it up

Insurance claims paid and the cost of insurance administration typically are close to the received premiums each year—and operating losses are common. There is, however, a multiyear gap between receipt of premiums and payment of claims. The investment income on premiums received during this time gap more than compensates for the annual losses. With this multiyear view, insurance companies convert unacceptably low annual operating profits to satisfactory multiyear financial profit.

The insurers are unable to actively plan, schedule, control, and close out insurance policies—processes that are central to project management. Long periods of consistent operation followed by large abrupt change—such as termination of all insurance sales in a state—may make sense from the insurer's standpoint but are puzzling to project management personnel.

Premiums are not precisely known until the end of the annual policy period
Annual premium exposures are estimated and then adjusted at the end of the period

Some premiums, such as for umbrella insurance, are priced as a fixed annual lump sum, but most are priced as a percentage of sales or payroll. Sales and payroll costs cannot be precisely known before the start of the policy period, so previous year costs, tempered by management's judgment, establish the estimates used in the premium calculation.

At the conclusion of the policy period, the insurer will audit the accounting documents of the insured and determine the actual sales and payroll figures. The auditor will also attempt to find any changes in operations, such as acquisition of significant quantities of new equipment or new more risky types of contracting activity, which might affect insurance risk ratings and premiums due.

This practice has two implications for construction project management. The first is that since actual insurance costs cannot be known early enough to permit management, cost control is compromised. The second is that for time and material contracts that seek a "to the penny" accounting of costs expended, the required multiyear look back can unexpectedly reduce previous year profit and current year cash flow. This look back accounting may be required by regulation on some government contracts. But for private contracts, this effort and uncertainty can be avoided by negotiating a stated rate that includes reasonable estimates of future costs for current insurance exposures.

Regulation is heavy and varies by state
Sound business judgment gets crowded out

Each state regulates its own insurance types, terms, and conditions. Requirements for generous property insurance for hurricane prone areas are one controversial example. Workers' compensation insurance rates and procedures can vary vastly by state—favoring either the employer or the employee. Unregulated carriers can, under some circumstances, operate in a state, but their lower claims paying intentions, capacity and efficiency may fail to meet the contractor's and project owner's minimum standards. The unregulated carrier's poor performance may not be discovered until the policy is in force and a claim is made—and then full correction is not feasible.

Insurance companies specialize in types of insurance, and kinds and sizes of companies insured. When regulatory requirements conflict with insurance companies' areas of expertise and competence, the insurance company may be forced to cease operations in that state.

Reconciliation of these government regulations and the insurer's own regulations and business requirements necessary to provide insurance is performed by the insurer's underwriters. Underwriters (parties who determine what insurance will be offered to whom and at what cost) must evaluate these regulatory requirements, multiyear statewide losses for each insurance type, and their company's return on investments. These factors can overwhelm the favorable payment and loss history of an individual insured. An insured who has paid all premiums on time and sustained no losses can still be denied insurance renewal. This prevents long-term continuously improving relations between insurer and insured.

Insurance agents work for the carrier—not the insured
Incentives do not always produce the best deal

Another unusual dimension of the insurance relationship is that, unlike a real estate transaction where the seller may have one agent and the buyer another, the insurance agent is always an agent for the insurance carrier. Insurance consultants representing the insured have been attempted rarely, and with little success.

A portion of insurance agents are monoline, selling insurance from only one carrier. Most are multiline insurance brokers who assemble an insurance package for the insured from different carriers.

Coordination of the efforts of multiple underwriters from multiple carriers to form a comprehensive insurance program is a time-consuming effort. For this reason, each carrier will only quote to one broker. This restricts meaningful competition between brokers.

A broker may favor a more familiar or friendly carrier, rather than the optimal carrier for the insured. Or, a broker may push the insured to a suboptimal carrier to receive a volume discount. When the insured discovers others in a similar position are getting a better deal, the broker may then claim that a better deal is not available for "technical reasons" or "present market conditions". The insured must then seek quotations from other brokers, which is both time consuming and terminates the present broker relationship.

Risk Classification and Rate Calculation

Confusing rating terms have big cost impacts that loss experience amplifies

Workers' compensation rating bureaus use confusing terms

The probability of injury and severity of injury varies by work activity. Classification of work activity by severity is performed by rating bureaus. The largest is the NCCI (National Council on Compensation Insurance). Some states self perform ratings.

The bureau's rating manual lists thousands of work classifications—with several hundreds for the construction industry. And few of these classifications use the terminology of the real world. For example, "carpentry, interior trim and millwork" describes the construction of office tenant build-out work. And "hauling" defines contract hauling apart from construction operations, and the "artisan and trades" classification describes construction company truck drivers.

Ratings can vary up to 1000% for similar sounding classifications. The manual rates for tradesmen can vary from about 4% to 90% of gross payroll, so proper classification is hugely important—one wrong word can produce incorrect insurance costs that wipe out a year's profit. The insured must meticulously and persistently question the broker until the correct classification is found.

Manual rates are modified by loss experience—a 5-year process

Manual (manual means taken from a book—a manual—and does not mean performed by hand) rates without modification are used for the first year of operation for newly formed construction companies. Then these rates begin to adjust up or down based on loss experience.

The loss experience is evaluated on a 5-year cycle: the current annual policy period, the previous year "green period," and then years 3, 4, and 5. The current and the green periods are ignored, and the three remaining years form the basis of loss evaluation. Premiums paid, industry expected losses for that classification, and actual losses are evaluated by a formula (modified by a sliding premium volume scale) developed by the rating bureaus. A single experience rating number is produced. A sample workers' compensation rating form is shown in the appendix.

Infrequent small losses have the least adverse effect, then infrequent large losses. Frequent large losses have the largest adverse affect. Newly formed companies have an experience modification of 1 and can change from .5 to just less than 3—a 600% variation. (The method of experience modification calculation has changed over time and does not have historical continuity.)

The experience modification is multiplied by the manual classification rate to adjust the premium basis. This premium can be reduced by carrier discounts or increased by expense constants and fixed fees.

A high experience modification (an experience modification of three times a 90% manual rate produces a premium cost of 270% of gross payroll) can eliminate profit or drive a company out of business. And it should be noted that with a 5-year evaluation cycle, a large loss or losses will not produce an adverse insurance cost for up to 2 years but will then persist for 3 years.

This timing is important for a company's business planning—and when evaluating subcontractors for future projects. Impairment or terminations of subcontractor operations caused by high insurance costs can disastrously affect a project. Analysis of a subcontractors' experience modification becomes part of the screening process prior to contract award. It is also frequently used by more sophisticated owners as a tollgate to screen construction managers—high experience modifications probably mean unsafe operations.

Liability and property rate calculation is less complex—a 3-year look back

Liability and property rate calculation has fewer calculations, is not performed by a rating bureau, and does not produce a single number. Loss runs, which are itemized detail of loss and cost of loss by insurance type, are used by the insurer to decide the costs and terms of insurance offered. The last 3 year's loss runs are usually considered.

Types of Insurance Have Very Different Structures

Different risks, time of coverage, and method of premium calculation

Commercial liability—for injury or damage to others and their property

Multiple different risks and perils

"General liability" covers damage to others' properties, and personal and advertising injury such as libel or false advertising.

"Auto liability" covers personal and property damage caused by on-road vehicles but does not cover damage to the owned or hired vehicle itself.

"Employers liability" covers injury or damage to your own employees who, for some reason, are not covered by workers' compensation insurance.

"Products and completed operations" covers damage caused by defects of completed projects.

Premiums are computed on a combination of a lump sum per year, and percentage of sales, subcontract cost, and payroll by classification. Rates for liability insurance vary hugely by the type of work a party normally performs. This can mean that a preferred contractor from a larger riskier project may be unsuitable for a smaller less risky project because of higher insurance rates. This challenges long-term continuously improving relationships.

Property—that the CM owns or is presently building

Closer in look and feel to common sense residential insurance

"Builders risk" covers damage to a partially completed project. It is intended to cover hard and soft costs necessary to restore the project to its previous condition. The premiums are computed as an annual or per project cost, and may be carried either by the contractor or by the owner.

"Contractor home office and equipment yards" coverage is similar in concept to insurance on a home. Premiums are an annual lump sum.

"Inland marine" (contractor mobile equipment) covers contractor equipment damaged or lost by a casualty event but not normal wear and tear. This insurance type was developed based on insurance experience for ships. It no longer has anything to do with ships, boats, or transportation by water. Insurance for these risks is called "wet marine." Premiums are an annual lump sum.

How equipment valuation is calculated and documented impacts management and record keeping. "Scheduled equipment" lists each piece of equipment with make, model, serial number, and acquisition cost. This requires submitting a new schedule to the insurance company each time equipment is added but commands a lower premium. If lost or damaged equipment is not on the schedule, it may not be covered at all. "All owned" equipment does not require these constant updates and avoids this possibility but commands a higher premium. The insured's estimate of the total value of "all owned" equipment must be truthful and reasonably accurate. If the insured presents an artificially low value to reduce premium costs, only a lower prorated share of each loss may be paid.

"Automobile collision and comprehensive" is similar to personal insurance of the same name and is usually computed as an annual premium.

Additional types of insurance

"Contractors professional liability," sometimes called "errors and omissions" insurance, is used when a contractor formally assumes responsibility for project design. When the design and construction firms are separately hired by the owner, this insurance is not purchased by the contractor. Premiums are most commonly an annual lump sum.

"Umbrella insurance" pays claims only after the underlying liability insurer has paid claims up to the limit of its policy. Premiums are computed as an annual lump sum.

Insurance limits vary by state, and contractor size and work performed

Limits define the insurance company's maximum payment liability for a claim. Workers' compensation limits are defined by a law in each state. Higher limits, even if desired for discretionary purposes, may be impossible to obtain. (Out-of-state owners demanding application of their home state insurance requirements may need explanation of local customs.)

When the maximum value of the loss can be precisely known for insurance types such as builders risk or inland marine, these exact values are used as the limits.

Liability limits are not specified by law or regulation—common practice and owner specific requirements govern. $1 million is the smallest generally available total liability limit and may be used for firms with a few employees. More sophisticated owners will escalate this limit to $5 million. Limits of $10–$20 million are customary for medium-sized contractors and specialty contractors engaging in higher risk work such as demolition, and structural steel erection. Limits may be increased to $50 million for still larger companies. These customary limits continually change—and there is no mathematical correlation with the single project value or the total annual project volume of a firm.

Bonding—Protection for Others from the Insured's Deficiencies
Coverage for others but not the insured

Bonding is a specialized form of insurance that protects someone else from the consequences of the insured's actions. But unlike most insurance where the premiums are intended to pay future claims, bond premiums are only intended to pay for the bonding company's services to promptly pay for remedies of the insured's specified deficiencies. The bonding company will seek reimbursement from the insured for all payments made, plus the cost of necessary litigation.

The common bond types in construction are listed below.

A "bid bond" will compensate the owner of a project when a contractor submits a bid but later refuses to construct the project. The amount to be paid for nonperformance is stated in the bond— usually 5%–10%, occasionally higher. Some excuse for nonperformance can usually be developed, so collection is difficult, and a legalistic argumentative mind is necessary to prevail.

A "payment bond" compensates the owner and/or the finance company if the contractor receives a payment from the owner but does not in turn pay the required amounts to the subcontractors and vendors. Payments made and payments required to be made are readily discernible by the sworn statement and canceled checks, so clear proof of legitimate claims is readily achievable. Payment on these bond claims is frequent.

A "performance bond" compensates the owner if the insured is unwilling or unable to complete the project. If the insured is unwilling to complete the project, real or fabricated disputes may make

Install facing—typically reinforced shotcrete.   *Soil nailing operations photo 5 of 6*

collection slow and costly. If the insured is not able to complete the project, their assets will be liquidated and the bonding company will secure another party to complete the work.

A "permit bond" compensates a city for damage to city property the insured caused but persistently refused to repair. Such negligent behavior and collection on permit bonds is rare.

"Bid and permit bonds" are provided to good customers at a nominal or no cost. Payment and performance bonds are quoted per project—a percentage of original project value—with premium adjustments to the final contract value made at the end of the project.

A bonding relationship first requires adequate capital, usually in the form of cash, marketable real estate, or large high value equipment. Accounts receivable and small tools are heavily or completely discounted. A ratio of $1 of capital for each $10 of project value—both bonded and unbonded—outstanding at one time is a common rule of thumb. In addition, those seeking bonds must execute a "personal undertaking" that pledges personal and company assets to satisfy bond claims. Larger companies with deep layers of management and more capital may sign this undertaking corporately but not personally.

Bond claims will only be paid if the claim can be indisputably shown to exist, and the contractor is unwilling and unable to defend against the claim. The bonding company will not hand over money to every hot head who wants to "call the bond" to get quick payment. There will be a fight. Collection on a claim usually means the contractor is driven out of business and the contractor's owners may be personally ruined. Contractor defense tends to be long and vigorous—exploiting every technicality of even the smallest claim defect.

Additional Complexity Must Be Managed

Unusual terms and clauses can have huge impacts

Insurance is governed by regulations, rules, and customs that are somewhat different than common sense expectations—as discussed above. Even more counterintuitive but common insurance practices are listed below.

The insured may be required to pay part of the claim

A deductible is a stated amount per claim, usually associated with automobile insurance. The insurer will pay the entire claim and then request reimbursement of the deductible by the insured. Self-insured retention is the deductible per year for umbrella insurance. Coinsurance requires the insured to pay a percentage of a claim—sometimes with a stop limit and sometimes unlimited. These variable methods and timing of calculation make definitive insurance risk pricing unfeasible—estimates must be used.

Definition of risks covered may be quite precise

"All risk" coverage will cover all risks except those specifically itemized as excluded. In contrast, "named perils" insurance specifically itemizes the perils to be covered and excludes all others. The first is more inclusive and preferable.

"Occurrence" insurance covers losses that occurred within the policy period, even if reported after the policy period. "Claims made" insurance covers only those losses that both occurred and were reported within the policy period. This can be crucial for losses that occur very near the end of the annual policy period. Poor communication or documentation can force the insured to absorb a claim that could have been covered by the insurer.

"Each occurrence" coverage specifies a limit per incident, and "general aggregate" specifies a limit for all claims in the policy period. This can result in the unfortunate situation where losses on a distant project unknown to a second project owner can exhaust the aggregate limits. So, despite convincing and legitimate documentation to the contrary, there may be no insurance coverage left.

Risk transfer clauses must reflect the risk management approach

"Indemnify and hold harmless" means to protect another against and compensate them for a loss. This is one of the first things out of a lawyer's mouth and a very common contract clause. But this transfer of risk should be approached with caution and resisted unless the receiving party has a superior ability to manage the risk.

"Subrogation" means to transfer the right of recovery to another party. For example, the insurer may pay a third party for a loss that a fourth party caused. The insured may still have the legal right to seek recovery from this fourth party. The insured may transfer (subrogate) this right of recovery to the insurer to recover the claim paid. Since the insured should only be made whole and not profit, this can be an entirely reasonable relationship.

If the insurer recovers the claim amount, the insured is entitled to subtract this recovery from their recorded losses—so that their loss runs and cost of future insurance are minimized. This adjustment is not automatic and must be actively pursued by the insured.

"Primary and noncontributory" means the insurance is first in line, even though common sense would indicate others are more responsible. For example, when a contractor requires a subcontractor to have primary noncontributory insurance, claims will become the first responsibility of the subcontractor and later or never the responsibility of the contractor. The injustice of this lawyerly approach tends to start fights rather than end them and attracts a lower tier of subcontractors and vendors.

Other Common Terms and Matters That Impact Management

"Additional insureds" are parties that have some relationship to the project and seek identification and notification of their status to preserve their claim rights. They must demonstrate an insurable interest and then will be named on the certificate of insurance. Architects, engineers, and project financiers are common "additional insureds."

"Certificate of insurance" is a document that specifies the types, limits and policy dates, and terms of cancellation for insurance coverage for a project. It will always name the project, insured, insurer, and owner, and may name additional insured. It will contain the financial rating of the insurance company (e.g., Best B+ or better) when requested. This certificate is almost always on the Acord form that presents the normal and customary insurance data in a standardized format. This standardization greatly enhances prompt review. The certificate of insurance is accepted as evidence of insurance and is a key document for a project start up. A specimen sample is shown in the appendix.

Certificates of insurance, including certificates of insurance for all subcontractors, have two important uses and functions. First, all certificates of insurance must be delivered to the owner, usually before construction start is permitted. Extensive additional insureds required by the owners, which can on occasion have multiple parties with precise wording running to two pages, must be included on each certificate of insurance with no typographical errors. Failure to give proper management attention to this clerically burdensome, but readily achievable, requirement can delay the project start and overall schedule.

The second function will be noticed during the workers' compensation audit at the end of the policy period. The construction manager is required to ensure that all subcontractors carry the required workers' compensation insurance. If a subcontractor fails to carry this insurance and provide convincing documentation of coverage, the construction manager must pay the subcontractors' workers' compensation premiums related to the work performed on the project. The auditor's default position may be that every penny paid to the subcontractor was for labor (assuming the subcontractor used no material or equipment and had no profit) and will seek premiums from the construction manager based on this entire amount paid—which would be a substantial unplanned expense.

This applies to subcontractors who perform installation work on site, not material only suppliers or vendors who fabricate solely off site and perform no on-site installation. Care must also be taken when one policy period ends and another starts during the middle of the subcontractor's work—two certificates are required to document continuous coverage.

The "assigned risk pool" is a government mandated mechanism to provide insurance that is unavailable in the private market. This usually applies to legally required workers' compensation and automobile insurance. When an insured's loss record is sufficiently poor that a number, frequently 3, insurance carriers refuse coverage, the insured is placed in an assigned risk pool. The government then forces an insurance carrier to provide coverage. Since the carrier does not want the insured in the first place, will probably lose money, and hopes never to see the insured again, premiums are sky-high, service is wretched, and questionable methods to further increase premiums or avoid paying claims will be used. This is the bottom of the barrel and end of the line of the insurance world.

"Reinsurance" is an agreement of the insured's carrier to transfer a portion of premiums and risks to another insurance company. This risk sharing agreement is usually unknown to the insured. If the unknown insurance company becomes financially troubled or goes out of business, the insured's carrier's obligation and ability to pay claims may be compromised.

Insurance Accounting Complicates Project Job Cost Accounting

The difference in timing of insurance accounting and project job cost accounting has a significant management impact. For the annual premiums, an annual project volume must be estimated to determine the percentage of the annual premium that must be allocated to each project. Further, the insurance policies will have an annual renewal date that will seldom coincide with a convenient meaningful project date. A project may have different insurance rate allocations from multiple policy periods.

Project cost accounting seeks to measure the effects of the efforts of the project participants in an intuitively obvious way, so current status and possibilities for improvement can be readily discerned. Periodic alteration of insurance costs clouds this picture.

In "open book" projects, the owner has the right to examine ongoing costs. The reaction to mid-project alteration of insurance rates can range from a frustrating nuisance to suspicion of accounting trickery. Identification of an estimated rate, and the times and method for adjustment at the project start can minimize these difficulties.

Real-World Construction Project Insurance Management

Insurance business practices and regulation resist project management techniques. Freedom to establish goals, methods to achieve the goals, implementation, and control are restricted. Understanding the insurance business, insurance types, rate calculation, and the complexity of terms defines the landscape that must be managed or worked around. The knowledge described above is a good start and exceeds the knowledge of 95% of most building teams.

But the limits of this knowledge should be recognized. Contractor assumption of design responsibility (design build), multistate operations, foreign operations, and owners and situations with different insurance regulations—such as some governments, the military, railroads, longshoremen areas, and marine construction—introduce new complexities.

A workable approach starts with identifying legally and owner required insurance types and limits. Next, supplement these limits and add insurance types to match your risk tolerance and financial capacity to bear the consequences of risk. Then, seek inclusion of qualifying terms that best reflect the real world risk distribution among project participants.

Seek the best possible relationship with the insurance agent but recognize that the restrictions in the insurance industry may prevent the optimization that you enjoy with other subcontractors and vendors. When venturing into a new situation or project type that exceeds your and your agent's everyday knowledge, outside counsel, such as insurance consultants, must be obtained. (Attorneys may be unqualified or unwilling to help. Insurance regulation complicates and sometimes overpowers the law.)

Summary

Insurance is a legal and owner mandated requirement that has a cost impact that can reduce profit and drive a contractor out of business. The insurance and construction businesses have different structures, regulations, timing, and attitudes. The insurance industry will not change for any one project, so the project manager must learn the insurance structure and manage within or work around it.

Insurance is but one tool of risk management and must be consistent with the attitudes and approach of the entire risk management program. The insurer's only source of money is the insureds. So the insureds pay for all claims over time—either present premiums or the increased cost of future premiums. Behave as if all claims will be paid with your own money, and structure the insurance that reflects the management style of your project management approach.

Review Questions (True or False)

1. Insurance costs can be greater than project profit, and preclude contractors from securing needed projects or even forcing them out of business.
2. Insurance trades responsibility for a specified portion of the consequence of an event for a premium payment, and this exchange can enhance business financial planning and avoid unbearable costs. Insurance at best restores the insured to the position enjoyed before the loss but does not provide position improvement or profit.
3. The insurer's premiums received each year must exceed administrative costs and claims paid each year.
4. All types of insurance are calculated either as a percentage of payroll or as a percentage of sales.

5. Premiums based on payroll are estimated at the beginning of the period and then audited and corrected at the end of the period, which can cause complexities for job cost accounting.

6. The Federal government regulates insurance types to produce standardization for all 50 states.

7. Sound construction project management practices require a broker who represents the construction management firm rather than the insurer.

8. Rating bureaus, such as NCCI, establish work classifications for workers compensation insurance to form the basis of the rate calculation.

9. The experience modification is a numerical modifier based on the loss experience of 3 of the last 5 years to adjust the manual workers compensation premium rates.

10. Liability and property insurance rate calculations are modified by lost runs that typically have a 3-year look back.

11. Builders risk insurance covers personal injuries that are not adequately covered by commercial liability and workers' compensation insurance.

12. Inland marine insurance is essential for contractors working on or near water but is not needed for contractors with solely land-based operations.

13. The construction manager's operations require frequent purchase of small tools throughout the year. "All owned" insurance coverage will be easier to administer than "scheduled" equipment coverage.

14. Insurance premiums are used by the insurer to permanently pay claims, but bond premiums are used by the insurer to temporarily pay claims. The insurer later expects full insured reimbursement of the bond claim amount paid.

15. A construction manager seeking bonds must have adequate capital, usually the form of cash, marketable real estate, or large high value equipment, and must execute a personal undertaking. This personal undertaking produces significant liability for the company.

16. Self-insured retention and coinsurance are methods the insured can use to avoid paying a deductible.

17. "General aggregate" coverage provides more comprehensive inclusive coverage for multiple claims in a policy period than with "each occurrence" coverage.

18. The construction manager must obtain the legally and owner required insurance types and limits, and then add other insurance types that match the construction manager's tolerance and financial capacity to bear the consequences of risk.

Test Your Understanding

1. You are considering subcontracting the reinforcing steel installation to a labor only subcontractor. Although this contractor is known for safe operations, they have just experienced a freak accident that seriously injured many workers. You are concerned that a large increase in their workers' compensation insurance premiums may cause them to cease operations. Will this potential rate increase be a factor if the subcontractor's work is completed in 1 year?—or if it is completed in 3 years?

2. Your construction management firm has an annual volume of $10 million and self performs significant portions of the work and owns significant tools and equipment. Your work volume is almost exclusively medical construction, and all design work is performed by others. What are the types of insurance you must and should carry?

   If your work volume were commercial offices performed with the design-build delivery system, what additional insurance should be added?

3. How can a potential subcontractor's workers' compensation experience modification be analyzed to assess the past and therefore probable future safety of their operations? Consider both the frequency and the severity of injuries.

CHAPTER
1.7

Laws, Regulations, Codes, and Standards

Single-family home and light commercial foundation walls are typically formed with preengineered reusable forms such as the Resi-Ply™ system shown. The highest quality installation and optimal productivity require a design that is constructable with the available form parts and pieces. The construction manager's constructibility input in design review can ensure these benefits are realized. *Photo courtesy: Symons.*

Laws, Regulations, Codes, and Standards

The regulatory framework for design and construction

The construction project manager must work within the framework of laws (restrictions and mandates written and adopted by legislators), regulations (restrictions and mandates written by unelected government staff and are usually more specific and applied "how to" than laws), codes (what can be built and general guidelines for performance—usually written by national code related organizations), and standards (installation performance standards and installation instructions)—usually developed by trade organizations.

The construction manager must understand the impact of this regulatory environment on company structure, project payment procedures, labor relations, and the technical aspects of construction—to effectively manage.

Laws and Regulations for the Building Industry

Corporate Law Establishes Company Structures and Regulations

Continuation of ownership, liability limitation, and income tax management

The players in the construction industry—building owners, construction managers, subcontractors, and designers—form companies to allow continuation through changes in ownership, and manage liability and income taxes. Companies are established in a state and are governed by that state's unique and significantly differing laws and regulations. Required administration and governance procedures must be used and annual reports documenting conformance must be filed with the state. Reports of other events affecting the company structure, such as change of ownership, must also be filed.

These forms of organization define control and governance procedures and limit the liability of the company owners. And the form of ownership has income tax consequences, which are critical for cash flow management and equipment acquisition. The purpose, type, and size of company influence the optimal structure.

"C" corporations for the largest companies

A "C" corporation is an entity owned by stockholders who elect a board of directors, which selects officers to manage and run the company. The "C" corporation has the most permissive regulations of classes of stock, number of shareholders, and foreign ownership of shares. Profits of the organization are subject to income tax. The largest firms of all types will typically be "C" corporations, but only a small portion of construction management or subcontracting firms will use this organizational type.

The passive stockholders are not fully liable for the consequences of the company's actions—their loss is limited to the value of stock owned. Company officers avoid most liability while performing their duties but can be liable for personal malfeasance and for unpaid company taxes.

"S" corporations for many small and midsized construction companies

An "S" corporation is similar to a "C" except the number of shareholders may be limited—such as to 99—and classes of shares and foreign ownership may be restricted. Small and midsized firms are seldom concerned with these types of restrictions.

Firm profits are not subject to income tax at the company level, but all firm profits are declared as personal income to the shareholders. If all profits are not distributed to the shareholders, these shareholders must pay taxes on profits they have not received—and shareholder hardship and hard feeling can result. (In contrast, "C" corporation profits are taxed twice—once on company profits and a second time on distributed dividends when received by the shareholders). Many small and midsize construction management and subcontracting firms are "S" corporations.

LLCs usually for professional service firms

An LLC (limited liability corporation) is similar to an "S" corporation except the annual record keeping requirements are minimized. In addition to the required income taxes on company profits, the shareholders must pay FICA (Federal Insurance Compensation Act) Social Security and Medicare at a current rate of 15.65% on all the firm's profit. (The amount of wages subject to FICA is capped for personal salary). This form of organization is popular with professionals, such as architects and engineers whose wages may be closer to the FICA cap and whose profit has less annual variation. But it is less common for construction managers, who may have higher wages and wild annual profit swings.

Partnerships or sole proprietorships are rarely used in construction

A partnership is an organization of individuals consisting of one or more general partners and one or more limited partners. The general partner has significant liability, responsibility, and decision-making authority. The limited partners' liability is limited to their investment, and their (usually lesser) decision-making authority is specified in the partnership agreement. Attorneys, accountants, architects, and engineers have significant personal liability due to their professional status—which cannot be fully discharged by a company structure—find this form of organization satisfactory.

Partnerships are also common for real estate ownership. But since construction management firms can have very large liability—such as physical project catastrophe that results in significant property damage and personal injury—construction management firms are rarely partnerships.

A sole proprietorship formalizes an individual operating under a business name in the eyes of the state. The individual is personally liable and responsible for income taxes. This form of ownership offers no advantages (besides being inexpensive and easy to establish) and many disadvantages for construction management firms, so is rarely used.

Project-Specific Temporary Organizational Structures

A joint venture is a temporary combination of companies for a project. Usually one party takes the lead and the share of risk and reward is specified in the joint venture agreement. At the conclusion of the project, joint venture is dissolved.

Joint ventures can combine the parties' technical knowledge, knowledge of local customs, people, and businesses, bonding capacity, and capital to provide superior project capabilities and diversify risk. Joint ventures can also be used to limit competition when two parties each enjoy dominant competitive positions in a market. These parties can form successive joint ventures and thus eliminate their largest competitor.

A land trust may own the project

A land trust is a form of organization frequently used to own land. The trust owns the land, and individuals or companies own the trust. This permits the owners of the trust to buy, sell, and pledge shares in the land trust without the time and expense and publicity of formally recording these changes in ownership with the government. (Real estate transactions must be formally recorded with the county, so this information becomes searchable in public records.)

This completed soil-nailed wall was later faced with conventionally placed concrete to provide the permanent foundation support.

Soil-nailed walls can permit rapid and economical installation, including curved surfaces. But there are restrictions and drawbacks. Soil-nailed walls are not practical in soft clays, and cohesionless, low-density, or saturated soils. The backside of the wall must be free of structures or utilities, and some deflection of the soil-nailed wall must be acceptable. *Photos courtesy of Hayward Baker Inc..*   *Soil nailing operations photo 6 of 6*

The form of company organization is rarely changed

Selection of the appropriate organizational form should be made, and then changes should be done rarely and with reasonable cause. Frequent changes of ownership to attempt to avoid income taxes are not permitted. Change from sole proprietorship to "S" to "C" is easier and less costly than the reverse.

Careful selection of the construction company's formal organization can provide the needed liability protection while minimizing administrative requirements and optimizing income tax management. Minimizing administrative requirements maximizes the time available for project management.

Construction Converts Personal Property into Real Property

This moving target confuses many

Personal Property Is Moveable and Real Property Is Attached to Land

Personal property is not permanently attached or committed to land. Personal property (with the exception of a few titled and licensed vehicles, such as cars and motorcycles) can be bought and sold without recording the transaction with the government.

Real estate, consisting of land and all the permanent improvements attached to the land, is called real property. Ownership and every alteration to ownership (including pledging the land for collateral) must be recorded with the government. Materials such as lumber and concrete (personal property) become real property when permanently installed. Services of architects, engineers, and surveyors—who helped make the building possible—become part of the real property's improved value.

Once permanently installed, these materials cannot be legally removed even if the owner fails to make payment. Generic materials such as lumber, conduit, and piping awaiting installation is still personal property and can be removed. However, custom fabricated equipment such as rooftop units on the job awaiting installation typically cannot be removed.

These laws are established at the state and county level—and vary hugely by jurisdiction, and even by the preferences of officials in the same jurisdiction. Very specific local knowledge about the law and its enforcement is needed.

Sworn statements document the conversion from personal to real property

Contractors, who improved the real estate and have not been paid, need an equitable remedy. Liens (a formal claim) on the property record the unpaid value of improvements. These liens produce very severe restrictions on the sale or financing of the property.

The liens must be filed within time limits tiered by the type of goods or services—such as 60 days for material suppliers, 90 days for subcontractors, and 120 days for general contractors. The liens must be "perfected" (a legal process to pursue the claim) within a specified time—usually 1–4 years—or the lien rights expire. Then, the claimed funds must be obtained by lawsuit—a time-consuming and expensive process.

To document lienable amounts, a sworn statement (an itemed listing of all parties working on the project and their total contract and completed values) is used. The construction manager has a master sworn statement for the entire project. Principal subcontractors have statements naming their principal vendors as well. The lower tier subcontractors (a sub to a sub to a sub) will be named but have progressively declining rights.

Proper preparation of the sworn statements has significant legal consequences and materially affects prompt payment. And each lending and title company can add further complexity with their own regulations. Truthful statements and meticulous documentation are time consuming but essential to avoid lien liability and achieve prompt payment. AIA (American Institute of Architects), AGC (Association of General Contractors), and some title companies provide paper and electronic sworn statement formats that are widely accepted.

Although preparation of sworn statement appears at first to be a clerical task that can be delegated, because it includes input from many subcontractors and vendors interwoven with the management of the project, some management guidance is needed. And since even the smallest clerical error or inconsistency can stop payment for the entire project—and money is the fuel that runs the project—the importance of this task cannot be underestimated. The project manager may have clerical assistance but must take personal responsibility for correct execution.

Labor Law in Construction

U.S. industrial and construction wages and working conditions in the late 1800s included long work weeks (maybe 80 hours) for straight time wages, no benefits, no child labor laws, and dangerous working conditions—producing maiming and deaths. By the mid-20th century, these conditions were gone or radically improved. The rise of unions and the improvement in wages and working conditions for all workers were parallel movements that drove these changes, as described below.

Unions Developed, Stabilized, then Declined

Union labor evolved from promanagement in 1896 to union acceptance in 1955

Unions organize workers into a group to more effectively bargain with management about compensation and working conditions. Unions seek and enforce uniform agreements on wages and benefits, hours of work, types of work performed, and safe and healthy working conditions. Guaranteed continuous employment, regardless of available work, is sometimes also sought.

AFL (skilled labor) and CIO (industrial labor) worked together and at odds

The skilled trade unions are the descendents of medieval trade guilds. Each trade organized a guild to increase the quality of the craft, preserve trade secrets, and limit competition to maintain higher prices. This included formation of societies and a feeling of "brotherhood" that produced group cohesion but also limited the number of tradesmen in the group. The trade frequently passed from father to son.

The skilled labor construction trades carry on this tradition in a more limited form. Unions train young new members in apprenticeship programs consisting of a combination of classroom and on-the-job training lasting about 4 years. Regular meetings and continuing education then increase the tradesman's skill level and dedication to the craft for the rest of his career of about 30 years.

The unskilled, originally industrial workers, sought the same improvements in wages and working conditions as the skilled trades. Instead of maintenance of trade skills, these unions sought "social justice" and in the 1930s were strongly aligned with the socialist and communist parties. (Before the cold war that began after World War II, "communist" did not have the hugely negative connotation it does today and was a significant political force in America.) Training, but not formal apprenticeship, exists in unskilled labor. The unskilled workers' value improved wages and working conditions but do not see the work as a vocation for a full career.

The AFL (American Federation of Labor) started to organize skilled labor in the late 1800s, and the CIO (Congress of Industrial Organizations) organized the unskilled workers in the 1930s. The AFL believed they were the sole representative of labor, but there are far more unskilled than skilled workers, and this imbalance began to threaten the power of the AFL. In 1955, these organizations formed a reluctant and uncomfortable alliance of necessity. The differences in personalities between these two branches result in court fights, threats, and a one-time defection of the carpenters' union from the alliance.

Laws Promoted and Followed Union Development and Legitimacy

In the late 1800s, the United States was still sparsely populated and sought and welcomed rapid industrialization. Large conglomerates that could move boldly and fast were initially welcomed. Steel mills, oil, railroads, and manufacturing employed increasingly large workforces concentrated in urban areas. Long hours, low wages, and dangerous working conditions became common.

The union movement to improve these working conditions started in the early 1900s but was initially met with an extremely probusiness reaction, including government injunctions against strikes and tolerance of management's use of physical force to discourage union activity. A series of laws then moved the pendulum from pro-business to union acceptance.

A brief history of key developments that promoted and managed unions

Sherman Antitrust Act (1890) attempted to curb monopolistic behavior of large companies in the oil, steel, and railroad industries that colluded to the disadvantage of smaller companies and consumers. Although the act was not originally intended to address labor organizations, it was later used to prohibit union organization.

AFL (1886) was established for skilled trades such as blacksmiths, cabinetmakers, and tanners. This pioneer labor organization produced little immediate effect for the workers.

Haymarket Riot (1886) was a labor–employer riot on the west side of Chicago streets where employers' security forces, with government approval, killed workers in the course of the clash. Although this event was not unique, it became a symbol of unacceptable employer overreach in labor relations.

Supreme Court ruling (1908) affirmed that the Sherman AntiTrust Act prohibited union organizing as monopolistic behavior.

Building and Construction Trades Council of the AFL (1908) is the start of construction industry unions.

Clayton Act (1914) attempted to counteract the labor impact of the Sherman Antitrust Act and the Supreme Court ruling of 1908 to permit union organizing at a single employer. But since unions were national and therefore multiemployer, the act seldom applied and was ineffective.

Davis–Bacon Act (1931) mandated payment of "prevailing wages" on some federally funded projects. But since Federal funds may be used for state, county, and city projects, this act had broad reach. Prevailing wages are almost always the union-established wage rates. Employers must submit certified payrolls to the U.S. Department or Labor to obtain project progress payments—a time-consuming task. This act is still in full force and is an actively and hotly contested by nonunion employer organizations and similarly supported by union lobbying groups.

Norris–La Guardia Act (1932) reversed the labor impact of the Sherman Anti-Trust Act and provided the regulatory and enforcement mechanisms that were unsuccessfully attempted by the Clayton Act. This act enabled the beginning of open, effective, and widespread union organization.

CIO (Committee for Industrial Organizations) 1935–1936 was organized for unskilled, primarily industrial workers. The AFL, believing it was the sole national organizing body, ordered the CIO to disband.

National Labor Relations Act (Wagner Act) 1935 established "Employer Unfair Labor Practices" that restricted employer antiunion activities, viewed labor as the weaker aggrieved party, and added rights to correct this perceived imbalance that greatly strengthened unions.

CIO (Congress of Industrial Organizations) (1938) was organized as a successor to the previous CIO. John L Lewis of the United Mine Workers was a driving force that developed a union that could and did survive.

Smith–ConnollyAct (War Labor Disputes Act) (1943) attempted to correct aggressive overreach by unions during the tight labor markets of World War II. Unions' exploitation of wartime labor shortages was thought to be unpatriotic and tainted the unions' public image.

Hobbs "Anti-Racketeering" Act (1946) addressed the unions' involvement in the same anticompetitive and violent behavior (by employers) that the unions originally fought to counteract.

Labor Management Relations Act (Taft–Hartley) (1947) attempted to correct the union imbalance of the Wagner Act of 1935 and defined "Union Unfair Labor Practices."

AFL-CIO formed (1955) by merger of AFL and CIO.

Landrum–Griffin Act (1959) attempted to further fine-tune the labor management balance of the Taft–Hartley Act.

State regulations were established usually to limit compulsory union membership, such as with "right to work" laws. New state regulations continue to be added to define union regulation.

This history documents the swing of the pendulum from physical violence by management to physical violence by workers, and from government injunctions against unions to regulations that tolerated and sometimes promoted unions.

Unions Won Improvements That Became Mainstream for the Entire Workforce

Work hours, wages, child labor, discrimination, benefits, and safety improved for all

Improvements in the working conditions for the entire workforce, both union and nonunion, occurred during the time of union development. Some of the landmark developments documenting this trend are listed below.

A brief history of labor regulation development (both union and nonunion)

Fair Labor Standards Act (1938) mandated overtime pay for workweeks over 40 hours and also mandated "equal pay for equal work." This was then a profound radical development that now is considered normal and customary.

Title IV Civil Rights Act (1964), amended (1972), (1991) prohibited discrimination for race, sex, or creed.

Equal Opportunity Commission (1964) was established to investigate and adjudicate discrimination claims.

Executive Order 11246 (1965) established "affirmative action" requirements for minorities for some federally funded projects. This requirement went beyond equal opportunity and required aggressive efforts to achieve stated percentages of minority participation. Satisfaction of these quotas is a large project cost, quality, and a schedule consideration when there are not enough qualified minorities available.

Executive Order 11375 (1968) extended affirmative action to women.

OSHA (Occupational Safety and Health Act) 1970 established safety standards, employer record keeping, administrative protocols, and methods to adjudicate claims of unsafe conditions.

Public Works Employment Act (1977) required award of 10% of a contract's value to minority general contractors, subcontractors, craft workers, or suppliers on some federally funded projects.

ERISA (Employee Retirement Income Security Act) (1974) is a Federal government agency that regulates the management record keeping and reporting of employer pension plans to attempt to protect the beneficiary interests. (Private pension plans such as IRAs individual retirement accounts and 401Ks employer sanctions but private pensions were established and grew rapidly in popularity at this time.)

Pension Benefit Guarantee Corporation (1974) is a Federal government agency that guarantees some, usually lower, pensions will be paid if an employer-sponsored pension plan fails.

Codifying these rights and limits, such as hours of work, overtime, and safety for the entire workforce, removed one of the competitive advantages that unions originally fought for and provided.

Present Labor Practices and Terms

As the pendulum swung from management to unions and back to the middle, the excesses of both sides produced some puzzling labor terms and practices. The historical development of laws and organizations described above can help understand the present landscape.

Closed shop. All employees must be union members at the time of hire and throughout their employment. Closed shop was restricted by the Taft—Hartley Act and remains illegal.

Union shop. It is the same as closed shop except employees do not need to be union members at the time of hire but must join promptly—usually within months.

Agency shop. Employees do not have to be union members but are governed by union rules and must pay dues and fees required of union employees. Agency shop is increasingly restricted or prohibited.

Open shop. Union or nonunion employees, material suppliers, and subcontractors may be hired and employed. Union members will not be represented by the union while working in an open shop.

Merit shop. It is a form of open shop promoted by the ABC (Associated Builders Congress) that promotes differential wage rates and promotion opportunities based on the employees' merit.

Right to work. States may ban requirements for union membership and union shop agreements that are otherwise permitted by the Taft–Hartley Act.

Project agreements. Project agreements cover union and nonunion workforces for wage and working conditions for a specific project that supersedes existing regional agreements. These projects are usually large and may include multiple projects. The project agreements are dissolved at project completion.

Apprenticeship programs. Construction unions are legally authorized to establish apprenticeship programs. (Nonunion organizations may also have apprenticeship programs, but these do not enjoy the same legal status.) Spreading the cost of facilities, equipment, training materials, and instructional staff over multiple employers (particularly small employers) is a competitive advantage.

Union apprenticeship regulations permit stepped lower wages for the early years of apprenticeship such as 40%, 60%, and 80% of prevailing wages. These lower wage rates are permitted for union, but not for nonunion, contractors on prevailing-wage (Davis–Bacon) projects. This inequity and competitive disadvantage is strenuously contested by the nonunion contractor organizations.

Collective bargaining agreements. In construction, national union organizations will grant charters to individual locals. In some areas, these locals may be associated in a district council. These locals or councils individually negotiate wages and working conditions with the local employer groups. (In contrast, industrial unions may negotiate nationwide contracts.)

Common-situs picketing. If some, but not all, contractors on a project are engaged in a labor dispute, separate gates may be used to minimize the effects of the dispute on the project progress. The NLRB (National Labor Relations Board is the Federal agency established by the Taft–Hartley Act to regulate and adjudicate union management relations) finds that if a gate is reserved for a contractor in a dispute, that gate may be picketed. But a second gate may be designated for the parties not in the dispute and may not be picketed. Only by knowing the history of labor law can this pointless and ineffective measure be understood.

Project Specific Regulations, Codes, and Standards

Code and regulatory analysis requires a structured sequential approach

Minimum standards, but not excellence, are sought

Laws and regulations seek to minimize the bad, but not achieve the good

Zoning codes, building codes, standards, and industry-specific regulations define the type of project that can be built at a site. These regulations must be viewed as a comprehensive whole and be applied in a defined sequence. Nothing out of sequence or context has a reliable meaning. "Ah-ha, here is the answer" will seldom produce the correct result.

These standards provide a needed and critical function but do not attempt to ensure uniform quality or that the completed project satisfies the owner's purpose. "It is all up to code" is a start but not the end of successful project definition.

Land-Use Restrictions First Define the Type of Project Allowed

Zoning restricts types of uses to achieve diverse goals

Zoning ordinances identify use classes such as industrial, manufacturing, commercial, office, institutional, retail, multifamily residential, and single-family residential. (There can be many subcategories and qualifications in each of these categories, and specific named use types such as "dry cleaners" or "pet store" may be prohibited or allowed.) Zoning ordinances were first concerned with noise, fumes, truck and rail traffic, and fire hazards. Regulations to segregate types of workers or clientele, such as liquor stores near schoolyards, were then added.

Increasingly, zoning ordinances are used either to provide a "look and feel," such as a certain architectural style, or to attract certain types of businesses that provide desired jobs or sales tax revenue. Higher densities served by public transportation or ratios of retail, commercial, and residential development that city planners feel optimal may also be added. Minimum lot areas, setbacks (that must be free from improvements), parking, site lighting, and landscaping requirements may be added.

Storm water management can have huge project impacts

Storm water management was once the responsibility of government organizations. Increasingly, property owners are required to temporarily retain storm water on their property to minimize the short-term surges that would further burden the government storm water infrastructure. This can hugely increase site development cost or prohibit the use of some sites. Environmental regulations both for pollution control and for preservation of wildlife habitats can add further restrictions.

Storm water management regulation is primarily regional (usually a county sized district related to the flow of storm water) but also city, state, and national. Cooperation frequently exists among these overlapping jurisdictions.

Building Codes Then Determine the Types of Building That Can Be Built

Building codes first governed building component size and capacity, then fire safety

Building codes first developed thousands of years ago in the Middle East and established some standards, but mostly penalties for structural collapse. Penalties were criminal in nature and severe, such as amputations or execution of the builder. (With few exceptions, most construction in many large cities up until the last 200 years was predominantly masonry, fire was a lesser concern.)

Increase in wood-frame construction produced an increase in fires. The Great Chicago Fire of 1871 destroyed the entire developed portion of the city. Chicago then instituted the Chicago Building Code with a heavy emphasis on fire prevention—a pioneering code that, with revisions, is still in use. Many other cities followed suit and developed municipal building codes. Requirements for light and ventilation, and controls of combustion and heating and pressure devices, as well as the purity of domestic water systems, were then added.

Codes transitioned from municipal to national

The move to standardize codes progressed throughout this second half of the 20th century. A uniform building code predominated in the west and northwest but was phased out in 1998. Four regional BOCA codes addressed the regional needs such as hurricanes, tornadoes, termites, frost penetration, snow loading, and high rain and moisture conditions. These four regions were combined into the International Building Code in 2000.

International Codes have volumes for building, mechanical, plumbing, and fire prevention. These codes are developed in a highly structured proposal, review, and revision process, involving large panels of code officials and design professionals. But installing contractors and manufacturing vendors are specifically prohibited from serving or contributing to this review process.

The NFPA (National Fire Protection Association) developed the NEC (National Electric Code), which is the dominant electrical code used throughout the United States in conjunction with the International Codes. The NFPA also publishes NFPA 101, which establishes basic life safety as a supplement to the International code—straddling the border between codes and standards. NFPA also publishes nearly 300 other standards specifying proper work execution. These standards and codes are developed with a review process similar to the international code, but the NFPA does include manufacturers and vendors in their review process. The NFPA seeks to expand their codes into the jurisdictions now occupied by the International codes.

These codes must be formally adopted by the government entity (city, township, or county) having jurisdiction. And the codes are revised at variable intervals, with 3 years most common. The revised editions must be adopted as well—but that adoption can be delayed years or decades. And each government agency may add amendments for their peculiar situations or the personal preferences of their officials. Still, other cities write their own codes from scratch. So, although national codes predominate, regional variations and arbitrary interpretations abound.

Project code analysis is sequential and no step can be skipped

After the zoning analysis determines the permitted uses at the project site, building code analysis determines the possible type and size and construction of the building.

The intended use must be translated into building code occupancy types.

Occupancy types in the International Building Code include

> Assembly A
> Business B
> Educational E
> Factory F
> High Hazard H
> Institutional I
> Mercantile M
> Residential R
> Storage S
> Utility and Miscellaneous U

There are subgroups for each of these occupancy groups

Once the occupancy classification is determined, the code then determines the permitted size, height, fire resistance, and structural capacity of the building needed for that occupancy. The headings of some of the chapters in the International Building Code used for this analysis are listed below.

> General Building Height and Area
> Types of Construction
> Fire-Resistant-Rated Construction
> Interior Finishes
> Fire Protection Systems
> Means of Egress
> Accessibility
> Interior Environment
> Energy Efficiency
> Exterior Walls
> Roof Assemblies and Rooftop Structures
> Structural Design
> Structural Test and Special Situations

Additional sections on building components such as concrete, aluminum, masonry, steel, and subsection for all sections are included. Other parts of the building code then determine the required and permitted standards of ventilation, heating, sanitation, and electrical safety.

Analysis must be performed in this order, and no step can be missed. This analysis produces requirements for a building of this occupancy type that is structurally adequate, reasonably safe, and meets minimum standards of light ventilation and sanitation.

Mechanical electrical trades analyze codes more than construction managers

But these performance criteria, with the exception of the NEC, provide few detailed instructions for execution of the work. (The NEC has far more detailed execution standards and provides guidance for both the design professional and the installing tradesman.)

This complete code analysis is performed by architects with the assistance of consulting engineers for certain portions of the work. This analysis produces the overall design of the building but speaks little to the execution of the construction. Therefore, construction managers must be familiar with and understand the code but do not consult it regularly when executing the work. In contrast, mechanical electrical codes contain detailed information relevant to the installation and are frequently consulted by the installing subcontractors. This distinction is critical for the construction manager—both to select appropriate subcontractors capable of performing the needed analysis and to schedule sufficient time to perform this subsequent analysis.

Then Additional Regulations May Be Added for Specific Project Types

Industry-specific regulatory bodies can require modification or addition to the building and zoning codes. These modifications can affect original design and construction and maintenance of the facility. Some common examples are listed below.

Departments of Public Health can alter mechanical electrical design and installation

Departments of Public Health regulate restaurants, hospitals, food processing, and water supply systems. These departments tend to be local—state, county, or city—and have only few technically trained personnel. These personnel may have personal preferences about installations and testing procedures.

Environmental agencies can alter design or kill a project

State and national environmental protection agencies establish standards and modify conformance of effluents from power plants, fuel-handling facilities, and heavy industrial facilities. These requirements can markedly affect the original design and construction, as well as ongoing maintenance.

Fire marshals can affect fire suppression and fire-resistive assemblies

State Fire Marshals are a separate entity substantially divorced from the building code and other regulatory systems. Coordination of requirements and enforcement is not normal. They are heavily involved in any storage and transmission of flammable liquids and gases, as well as installation of fire protection sprinkler and fire alarm systems. They can also become involved with fire separations and exit ways, particularly for institutional (hospitals, schools, nursing homes) and assembly (theatres and sports stadiums). They typically do not develop their own codes and standards but rather adopt and slightly modify standards by others. But their interpretation and preferences can produce variable interpretation and enforcement.

Further Voluntary Standards Seek to Improve Project Outcomes

Exceeding minimum standards and achieving target goals

As described above, the building codes and regulations seek to achieve but not exceed minimum standards, and these codes are not intend to and do not provide detailed installation instructions. But many projects seek more than the minimum level of quality. Supplemental standards provide this necessary and desirable additional detail.

Supplementary standards to assist execution

Standards developed by NFPA, ANSI (American National Standards Institute), ASHREA (American Society of Heating and Air-conditioning Engineers) may be formally adopted or adopted by reference in the building codes. Installation standards are provided by the trade associations for masonry, roofing, doors, and windows. These standards, which are sometimes used by the design professionals, but more heavily by construction managers and specialty trades, are needed to design and install "best practices" installations.

Certification is sought by some project owners

Some individuals or industries seek certification of achievement of higher standards. The JCAHC (Joint Commission on Accreditation of Health Care Facilities) and the AAHA (American Animal Hospital

Association) establish quality standards and inspection protocols to accredit and certify facilities. LEED (Leadership in Energy and Environmental Design) certification standards similarly specify design standards to provide environmental certification. Adoption of these voluntary standards can materially affect the design, construction, and maintenance of the structure.

Regulation, codes, and standards become everyone's responsibility

The construction manager could take the position that conformance to codes is the designer's responsibility. But even if this were entirely true (as might occur in hard bid jobs), understanding of the thought process and analysis behind the designer's work aids effective installation.

And the execution of the work and the standards needed to achieve the desired high level of quality does require understanding of the inner relationship between codes, regulation laws, and standards. Finally, understanding of this process can greatly assist the construction managers' input in the project development process that can greatly increase the value and the desirability of preconstruction services.

Summary

The regulatory framework for design and construction must be understood to achieve conformance with minimal effort, so the construction managers' focus can remain on project management.

Careful selection of the construction management company's formal organization can provide the needed liability protections while minimizing administrative requirements and optimizing income tax management. It is easier to start small and grow, than to shrink and dissolve.

Labor-management project disharmony can adversely affect the project schedule and cost. An understanding of the origin and history of labor law can assist understanding of the present labor environment. But this environment has significant regional variations and is changing rapidly. The labor environment for each project must be specifically analyzed and the impacts included in project planning.

Conformance to codes, regulations, and standards involves all project participants. Land-use regulations, building codes, and additional regulations for specific project types, further voluntary standards, and standards for execution must be analyzed in a structured sequence. But it must be recognized that some of the later steps can subsequently affect the earlier steps, so several iterations of this cycle may be required. Local authorities having jurisdiction have personal opinions and preferences that affect interpretation. Careful analysis must be performed for each project.

Laws, regulations, codes, and standards seek to enforce minimum standards but do not seek to achieve project excellence. So regulatory conformance is a starting but not an end point.

Review Questions (True or False)

1. Laws by legislatures, regulations by unelected government staff, codes by national code-related organizations, and standards by trade organizations all establish the regulatory framework for construction projects.

2. Corporations are established and regulated by the federal government and permit continuity of ownership and a reduction in the liability of the company owners.

3. Most construction firms are either "C" or "S" corporations. The profits of a "C" corporation are taxed at the corporate level and again at the personal level when dividends are distributed. "S" corporations are taxed only at the personal level.

4. A joint venture is a temporary combination of companies for a project that pools technical knowledge, knowledge of local customs, people, and businesses, bonding capacity, and capital to gain a competitive advantage.

5. Construction converts personal property that is movable to real property that is permanently attached to the land. Sworn statements for payment document this conversion.

6. In the United States, unions started developing in the late 1800s to more effectively bargain with management about compensation and working conditions.

7. The Sherman Antitrust, Clayton, Norris–La Guardia, Wagner, and Smith-Connelly acts all increased the management's bargaining power with the unions.

8. The Fair Labor Standards Act of 1938, OSHA, and ERISA sought to improve employees' working hour regulation, safety, and pensions.

9. The closed shop that requires all workers to be union members at the time of hire is illegal, but the union shop, which does not require workers to be union at time of hire but does require them to join the union promptly, is legal.

10. A merit shop promotes differential wage rates and promotion opportunities based on the employees' merit, and right to work states ban requirements for union membership and union shop agreements.

11. Construction unions are legally authorized to establish apprenticeship program with a lower wage rates for apprentices. Both union and non-union contractors may legally pay these lower wage rates on prevailing wage (Davis–Bacon) projects.

12. If some but not all contractors on a project are engaged in a labor dispute, one gate (that may be picketed) may be established for the contractors in the dispute, and a second gate (that may not be picketed) is established for the parties not in dispute.

13. Zoning ordinances that restrict the types of business uses and control noise, fumes, and traffic are fully integrated with building codes.

14. International Building Codes cover buildings, mechanical, plumbing, and fire protection, and are developed in a highly structured proposal review and revision process involving code officials, design professionals, installing contractors, and manufacturing vendors.

15. The building code analysis is sequential—first determining occupancy types and then determining permitted building size, height, fire resistance, structural capacity, and mechanical electrical system characteristics.

16. Additional regulations may be added for specific project type by Departments of Public Health, environmental agencies, and fire marshals.

17. Projects seeking accreditation such as JCAHC or LEED may voluntarily adopt additional standards.

Test Your Understanding

1. Find from a family member, relative, or friend the form of organization (Corporation C or S, LLC, partnership, or sole proprietorship) of their employing organization. Ask what impact this form of organization has on day-to-day operations, management of liability, and income taxes.

2. Find an advertisement for construction bids in a newspaper and note the impact of regulations included such as "prevailing wage," "equal opportunity," or minority set-asides.

3. Find a city zoning code on a city's website and analyze restrictions on construction of an automobile dealership. Note permitted zoning districts, lot size and setbacks, and maximum building height specifications.

Introduction Part II
Winning the Job and Initiating the Project

All projects must be developed from initial concept through design development to provide instructions and documents needed for construction. Construction managers or general contractors using all project delivery systems—from hard bid to service oriented construction management firms—are affected by the project development process. But the time and nature of involvement varies.

The hard bid contractors start when the documents are ready to bid and do not participate in early project development. But understanding the development process can assist these contractors select the most viable high-profit projects. If the contractor determines that a project is poorly conceived and coordinated and the owner has limited financial resources, the project may be deemed too risky and avoided. However, if a different owner of this same project had sufficient financial resources, the project might be accepted anticipating many high-profit change orders. Understanding the project development process is like getting a copy of the other team's playbook—a huge competitive advantage.

Construction managers providing a range of services from preconstruction, value engineering, constructability analysis, and construction can add significant value during project development. Early service fees can be obtained, performance and outcomes managed, risk of project execution reduced, and development of a preference for the CM's services that reduces competition gained.

All contractors can benefit from knowledge of the development process—only how and when this information is used differs.

And construction managers also require the skills needed to "get the job"—cost and estimating, time planning and scheduling, and bidding and buying the job. This text provides both the needed theory and practical application—with particular emphasis on integration of these knowledge areas.

CHAPTER
2.1

A Workable Purpose Must Be Designed First

The Steel-Ply® steel concrete forming systems can be handset or gang formed using more than 80 standard panel sizes and fillers. With this versatility, a construction manager can own the forms and amortize the cost over multiple projects. *Photo courtesy: Symons.*

A Workable Purpose Must Be Designed First

Project success must start with clear definitions and priorities

Achieving excellent and predictable performance—project success—must start with defining a workable purpose. This must be followed by establishing a workable approach that makes achieving this purpose highly probable. Failure to define the purpose—before initiating the project—usually ensures failure to achieve the purpose.

Construction project manager involvement in early project development adds value. Clear definition of the reason and purpose for the project and early determination that the intended scope, time, and cost are feasible speed execution and minimize mid-project scope corrections. The intended results are precisely achieved faster and at a lower cost.

Purpose definition is essential for construction management, and valuable for hard bid delivery as well

The project owner may exclude the construction manager from the steps described in this chapter and presents the project as an accomplished fact—"we know what we want, so how long will it take, and how much will it cost?" Backing up and performing the needed initial steps can produce the optimal results—but does require the owner's cooperation, which may not always be present.

On the far end of the spectrum, hard bid lump sum contracts always exclude the contractor from initial planning. In these cases, the contractor will still make some determination of the quality of the owner's definition of the reason and purpose, and choose an appropriate reaction.

A project for which the reason and purpose are poorly defined may be avoided, or additional management cost included in the contractor's proposal to cover the needed additional management time. Or the contractor may attempt to serve the owner better and solve the problems—hoping to develop a long-term relationship.

Alternatively, the contractor may choose to take the project and increase profit through numerous high-priced change requests. Understanding the quality of the owner's reason and purpose is similar to obtaining an opposing team's playbook before the contest—a huge competitive advantage. But this profit maximization will probably reduce the customer's preference for a long-term relationship.

Whether maximizing the value of the project or maximizing the contractor's profit is sought, the analysis of the project reason and purpose is the same, as described below.

Defining a Workable Purpose Starts with the Use of the Project

Getting it right the first time means knowing what "it" is. To begin a project, one must know the purpose—consisting of use to be served, and the reason for the project. Definition of intended use and reason, including grade of materials, time, and likely cost (the triple constraint), must be set to determine if the project is probably feasible. Once a feasible purpose is defined, workable approaches can be selected to achieve this purpose, and success will be possible. Hoping to get lucky later is not a plan. Starting a project with "we can work that out later" or "we just need to get some ideas and input" makes partial or complete failure probable.

Use of the completed project—what functions will it serve?

State the project's intended use.

Examples:

> Apartment building
> Church
> Manufacturing facility
> Retail store
> Vacation home
> Interstate highway
> Municipal sewage treatment plant

Specify few uses—one is best

Some projects legitimately have multiple uses—such as an office warehouse or a high-rise facility combining retail, office, and residential. Most mixed-use facilities, however, do *not* have a legitimate use. Instead they represent cloudy and confused thinking that must be corrected before the project proceeds. For example, an owner's manufacturing facility that will also house his antique car collection, or a church that wishes to add rental retail facilities in a portion of the building—to get income to "help out with the expenses." A good project should serve only the essential and necessary use.

A mixed-use facility will cost more and take more time to build than either of the single uses. This is true because each use will have unique site development considerations such as parking, truck access, site lighting, storm drainage, structural systems related to clear spans and floor loading capacities, floor-to-floor heights, heating, ventilation, air-conditioning, and electrical systems. Also, it is usually true that the more complicated and expensive requirement of one use will be imposed to some degree on the other uses. Further, there are usually additional design considerations, such as fire walls that separate the two uses. All these will increase the cost of a mixed-use project.

Contributing to the design problems of a mixed-use project is the fact that different companies and different personnel usually specialize in each type of project. For example, one type of company and set of personnel would perform road construction, and a different set would perform interior construction of high-rise residential units. Neither is adequately suited to do the other's work. For uses with more similar construction types and owner uses, such as an office warehouse, similar differences in firm and personnel capabilities exist. A single company will typically try to perform both, but one or more of the tasks will be performed at a less-than-optimal level.

If multiple uses are essential for a project, then proceed knowing that additional time, cost, and management effort will be needed. If multiple uses for the project are not essential, or worth the resulting cost and time premium, make the hard decision—before starting—and delete the unnecessary part of the project.

Then Define the Project Reason—Why Is It Being Built

The reason for the project is defined by the most important characteristics sought—expressed in both qualitative and quantitative terms for grade of material, cost, and time.

For example:

Apartments
Apartments are built for investment, to achieve a 7% return on investment for market rate housing in a specified area. The grade of materials will be the lowest acceptable for the market area, and a minimal time of construction to minimize construction financing costs is required.

Manufacturing facility
A manufacturing facility requires precision and consistency of the manufacturing processes and rapid manufacturing line changeovers, so grade of materials and reliability of mechanical systems cannot be

compromised. Construction cost is not critical, and time may or may not be critical, depending on the prevailing market demand for the product to be manufactured.

Hotel interior construction
A "new" image is required every 3 years, so the selected finishes and furnishings cannot be compromised. Construction in the slow season—with minimum downtime—is required to minimize revenue loss. Cost is of medium importance, and the short intended useful life means long-term material durability is of no concern.

Government projects
Allocation of political favors to certain persons or groups can be a primary purpose, so a high cost is desired (more favors to pass out). Grade of materials and functional use may be of little concern. Time of construction is only important to produce a big show around election time.

Truthful statements are critical

Truthful statement of some reasons(s) such as "the highest cost is best," "grade of materials doesn't matter," "time of completion isn't important" are awkward and usually must be disguised for public consumption. But truthful internal statements must be made to define the reason for the project. Such statements can best be made by the highest ranking decision-maker(s)—even if guided by subordinates—but they must be made. Subordinates telling the boss what he wants to hear, then telling him the bad news later, avoids defining the reason and will fail to provide needed project definition.

Be definite only when really needed

State only the essentials definitely—with both qualitative and precise quantitative definitions. For the qualities that are not essential, state a range or qualitative description only. The fewer definite statements made, the more achievable the project. Three definite statements is usually the limit for achievable projects.

State requirements only if required for your purpose. Requiring the highest grade of materials, at an impossibly low price, in an impossibly short time, because "if we start high, we can always go down from there," is a failure to decide. A demanding, unnecessary requirement will compete with necessary requirements, and the necessary requirements may lose.

Setting priorities early is essential

After establishing all the essentials of the project, the needed characteristics must be ranked in the order of importance. Everything cannot be first and equally important—set priorities early. Failure to set priorities at the start of the project will let somebody else decide as the project unfolds—and the real goals may not be achieved!

This is true first because the project will proceed without turning back from the starting requirements. To make a mid-project correction and start over from a clean slate requires a person who is willing to say that they were completely wrong at the beginning. The need for such people always exceeds the supply. Second, once the project is underway and time constraints have been established, the clock is running. There is usually no time to completely start over. Finally, the project participants can only partially change their point of view of the project purpose, reason, and approach. They will have vested interests, partial work done they wish to salvage, and attitudes that cannot be changed easily or completely. Midcourse correction of use and reason is a patch-and-repair operation that cannot achieve excellent results.

A forceful personality with better communication skills, a more competent company, or someone with a quicker response will be heard first and better. Decisions will be made randomly, and the wrong things may win and lose. This will produce at best mediocre results and failure to achieve some or all of the needed goals.

The project sponsor—a project champion and owner liaison

The construction project manager's skills and work drive development of the workable purpose—but an owner counterpart is required as well. This counterpart, the project "sponsor," champions the project and acts as a liaison to the project owner's senior management. The project sponsor will state the project needs, work with the construction project manager to refine the needs, and gain senior management project approval, including financial commitment. For very small companies, the sponsor may be a member of senior management. For larger companies, the sponsor may be a member of the facilities, construction, or real estate departments.

The project sponsor will usually not be involved in day-to-day project management, unless the project performance falls below agreed limits or the owner requests major scope changes.

Once the Purpose and Reason Are Clear, Feasibility Can and Must Be Checked

This chapter describes clear thinking about the project reason and purpose that is an essential first step. Once these priorities are established, the next steps in the project management process can work to plan and execute these priorities. Without these definitions, the following steps will struggle to establish priorities after the fact—an inefficient exercise that can only partially succeed. The next chapter describes evaluation of the feasibility of the priorities and begins to establish quantitative and qualitative definitions needed to plan and execute the project.

An exterior scaffolding and access system must simultaneously consider the materials to be installed, installation equipment needed, and the safety and productivity of the installing workers. The cost of the access system and productivity of the workers must be balanced to achieve the needed project cost and schedule. This scaffolding system for the Aldgate House London, England, included the CUPLOK® and MCWP (mast climbing work platform) and traditional tube and fitting scaffolding. *Photo courtesy of Harsco Infrastructure.*

Summary

Define the project purpose—consisting of the purpose and reason—and specify grade of material, cost, and time—before starting. Make definite requirements only when really needed—otherwise provide a range or qualitative description. Set priorities and rank requirements in order of importance. Do not proceed with the project until the use and reasons are known and ranked in order of importance. Ranking helps ensure that all important points are considered, and priorities set.

Mid-project correction of use and reason cannot produce excellent results. Clear definition of purpose before the start of the project makes determination of a workable approach and project planning, execution, and success possible.

Review Questions (True or False)

1. Achieving excellent and predictable performance must start with defining a workable purpose, followed by establishing a workable approach that makes achieving this purpose highly probable.
2. A project manager can add maximum value through early involvement in project planning.
3. Purpose definition is essential for construction project management but not for lump sum hard bid project delivery.
4. Defining a workable purpose starts with the use of the project.
5. Mixed-use projects can usually be built in the same time and for the same cost as single-use projects.
6. The reason for the project is defined by the most important characteristics sought.
7. Truthful internal statements must be made to define the reason for a project, and these statements must also be presented to all project participants and senior management.
8. State the project essentials definitively, both qualitatively and quantitatively, but state nonessential characteristics with a quantitative range or qualitative description only.
9. All characteristics of a project must be given equal weight and consideration.
10. The owner's representative, called a project sponsor, champions the project, acts as a liaison with the project owner's senior management, helps define project need, and gains approval and financing.

Test Your Understanding

1. For a project you are familiar with through personal experience or case study, state the reason and purpose of the project and rank the criteria in order of importance.
2. For one of your extracurricular activities such as sports, music, or service organizations, state the reason and purpose of your involvement.
3. For a project for which the initial reason and purpose were poorly defined, discuss how effectively (from the project owner's standpoint of owner administrative time, and project schedule and cost) the following project delivery methods can achieve the needed mid-project correction.

   Construction management with reimbursable cost of work plus a fixed fee
   Construction management with a guaranteed maximum price and shared savings
   Lump sum hard bid
   Time and material

CHAPTER
2.2

A Qualitative Understanding and Definition of Feasible Limits Come Next

Selection of scaffolding systems for exterior renovation projects is a critical project decision affecting both cost and time. Successful selection requires collaboration of the construction manager and field superintendent. This scaffolding system for the Buffalo City Hall Buffalo, New York, combined QES® scaffolding and Trouble Saver sectional frames needed for stonework repairs. *Photo courtesy of Harsco Infrastructure.*

A Qualitative Understanding and Definition of Feasible Limits Come Next

Approximating project size, difficulty, ingredients, opportunities, and obstacles

Finding Probable Workable Approaches

A "workable approach" is one that can and probably will achieve the workable purpose with the scope, cost, and time required. Determining the "workable approach" to a project is similar to getting the right tool for a task. However, it is quite different in timing and impact. If the wrong tool is selected, the right tool can be quickly substituted—and the consequences will probably be minor. If the wrong project approach is selected, the error will be noticed at the middle or end of the project—when partial or total failure is admitted. "I can do anything, just let me get started" or "Do it like we did last time" will frequently end in delay, cost over-runs, or failure.

Determining a workable approach is 95% hard work—counting, measuring, checking, and organizing. But the approximate size, scope, look, and feel of the project must be known before an approach can be approximated, counted, and measured.

Finding an intuitive understanding and feasible project limits involves:
1. Gaining an intuitive understanding of the project—in an organized format
2. Evaluating the ingredients for problems and opportunities—including some counting and measuring
3. Evaluating the risk of obstacles
4. Finding the feasible approach limits using this information

This chapter describes the initial processes to find the limits of feasible approaches—and determines that the project can probably be made to work. Several cycles of evaluation are frequently needed to reach this conclusion—but this preliminary step is heavy on intuition and analysis and lighter on quantitative data. The next step, adding further quantitative analysis that establishes a project charter that starts project planning and execution, is discussed in the following chapter.

First an Intuitive Understanding—in a Framework for Evaluation

Determining a workable approach builds the project mentally and on paper—before touching a shovel. A workable purpose (described in the previous chapter) must precede a workable approach, or there will be no way of knowing if the approach will achieve the purpose. "If you don't know where you are going, you can't know how to get there, or that you have arrived." Although this is obvious common sense, it is frequently omitted, and the project partially or completely fails.

Determining a workable approach consists of understanding the project, counting all the building blocks, and then organizing the building blocks into relationships and sequences to achieve the purpose. Knowledge gives power, and knowledge requires both intuition and experience—and facts.

Obtaining, organizing, and analyzing facts take the most time and effort. The process is 5% inspiration (fun—intuitive understanding of what the project might be) and 95% perspiration (work, counting, checking availability). Without intuitive understanding, one will not know what to count. Without counting the facts problems and opportunities for improvement and innovation cannot be known and results cannot be checked.

Determine the scale and "look and feel" and nature of the project

Start with intuitive judgment of about how big and difficult the project is—but keep an open mind—it may be wrong. The following broad categories are starters:

Epic—Unprecedented size, unproven techniques, vast time frames. Examples include the Great Wall of China, the Great Pyramids of Egypt, the cathedrals of Medieval Europe (taking up to 300 years to complete), the Panama Canal, and the first man on the moon.

Massive—One of the largest projects under construction in the world, techniques are difficult but have been previously completed, time frames are over 5 years but within one person's lifetime. Examples include Hoover Dam, tunnel under the English Channel, and Three Gorges Dam in China.

Large—Large size (but many similar projects also underway at other remote locations), techniques have been completed many times, completion under 5 years. Examples include 80-story office building, lock and dam, refinery, suspension bridge.

Medium—Size similar to many surrounding completed projects in the area, techniques off the shelf, completion in 1–5 years. Examples include 6-story suburban office building, new public school, and highway cloverleaf interchange.

Small—Size identical to projects completed and underway in the area, component are off the shelf or field fabricated with supply house material, completion under 1 year. Examples include single-family homes, office tenant build outs, and chain store construction.

Although this is a progression from large to small, it is not a progression from hard to easy. All projects require similar intuitive thought and detailed analysis. The short time frames of smaller projects, in fact, make recovery from project approach errors more difficult.

Qualitative and quantitative impressions are needed to find the best "workable approach." Since this is done before the project starts—before design, cost estimates, or detailed evaluations are made—the estimates of quantities for each project ingredient are an approximation based on specific knowledge from prior projects. These quantitative impressions coupled with intuition ask the following questions:

"What is probably going to be a challenge on this project?"

"Where are the opportunities for improvement?"

"What project is this most similar to?"

"Could we look at this project in a different way?"

"Does this feel about right?"

This is the last opportunity to resolve the quantitative and qualitative impressions and to view the project in a different light—to reduce the time, cost, and effort of the approach—and still achieve the intended result. For example, a government office building will require the most effort, cost, and time; a custom-designed private office building will require a medium amount; and an adaptation of a previously completed private office design will require the least. Three approaches may produce the same building but have vastly different costs and times of completion.

Early clear thinking can produce large benefit, but it must be early. Once the approach is chosen, management and field forces will be assigned, and vendors contracted, effort, cost, and time cannot decrease easily or much.

Can the Available Project Ingredients Support the Approach?

Estimating an approach is a valuable start, but most projects are too large and complex for anyone to grasp them entirely at once. An estimated approach must be verified and adjusted by individually evaluating the availability of each ingredient for a project's specific time, price, and location. Assumptions must all be checked with information and knowledge specifically gathered for this project.

What is required and available is influenced by the price to be paid, time available, and normal variation (such as plant shutdowns, material or labor shortage, arbitrary whim of governing authorities).

The Washington National Cathedral in Washington, DC, required repair of stonework that was loosened by lightning strikes. Double-cantilevered INTERFORM® shoring tables were moved around and used to support the QES scaffolding above. *Photo courtesy of Harsco Infrastructure.*

Since these can change instantly, even identical projects in different places or times can have very different ingredient effort, time, and cost. Specific estimates by component must be obtained. Every single ingredient is necessary for project completion, so no detail can be entirely missed or misunderstood.

Project Ingredients

Labor of the needed capacity and character must be verified

The quantity of labor—of the character and capacity required for the project—must be estimated. Skilled labor is limited at a specific location, price, and time, so an approximation of the amount of each labor type—unskilled, skilled, technical, and management—for the project must be made to ensure sufficient labor is available. If the "required" field labor is unacceptably expensive, more mechanized on-site production, or subcontracted off-site component production may be substituted to lower cost. If there is a shortage of available labor, wages can be raised, or additional compensation offered to attract more labor—reattracting skilled labor temporarily employed in other pursuits or attracting skilled labor from outside the normal geographical area. Training of the available, insufficiently skilled labor is another option, but takes time and money. There are limits, and once reached, more time and/or money must be allocated or the project must be deemed unfeasible.

There are also limits to the density of labor on the job site at one time. Increases in the density will reduce productivity and quality and increase accidents. Increasing labor by adding shifts will increase cost. "We can always add more people" is not always true.

Materials will be scarce at a price and location

The quantities of each required material must be estimated. All materials are scarce at some price, time, and place, so quantities and availability must be estimated for the specific project. Water for human use, construction cleaning, and concrete mixing will be scarce and expensive for desert projects. Water is available at city projects by turning on the tap. Basic materials such as steel, cement, copper, oil, and aluminum vary wildly in price and availability—due to variations in demand, plant shutdowns, and short-term manipulation of prices. Manufactured equipment can have even greater variation.

Outside companies—designers, subcontractors, and vendors—are scarce also

Designers, vendors, and subcontractors are required on all projects. At a given price level, a limited group will be available. These groups' capabilities for technical expertise and capacity for quality and quantity of delivery must be estimated. Their size provides some guidelines, as explained below:

1. One-man shop—One person furnishes proposals, does the work, and does the books with no other employees. May be extremely responsive, somewhat limited in technical innovation, and strictly limited in quantity of output.
2. Small shop—One person oversees everything and can do all or most tasks, but has employees. Same as one-man shop but fewer restrictions on technical innovation, and greater output is possible.
3. Medium-size shop—One or two owners who each may be able to perform only some of the tasks. Valued and skilled long-term employees may perform all functions of the business. This size shop is limited to the number of employees owners know personally and interact with daily or many times per week. Management can be by the force of the owners' personalities, with little formal structure, and can be responsive and innovative and expand output beyond normal capacity. Geographical reach may be limited.
4. Large shop—One or many owners who perform few or no online tasks. More than one key employee can perform each key task. Formal management structure restricts responsiveness and innovation. Can have major management failures and quality control deficiencies that are not promptly detected. Capable of large quantities of output with long geographical reach.

Small firms cannot do all that large firms do. The large firms cannot do well what the small firms do. The vast majority of subcontractors and vendors are small and medium sized. The smallest firm suitable for the project tends to be the best fit. An evaluation of the firms available must be made, so the assignment of tasks to firms matches their execution capability. There may be many names in the phone book, but few or no optimal firms may be available for a specific project at a specific time.

Time is always critical, but frequently not carefully considered

Possible construction times to achieve optimal quality and cost must be estimated and compared with the desired cost. Every project has a small range of completion times that can be achieved with maximum productivity and performance standards. If a project "must" be done by a time that is unfeasible with the available straight time labor at an acceptable cost, an alternate time or cost premium must be selected. "Drop dead" times usually mean that costs must increase or performance standards decrease or both.

There are also limits to the time of material installation—governed by chemical cure times. Concrete cures in 28 days. "High early" concrete can achieve (for additional cost) the design strength earlier than

28 days but will not be fully cured to properly accept chemical coatings and adhesives. Similarly, the coatings and adhesives have cure times between coats that can be shortened somewhat but not eliminated.

Cost is only evaluated for approximate feasibility at this stage

Cost is frequently one of the most compelling parts of the triple constraint. But unlike other areas of project management, the range of acceptable costs in construction is frequently quite narrow—a 10% range is huge, and a couple percent is more common. But this level of precision requires more quantitative analysis, so cost at the stage of analysis is more a "tollgate" than a quantitative commitment. Questions such as "Is the cost for this project approximately in line with past completed projects of similar nature?" or if the project is innovative or has high hazard risks "Is the needed cost premium included?"

If a small portion—such as only half of the reasonable project cost—is included in the approach, the approach must be revised or the project abandoned. If the costs are in a reasonable range, further quantitative analysis and cost refinement are then performed as discussed in the following chapters.

Obstacles Can Kill a Project—Risk Evaluation Is Required

Major forces must be considered

War surrounding a job site, war or revolution in a remote country that supplies an important component of the project, trade disruptions between countries, destruction of a plant producing a required material, labor strikes, and catastrophic weather can radically affect project completion. Although wars surrounding the job site are unlikely for most projects, disruptions in other countries that increase the cost or delay or prevent delivery of critical components are quite common. Oil prices, exotic hardwood, or granite and marble are materials subject to price swings or reduced availability. Although the time of disruption cannot be predicted, recognition that a project includes such materials allows alternate plans to manage the disruption—such as stockpile early, or have contingency plans for alternate materials.

Government force (taxes, fees, regulation, and permissions) can raise costs

The impact (in time and cost) of government regulation on a project must be estimated. Permit, zoning, land use, and "impact" fees are only partly specified by written regulation. A reasonable person can determine the probable impact of the regulation. However, the government is also political, so a reasonable interpretation may not be enough. A portion of the fees can also be arbitrary. For example, a politically influenced tax on the project, completely unrelated to any regulation or government service rendered may be imposed. In predictability and project impact, these fees are similar to bribes paid to corrupt politicians. Additional time, money, and increased risk of further arbitrary demands are possible and could delay or prevent the completion of the project.

Any interaction with the government will take time and have a cost. If multiple successive approvals are required—first environmental approval, then zoning approval, then building approval—the time and money required could rapidly escalate out of control, rendering the project unfeasible at the required time and cost.

Innovation can have extra costs too

If a portion of the building, such as structural or mechanical system, has never been built before in the project area, additional expertise, time, and money must be allowed to learn the new building systems and learn the implications on the other parts of the building. Substantial redesign of other building components, which are necessary to accommodate the innovative portion, will have cost and time implications. If multiple innovative systems interact on one project, such as a new curtain wall system and a new structural system, both of which require regulatory approval, then significant impacts in management, technical expertise, time, and money must be anticipated.

Summary

A workable approach will probably succeed—with hard work

Approximating the quantity and availability of ingredients—and the magnitude of obstacles for a project—helps select a workable approach. These approximations are compared to the project's "required" ranges for products, costs, and time. The project approach, design, and the ingredients are then refined with increasing precision until what is "required" is within the feasible range of what is available—a workable approach.

Once the selected workable approach makes timely and cost-effective availability of the project ingredients feasible, then the triple constraint is quantitatively refined to produce a project charter as discussed in the next chapter.

Review Questions (True or False)

1. A workable approach is one that can and probably will achieve the workable purpose with the scope, cost, and time required. It involves both quantitative work—counting, measuring, and checking—and an intuitive understanding.
2. The order of the steps to determine a workable approach is: quantitative analysis, intuitive understanding, and determining a workable purpose.
3. Evaluation of the project scale from epic to small is needed to gain a qualitative impression of the effort, cost, and time for the project.
4. Projects of all scales require similar intuitive thought and detailed analysis. Smaller projects with shorter time frames make recovery from project approach errors more difficult.
5. Labor of the needed capacity and character can always be obtained for a project by increasing compensation.
6. The maximum job site labor density that can be maintained without reducing productivity, quality, or safety is a schedule constraint that must be included in project planning.
7. Subcontractors and vendors must be appropriately selected for the project. Small firms cannot do all that large firms do, and large firms cannot do well what small firms do. The smallest firm suitable for the project tends to be the best fit.
8. Newly developed materials can eliminate chemical cure times as a schedule constraint.
9. Acceptable cost ranges for construction projects are quite small—often only a few percent. When evaluating project feasibility, cost is used as a "tollgate" to evaluate project feasibility.
10. Risk evaluation of labor or material disruptions, government decisions, and the technical, time, and schedule demands of innovation all must be included in project planning.

Test Your Understanding

1. Identify one large, one medium, and one small projects now under construction in your area.
2. A medium-sized commercial project will probably require the subtrades of excavation, structural steel erection, and fire-protection sprinklers. Using a local trade directory or phone book, identify the number of each of these subcontractors within 30 miles of your location. If only 25% of these subcontractors are capable and willing and available to work on the project, can you get three bids for each trade?
3. For a 10,000-square-foot renovation project, you have determined from past experience that the maximum productive labor density is 1 man per 1000 square feet. 600 trade labor workdays are estimated. What is a theoretical shortest schedule that can be achieved without reducing productivity?

CHAPTER
2.3

Risks Must Be Evaluated, and Responses Planned and Managed

Large mechanical and electrical equipment may be installed most economically very early in the construction before obstructions are installed and when optimal hoisting equipment can be used. The 625 and 1,200-ton Carrier chillers at the Dearborn Center 131 S. Dearborn Chicago, Illinois, were set on the structural steel before the surrounding concrete floors were poured. Such early placement may require equipment preorder during preconstruction services. *Photo courtesy: Temperature Equipment Corporation.*

Risks Must Be Evaluated, and Responses Planned and Managed

Project planning is the critical first step, management then follows

What is risk?

Managing variation to stay within acceptable limits

Risk is the probability that the achieved outcomes will be less favorable than the planned and anticipated outcomes. The physical and human world is uncertain and variable, so risk is everywhere. Commitment to a project commits to the risk that comes with it. Risk can be minimized and managed but not eliminated. All possible risks must be considered to identify risks that are unacceptable or impossible to bear.

Construction project risk management has four steps: planning, identification and analysis, management, and control, which are discussed below.

Plan Your Risk Comfort Zone

Some risks are desirable

You get paid for managing risk, so some risk can be good

Risky investments command a higher rate of return, and risk also pays well in construction project management. So, there is a strong incentive to seek risk, but only risk that you have the full capacity and desire to control. If you are good at what you do, assume the risk, and you will profit and help others.

Screen projects exceeding your risk tolerance

A go or no-go decision

Examples of possibly unacceptable risks are as follows:

Wars and civil disorder
Operating in or securing materials from places where there is an absence of law and order, such as countries at war, civil war, or heavily influenced by gang warfare, can be unacceptable for many. Since World War II, the United States has been in five wars, and a war has started about every 18 months somewhere in the world. (A war can stop raw material production in and shipping near the war zone, which can affect projects on the other side of the earth.)

Natural catastrophes
Catastrophic geological and weather conditions, such as earthquakes, mudslides, arctic temperatures, and hurricanes, occur weekly. (Shipping can be affected.)

Unstable governments
Unstable dysfunctional governments may be hostile to the project. Since World War II, governments such as India, Pakistan, and Bangladesh, and many African countries have emerged from the ashes of former colonial empires. North Korea and Cuba have been closed to the outside world. And Nigeria has experienced civil war, gang warfare, and frequent government collapse.

Projects requiring financing are influenced by major interest rate variation. The U.S. prime rate (a benchmark rate for those of high credit quality) continually varies, with a low of 1.75% in 1947 and a high of 21.50% in 1980. A ¼% rate change can kill some projects.

Projects are possible in all these adverse conditions for those who have the capacity, appetite, and experience. Mining operations are started in continually war-torn countries. Oil exploration and extraction flourishes in Nigeria's political unrest and in the Gulf of Mexico, which is regularly ravaged by hurricanes. And construction projects are built in chaotic countries plagued by military dictatorships and frequent coups. At the same time, others may be unable or unwilling to undertake a project in a bad part of town five miles from their home office.

There are few totally unacceptable risks for all parties. But you must rule out your unacceptable risks at a specific time and location, and reject projects with these risks.

Find an acceptable range of risks you can manage
Both capital and experience are essential

A company's culture, experience, and capital structure—and the profit margins available for the project—determine acceptable risk levels. All projects require some temporary funding to cover cash flow. Project evaluation and start up require sufficient capital to cover costs until the project is started and profit from the project is received. An owner may pay promptly but not instantly.

Start with familiar project types, sizes, and locations. If a different project type is sought, a cautious approach is needed. A full size first-time project can rarely succeed. Tiptoe in with a joint venture, or attempt a very small version of the project type. If an unfamiliar project is undertaken, a premium of 500%–1000% must be added in cost and time to the project's unfamiliar aspects.

Identify All Risks—Both Global and Project Specific

Global Risks are Analyzed First
Get the few big things right, and never forget them

Identify catastrophes—large events that do not occur every year at your project location
Rare natural and man-made occurrences on the other side of the world can have sudden effects on a local project. For example, wars and other civil disruptions, dissolution of governments or government relationships with other countries, evaporation of the value of a country's currency, temporary freezing of credit markets, acute shortages of required materials, and disruptions in shipping (just to name a few) are risks that can make a project unfeasible or impossible. Identification of the necessary global conditions that are assumed to exist for a project—and identification of the probability and consequence of interruption of these conditions—are needed for risk management.

Separate global from project-specific risk
Although these events are global in origin and must be considered, they are part project specific and part global. The normal temperature and humidity range for the project area can be well known from established sources, such as weather bureaus and geological services. Primitive records have been kept since the 1700s, adequate records since the 1800s, and detailed consistent records since the early 1900s. These normal annual ranges should be included in project planning—and not be considered global events.

Events that do not occur annually, such as 100 and 500 year floods, volcanic eruptions, and earthquakes in areas that rarely have quakes (Missouri's last destructive earthquakes were in the 1830s), should be treated as global events with an estimated probability of occurrence and anticipated project consequence. Areas such as California where earthquakes occur every year have superior records that aid prediction. These earthquakes should be included in project planning.

Never forget which conditions are needed for the project

A keen understanding of underlying assumptions and necessary requirements for a project—and a general understanding of global conditions affecting these requirements—are needed to begin project planning. Awareness of clues for changes in these essential conditions is needed for project management, but daily monitoring of international news is usually not required or productive. Because of the limited quantity and quality of information on global events, qualitative methods alone are usually used.

When a new project is considered, assumed global conditions must be reviewed to see if these assumed conditions are still valid—and are likely to remain valid for the life of the project. When a project outside the normal comfort zone in size, type, cost, or location is being considered, the project decision makers must make a more detailed evaluation.

A global analysis is essential to avoid occasional disastrous outcomes—but it should only occupy a tiny fraction of project management time. Once projects totally out of the comfort zone are eliminated—and the project is accepted—then risks must be identified, analyzed, managed, assigned, and controlled, as described below.

Risk registers can list all risks and probability of occurrence

Project management for activities such as new product development or software implementation can use risk registers to list each possible risk. Since these are genuinely new activities, everything must be freshly considered and then a risk register developed.

An example of a risk register for a few construction activities might be as follows:

Risk ID	Risk	Responses	Root Cause
1	Structural steel price increase possible	Fixed-price material contract	High construction volume and some foreign mills down for maintenance
2	Pipefitter labor shortage	Shop assemble some components off site	Full pipefitter employment in project area
3	Design completed when needed	Fast track schedule	Owner demands for schedule acceleration due to their changing market conditions
4	Rainy season may hamper foundation installation	Obtain foundation only permit and start foundation early	Planned construction start falls near start of rainy season

In construction, the global risks must be freshly considered for each project, and all risks identified and listed. This list is critically important but usually short—frequently five or fewer items. But risks that occur on all projects—liability, safety, cost over-runs, schedule creep—are not identified in the risk register but rather by standard operating procedures used on all projects.

The activities are identified in the WBS (work breakdown structure) developed in the planning and cost estimating stages of the project. (In construction, cost estimates are started earlier in project planning than in other industries, and cost estimating is more highly developed.) Construction estimating identifies, counts, and measures each activity and develops and refines the WBS. The risks associated with each of these common repetitive tasks are managed by standard operating procedures, as described below.

Probabilities can help evaluate risks

Project management in nonconstruction fields—such as manufacturing, which have long continuous processes—sometimes use "probability matrixes" to rank risks—0% (never occurs) to 100% (always occurs). The probability of occurrence of a risk could be statistically determined in construction as well if a sufficiently large relevant data set was available—but such high-quality data rarely exists. Although the thinking from statistics, such as viewing events as part of a normal distribution is used, probability assignment is largely subjective for most activities on most projects. With such limited data, a scale of whole number from 1 to 3 or 5 may be a more appropriate.

Do not get too fancy—limiting the number of good observations keeps analysis simple

In the 1980s, sophisticated risk evaluation and pricing techniques were developed. The Black–Scholes risk pricing model—developed in 1973 by Fischer Black and Myron Scholes—used mathematics "too sophisticated to explain" to price risk. This risk pricing was thought by some to render risk obsolete. It was used by the Long-Term Capital Holdings Group, founded in 1994 by Mr. Scholes and others, in their financial trading operations. One of the sophisticated risk management model's necessary assumptions was that all major international currencies would remain continuously viable.

This pricing model appeared to work until Russia temporarily froze trading in their currency in 1998. The bank was unable to honor its obligations and collapsed. The failure of one assumed condition overcame fancy mathematics.

Risks That Always Occur Are Managed by Standard Procedures

Standard operating procedures must address management of common risks

Liability and Injury Risks

Property damage caused by project personnel or others must be managed

This includes project damage or destruction by weather, fire, or vandalism—or home office building and equipment yard damage or destruction—mobile property damage, such as vehicles, equipment, or materials in transit or awaiting installation at the project.

Since contractors construct buildings that require equipment, they well understand the management of the risks related to property and equipment. Fire protection, electrical grounding programs, security, properly constructed hoisting and scaffolding, and a planned equipment maintenance program are known—and can be enhanced by the input of consultants. Safety audits by insurance carriers are also common. These preventative measures are the first and most effective way to manage these risks.

Property insurance on the partially completed building and material and equipment on site awaiting installation is called builder's risk insurance, and may be purchased either by the owner or by the contractor. Insurance on the contractors' buildings and equipment is voluntary but essential for good business practice. Over-the-road vehicle insurance is usually mandated both by law and by building owners.

Liability caused (or claimed to be caused) by project personnel must be managed

Liability is the consequence of damage or injury to people (but not physical injury to employees, which is covered by workers' compensation insurance), others' operations and reputation, such as loss of business and reputation damage, or property damage resulting from actions of project employees, vendors, and subcontractors. Actual damage caused and falsely claimed damage (which must be disproved)—both must be analyzed (and managed).

Over-the-road vehicles remain one of the most frequent and large causes of damage and liability. Settlement and erosion of adjacent properties and fires, explosions, dust, noise, dirty or crowded streets, or liquid overflows onto neighboring properties range from a temporary nuisance to an event that can terminate the project. Earth retention systems, and temporary facilities and services (general conditions) minimize and manage these risks. Prompt repair of damage by the contractor, where possible, is frequently the most cost effective approach.

These efforts can be supplemented by contractor purchased liability insurance. Liability insurance is required by many municipalities to cover damage to city property—and by all commercial and industrial building owners.

Safety management plays a large risk management role
Inclusion in both project planning and execution is key

Construction can, if not properly managed, be dangerous and can cause personal injury, death, and destruction of property. These perils are risks that must be managed. Fortunately, safety management can produce large improvements if included in project planning and execution. A later chapter on safety is devoted to these subjects.

Project performance risks always exist and are the project manager's responsibility

Deficiencies in grade, cost, and schedule of the installed work are a risk on every project. Building owners see this deficient performance as a great project risk. And every contractor is one bad job away from going out of business—a huge risk. There is no commonly available or satisfactory insurance for this risk. The buck stops with the project manager.

Since project performance risks exist on all projects, identification and management of these risks will be discussed together below.

Managing the Risk—Planning through Closeout

Risk Management Starts as Part of the Project Planning Process
Another dimension of the process, not another subject

Risk management is not a separate department at the end of the hall that does something about insurance. And it is not just a task that is passed off to the safety director. It is a dimension of all the aspects of project management. Integration in the process is essential for optimal results.

Safety of workers is one of the first risk topics to consider but fortunately—with management commitment—safety procedures can be implemented and safe operations achieved. And safe operations have a significant effect on preservation of reputation and continuing business relationships while achieving an acceptable profit. A safety program and a good and improving safety record are necessary and desirable, but only a good start on risk management.

Avoiding the risk of project failure due to insufficient or poor planning is more difficult and time consuming and is not always achieved. Success (avoiding failure) is achieved by the scope definition, and time, cost, and resource management parts of project development and the project management process.

Assign the Risk to the Appropriate Party
First, identify the legally responsible party, then seek the party best able to manage the risk

Once the maximum amount of risk has been identified and eliminated or managed, the remainder must be assigned to the appropriate party. Some parties will be required by law or overwhelming tradition to assume some risks. No project participant can legally or practically transfer all risk. And assigning risk forfeits the ability to manage it. Risk can be best managed by assigning it to the party best able to manage it. These possible parties are identified below.

Government and quasi-government agencies legally must assume certain risks

Governments, utility companies, railroads, and mass transit providers own and maintain the surrounding streets and infrastructure. They are responsible both for the maintenance of their property and for any consequential damages that arise because of the malfunction of their property—such as explosion, collapse, or leakage. This responsibility can only be enforced if their strict rules are followed—and the proper notifications are given. Similarly, some government agencies have area-wide responsibilities, such as environmental cleanup and storm water management, which can minimize or eliminate project responsibility for this liability.

The owner of the land and project must assume other risks

The owner inherently has responsibility for the condition of his property. Any issues about legal easements, existing environmental difficulties, and some storm water management concerns can best be handled by contractually ensuring that the owner remains fully responsible for management.

Contractors have their risks plus some portion of the risk of those they hire

The contractor has primary responsibility for care, custody, and control of the project area throughout construction operations. This includes maintenance of the property, both permanent and temporary, and the safety of the workforce. Attempts by some contractors to make subcontractors primarily responsible (for both the contractor's and the subcontractor's actions) have generated disputes and discord, and attract a lower caliber of subcontractors and vendors to the project.

Subcontractors have similar risks as the contractor

Subcontractors who have an ongoing workforce on the site are responsible for the safety of their own workers and their tools and equipment, including provision of related insurance. If subcontractors can effectively perform part of the temporary construction, such as an electrical contractor installing and maintaining temporary electrical service, additional project-wide responsibility may be appropriately assumed.

Vendors' delivery liability, and material quality assurance and warranty

Suppliers of material only to the site will always be responsible for the safe operation of delivery trucks and delivery personnel, including related insurance. The ownership of stored material—and the responsibility of proper storage and loss—transfers to the contractor at the time of delivery, and then to the owner at installation.

Quality assurance of agreed grades is covered by the vendor's explicit or implied warranties.

Insurance companies can be paid to assume some portion of some risks

Insurance companies will agree to assume a portion of some of the risks in exchange for premium payments as described above. But payment of claims rarely fully compensates for the loss. So, insurance should be considered a supplemental, not primary, method of risk management.

Project Performance Risks

The project manager's long term and daily task

Low worker productivity means cost over-runs and schedule extension

Failure to achieve the required productivity of the contractor's own workers is one of the largest project risks. Project scope, cost, and schedule planning to determine a workable approach are essential. Equipment selection, optimal crew size, and field management are also key.

Material cost over-runs

If the original cost estimate correctly identified all materials and assigned appropriate cost, material cost over-runs seldom occur—and require limited management attention. If material cost over-runs occur, the causes may be as follows: poor material storage and handling that unnecessarily damages material or poor trade skills that produce excessive waste, theft, and false quantities (rigged scales and false delivery tickets). Field management can diagnose and correct these problems. Material cost increases can be avoided by getting firm preproject cost agreements with vendors.

Unbudgeted subcontractor claims for additional compensation can mean cost over-runs

Unbudgeted claims for additional compensation by subcontractors and vendors can cause cost over-runs that will degrade or prevent successful project completion. The first and most effective way to manage this risk is project scope definition—and cost and schedule planning. A planned integration of scope, cost, and schedule defines—with some give and go—an approach that can be made to work.

Screening out some subcontractors—those who initially price artificially low, and then use clever but meritless arguments to request high-priced extra compensation—is essential. Efforts to defeat these claims will be time consuming, and slow the progress of the job, and will rarely be completely successful. Field management—to maintain the progress of the job—will actively reduce extra claims. A fast moving project increases productivity and profit, and leaves less time to contemplate mischief. Killer contract provisions that attempt to bar all claims for extras will only start arguments. This problem may be first noticed when the contractor begins making noises such as "this project is poorly organized," "you are not giving me enough time to do my work, what is the hurry?" or "I can't get any hoist time." This may be followed by a trumped up claim for extra compensation on an entirely unrelated activity.

Defective construction and materials hurts schedule, cost, quality, and produces disputes

Defective workmanship such as missing components, assemblies out of tolerance, and unworkable equipment are recognizable. Defective materials can be more difficult to identify, particularly if the exact specified material was installed, but still fails to perform satisfactorily. And a building is an assembly of exactly specified materials—which compounds the problem.

Defective design and engineering extends schedule and can compromise quality

Although it is not the contractor's legal responsibility or normal practice to independently verify a design, it will suffer some consequence from defective design. Continual questioning of how and why something works and questions posed on shop drawings and submittals frequently flush out design errors—allowing early, economical correction. When the design and construction firms are separate, the design firm maintains errors and omissions insurance. But reimbursement for a claim usually goes to the owner (not the contractor) long after the event, and is extremely difficult and time consuming to prove.

Warranties only assist solution

A 1-year overall warranty on the entire building is a common practice and contract provision. But laws may extend this warranty. Components such as roofing, some coatings, and mechanical components such as compressors may have a longer factory warranty—as stated in the specifications or contract.

Some warranty claims are straightforward and promptly honored, but most can be extremely time consuming and difficult to present and prove. Many honor only a portion of the repair cost (material only) and then only a declining proration of the useful life, and consequential damage from a defect is usually excluded. Warranties will not completely restore the original condition at no cost, so should be sought, but not considered a substitute for correct initial installation.

Some contractors take a very legalistic and detailed approach to prove that very few things are ultimately their responsibility and merit correction. One such view is that a material problem is a product liability problem and will only be remedied if and when the material supplier agrees to the remedy. But a more common view is to promptly repair or replace defective items, even if the responsibility is not entirely clear. Avoidance of additional future damage and maintenance of a reputation for quality work is thought to outweigh the cost of the corrective work. Completed operations insurance is available and frequently used. Other forms of insurance—for defects noticed after completion—are available but less frequently used.

Global risk management requires plans for alternate scenarios

If a project in a highly hazardous area was considered, analyzed, and accepted, then these high risks are managed as project-specific risks. However, if materials for a project in a safe area must come from or ship through a highly hazardous area, supply disruptions must be considered. One solution is to find and plan for an alternate fallback product. If no acceptable fallback product is available, the critical product must be physically obtained and stored in a safe location early in the project execution.

Management's continued commitment to safe conditions is essential

Safe operations must start with safe equipment. Since it is management's decision to purchase and maintain equipment, safe operations require this management commitment. A well-trained, stable workforce is also essential, which requires both management and worker commitment. This combined management and worker commitment can routinely solve most of the "safety problem." And management can further improve safety through project planning—temporary facilities, construction means and methods, and scheduling to optimize job site density—which will increase both safety and productivity.

Implementation of a safety program is essential, but only works within this context of management commitment. Management must establish the safety program, with safety manuals, and mandate and allocate costs for required training. Workers then must work within this established framework. Both management commitment and worker cooperation are essential.

Project Failure and Termination

A contractor unable to complete the project hurts cost, time, and probably quality

A performance bond secured before the start of the project can protect the owner if the contractor fails to complete the project. This usually involves driving the contractor out of business and seizing personal assets—and is a time-consuming unpleasant process that all seek to avoid.

Owner failure to make agreed payments to the contractor can slow or stop a project

This can be a huge risk when working for small, private one-project owners—and a lesser risk for large established multiproject owners—but it should be considered in all cases. Owners who do not have the money or the capacity to obtain the money for the project must be screened out in early project evaluation.

For larger or more substantial owners, guaranteed availability of funds for the project must be verified. Large private owners with apparent vast resources may be seeking project funds from a financing source that may not become available at the time required, or at all. Similarly, some government projects are not funded by the full faith and credit of the government agency but rather by a fixed amount of dedicated project funds. If the project cost exceeds the amount of these funds, the shortfall may not be remedied promptly or at all.

The available payment remedies are not entirely workable or satisfactory. Acceleration of payments in the form of deposits or "front ending" (overbilling work in progress) conflicts with construction lien law and the requirements of many lending institutions. Letters of credit (where a bank will release funds to the contractor directly upon receipt of the appropriate documents) can sometimes be used for international purchase of materials and equipment but has virtually no acceptance for routine construction project payments.

Early screening of owners who lack the character and capacity to pay as required is the first and best line of defense. Monthly payments for the full value of work completed are essential. Some early payment in full for preconstruction services can frequently be negotiated. Finally, the contract should clarify the remedies for owner default, which generally should, for private work, include a lien claim against the property. (Government entities frequently must consent to be sued, so this option is not available.) These remedies reduce, but do not eliminate, the impact of insufficient owner's funds.

Contractor failure to make agreed payments to subcontractors hurts schedule and cost, degrades communication, and produces disputes

When the contractor receives partial payment from the owner, the portions of that payment due to the subcontractors and vendors must be promptly paid. Subcontractors have large cash needs and short time horizons—fast cash keeps them quiet and cooperative. Late and irregular payments can disrupt communication and the schedule. A payment bond secured at the start of the project can compensate the owner if the contractor fails to make these required payments.

Project termination for owner's convenience can be legitimate—and must be managed

The project owner may have the legitimate need and contractual right to terminate the project before completion. The evaporation of the market for the goods or services the building was intended to provide would be one such reason. The contractor then needs to receive proper final payment.

The method for determining what is proper must be specified in the contract. Material and labor installed are rarely controversial, but work in progress off site may be. Removal of temporary facilities and equipment and any measures necessary to render the abandoned project safe and acceptable are gray areas. General condition service fees and home office overhead and profit are frequently controversial.

When an agreement on these items is reached and documented in the contract, it is important that all billing and ongoing project documentation identify line item costs specified by these agreements. Calculation of termination cost frequently involves low-level accounting or auditing persons new to the project, so clear documentation will make their job easier and the contractor's outcome better.

Monitoring and Control Risk

Risk management and project management controls can and should become the same

Project Planning Offers the Largest Possibilities for Control

The planning of the project workflow, particularly the timing of the project, will have a significant impact on risk management. If the project schedule strives for level consistent manpower requirements, the workers will be more familiar with the project conditions and therefore safer. The pace of the project and scheduling of material deliveries can maintain the project work areas unencumbered. This both improves and promotes safety and productivity.

Selection of construction means and methods—such as hand or gang forming concrete columns and decks, and anchorage details for curtain walls that can be installed from the interior—can have similar effects—both in productivity and safety.

The planning and selection of the general condition items such as haul roads, hoisting, scaffolding, fall protection, and temporary utilities must be correctly planned and costed to correspond to the project approach. This is part of project scope definition that must be done in the project planning stage to have maximum effect.

Project Cost and Schedule Control is Achievable for a Well Planned Project

Material and labor job costing is a key focus of control
The canary in the coal mine

Weekly analysis of expended labor and material (not subcontract amounts) is essential and readily achievable with a properly prepared estimate with a recognized WBS. Trade labor is paid weekly, and material vendors bill at the time of delivery. Project material and labor expended to date—and noted variances from planned quantities—should be available for analysis every Tuesday morning. No exceptions, no excuses.

This both documents cost status and also is an early warning sign of labor overage that may suggest an emerging schedule problem. (If it takes longer to do, it may take longer to get done.) Find the problem, devise a solution, and attack it. Since expended labor and work completed can be quantitatively measured with precision every week, early detection and correction can keep an emerging problem from altering the planned project outcome. (Note: "paper generals" or construction managers who employ little or no trade labor miss this early warning.)

Change request control starts in planning and continues through closeout
Subcontractors are under contract and bill a portion of the contract monthly, so subcontractor change request management requires a different approach. A well planned project with a defined workable scope and work packages will make a subcontractor's successful and profitable performance feasible. But this feasible performance will not always be achieved. And some subcontractors may seek to make up their shortfall by claiming unjustifiable requests for additional compensation. (Standard contract provisions that restrict the method and timing of claims may exist but may only be partially acknowledged and costly to enforce.)

The management time frame is longer than 1 week for material and labor described above, but the process is similar. Separate the belly aching and meaningless complaints, and then analyze the problem to see if they may have a point. Congestion of work areas, haul roads, storage areas, and access to crane and hoist time all impact productivity, and can be managed. Work to devise and implement a solution, and then qualitatively monitor the results. Increased subcontractor productivity will reduce both the need and the tendency to fabricate claims for additional cost.

Some large construction managers pride themselves on taking an extremely hard-line on requested extras. "Whatever the question, the answer is no." This ignores—not solves—the problem. Subcontractors can then compromise quality, perform at erratic times better for their productivity than the project's schedule, or wait for an owner requested change request and pile on additional cost. The project suffers, and no one wins.

Steel truss erection—Most of the Wheaton Bible Church structure used lighter structural steel and bar joists, but the large sanctuary required a structural steel truss. Well-planned detailing of the truss components and connections during shop drawing development and review can optimize trucking to this site, the balance of shop and field assembly, and permitted hoisting points. Management of these considerations can increase field labor productivity, optimize the number and types of cranes needed, and accelerate the schedule—which can simultaneously optimize profit and safety.

Photo 1 of 5

Schedule maintenance follows cost and schedule management

The schedule must be monitored as well. If the schedule was originally properly constructed using actual estimating data and WBSs, it will be workable. The schedule documents planning decisions and results to be achieved, so correction of schedule variation focuses on these inputs and outputs. The schedule building blocks of material, labor, and subcontractor performance must be monitored and controlled to manage schedule variation, as described above. If the schedule was not originally workable, more drastic revisiting of the project planning process and implementation of necessary corrective activities will be required.

Quality control of work in progress must be built in

Quality control of the work in progress is the project manager's responsibility. Verification of documentation such as mill certificates (showing the laboratory test strength of a batch of steel) for steel and concrete cylinder test breaks (to confirm strength achieved) must be ongoing. Walking around to determine if things "look right" and questioning the installing trades to smoke out their concerns can produce useful early warnings. And finally, commissioning portions of the project early with the accompanying quantitative test results can aid early detection of difficulties. Monitoring of quality and correction of defects as close to the timing of installation as possible maximize benefits.

Do not rely on outside inspectors to ensure quality conformance—the responsibility remains with project management. Civil projects—such as roads—usually have full-time on-site engineering inspectors, but the building project inspectors may come weekly or monthly, when much of the work is installed and concealed. Government inspectors will only come when called at specific project milestones. These inspections may be a contractual or legal requirement, must be performed, and are a substantial defense in litigation but do not guarantee or certify that the intended quality was achieved.

Summary

Risk management is a dimension of the project management process that seeks to manage variabilities of outcomes to achieve the project purpose. It starts with a global analysis to screen out projects exceeding identified risk tolerance and capacity, and then moves to project-specific risk analysis.

It includes safety—with the accompanying management and worker commitments—and insurance. But the largest benefit comes by viewing risk management as a dimension of the project management process—not as a separate subject. Project planning and project controls operate together to achieve safe and productive operations—while maintaining scope, quality, cost, and schedule—to more precisely achieve the project purpose.

Review Questions (True or False)

1. Risk is the probability that the achieved outcomes will be less favorable than planned and anticipated.
2. Construction project risk management has five steps: planning, identification and analysis, assignment and avoidance, management, and control.
3. Risk carries a higher reward (profit), so some risk within your risk comfort zone may be desirable.
4. Global risk such as wars and civil disorders, natural catastrophes, and huge interest rate fluctuations must be evaluated to screen out unacceptable projects.
5. The impact of weather and natural disasters is always considered a global risk.
6. The risk register lists risks and their planned responses and root causes.
7. Both property damage and liability for damage must be managed first by effective operations that minimize exposure to these risk, and then by insurance.
8. Risk management starts at the time of on-site mobilization.
9. Risk can be minimized and managed but not entirely avoided. The unavoidable risk should be assigned to the party best able to manage it.
10. Governments and quasi-government agencies and the owner of the land and project legally must retain certain risks, but the construction manager must follow very specific rules and procedures to enforce this risk retention.
11. The construction manager can and must develop firm contractual agreements to force subcontractors and vendors to retain all risks related to their work.
12. Construction job site management focuses on managing the risks of worker productivity, material costs, subcontractor claims for extras, the quality of the installed work, and schedule.
13. The risk of project failure due to owner's failure to make agreed payments on time or termination of the project must be managed both by early evaluation of the project to screen out unacceptable risks, and by appropriately structured contractual terms related to termination.
14. Managing cost, schedule, and quality risks must start in planning and continue through project execution, monitoring, and control.

Test Your Understanding

1. Material availability and price is a risk for all projects, including projects that seem to be strictly local.

   From a statistical abstract or economic atlas, find the top five producing countries for

   Lumber

   Steel

   Oil

   Cement

   Find the population and annual GDP (gross domestic product) for

   United States

   Japan

   India

   China

   Discuss how disruption in one of the major material producing countries and increased building volume in one of the developing countries can affect material cost and availability for a local project.

2. Managing material cost, worker productivity, and subcontractor requests for extra compensation are all project risks. Discuss how the tools or activities listed below can help manage these risks.

   Planned project approach

   Weekly job cost analysis

   Preaward subcontractor proposal analysis for completeness and feasibility

   Hard bids on material unit costs

   Firm contract procedures for claims for additional costs

   Assignment of risk to those best able to manage it

3. Discuss your personal risk comfort zone for projects you are building or seek to build. Use the continuum from projects in unstable third world countries requiring capable security forces or alliances with local militaries, to local projects in safe areas for which you have a long-term and possibly social relationship with most participants.

CHAPTER

2.4

The Integrated Project Scope and Approach Must Be Defined and Accepted

The Trump Tower in Chicago, Illinois, required four 1,175-ton Carrier centrifugal chillers. Placement in the lower level was required early in the construction sequence. *Photo courtesy: Temperature Equipment Corporation.*

The Integrated Project Scope and Approach Must Be Defined and Accepted

An intuitive understanding, a framework for facts, count everything, observe the implications and impacts, refine the approach and commit

Previous chapters discussed precision and organization and development of an approximation of the workable approach. This chapter continues development of the approach adding more quantitative verification. The result is the project charter that defines the agreed scope, time, and cost. Once the charter is established, the project proceeds to planning and execution.

Use Intuition and Organized Facts to Refine a Workable Approach

Designing a workable approach is a circular three-step process.
1. Develop a qualitative, intuitive understanding of the nature of the project, and its building blocks.
2. Count the building blocks and obtain the facts about the building blocks (purchasing methods, engineering and fabrication, distribution and shipping, and costs).
3. Determine the implications and impact of this information on the understanding of the nature of the project.
4. Go back to step 1 and repeat the three steps above until done.

This circular process is repeated with increasing information, understanding, and precision. In the real world, determining a workable approach is neither starting with a blank slate, and determining everything from scratch, nor is it slight modifications of "what we did last time." An approximate project type that closely resembles the present project is selected from a file of past efforts—recognizing it will change—and this approximation is probably partially or maybe even completely wrong. The building blocks of the selected project are listed and counted, and the possible project type is confirmed, modified, or rejected. Continuing this circular process eventually develops a workable approach to a new project.

What to Count

All the work items listed in the information framework must be counted, as well as the building blocks that make up the work items. Full itemization that is understood and useable by all is needed. So this is a mechanical counting, but in a manner that communicates effectively.

The following guidelines may be helpful:
1. Count physical things and systems of things. For example, cubic yards of concrete, square feet of ceiling tile, or lineal feet of piping in sanitary waste risers, using standard units of measure.
2. Show the relevance to all project participants. "What about me?", "Where's my stuff?" must be answered. The work of all project participants of even very small consequence must be identified and counted. Listing all categories in the CSI (Construction Specification Institute) organizational format will identify most of these people, but also check by lists of project personnel (by job and description not name), including the project management staff.
3. If a contract is awarded or a purchase order is issued to a vendor, count their stuff. If a dedicated workgroup is working on an item, count their stuff.

4. If an outside party, owner, architect, financial institution, or a government agency is identified as important for the project, count their stuff. If parties do part of a task in succession, count each parties' tasks.

5. Break into bite size pieces. Long tasks must be subdivided into tasks with maximum 2-week on-site work duration. Tasks must be able to be broken down into parts of the project (floors) and systems (sanitary waste, phone and data cabling). The task subdivison must be able to be organized into milestones that are unmissable and indisputable. For example, weather enclosure of a building, permanent electrical power on, heated and air-conditioning air is being delivered—not "we are two-thirds complete."

6. Analyze things, not ideas. Count objects that can be seen and touched. Use standard units of measure, so communication is possible.

Building Blocks to Be Counted, Measured, and Checked

The common building blocks that must be counted, measured, and evaluated are listed below.

People of needed capacity and character—availability must be checked

The capacity, skill, and experience to perform a task are critical to selecting good people. But character, disposition, and tendencies of people must also be recognized. Although it is frequently stated, "we can always add more people," this is not always true. Every employer states that getting good help is a large problem. Good help is always in short supply.

Capital—can the needed funds be available when required

Capital is the owner's and construction manager's available money to perform a project. The owner's capital is the long-term ability to pay for the work as it is completed, and finally pay the entire amount. The construction manager's capital is the money required between the owner's payments.

Materials (from supply houses and lumberyards)—current prices and availability must be checked

Materials are generic stock products not made to order for the job. Materials typically have no serial numbers, and no project-specific product data. Materials are abundant at one price, location, and time, and scarce at others. Present conditions must be checked for the project location.

Equipment (that will become part of the permanent building) lead times must be verified

Equipment is a product made to order for each job, frequently has serial numbers, and has job-specific technical data. Equipment made to order requires a sequence of ordering, engineering, fabrication, and shipment. Each step takes time and costs money—and should be accounted for.

Companies (subcontractors and suppliers)—present work volume and future availability

A company consists of an assembled workforce with shared knowledge, tools and equipment, and capital. If a company has patents on processes, or has specialized high-value equipment that is paid for and still serviceable, an advantage exists. For the vast majority of companies, this advantage does not exist. The people are the most important ingredient—and the bench of people of each competency are usually only one or two deep. So their availability for the project must be verified.

Constraints to Be Identified and Managed

Information is always scarce—can needed information be obtained when required

When building products were simpler, everything necessary was known about them from past use, and information was not considered a building block. Now, with proprietary products containing sophisticated systems, chemicals, and computer-controlled mechanical electrical components, specific information for each product for each project is required. Information always has a cost and is always in short supply. Even parties who want to help may not fully know about their products or services, and competitors will attempt to prevent access to necessary information. Future outcomes cannot be completely known. Facts, information, and knowledge are always in short supply.

Identify constraints, obstacles—are the risks manageable?

Constraints include changing economic conditions that may affect prices of material, or the availability of capital. Politicians may restrict or block all or part of a project. Nonrational decisions by the owner, designer, and/or government agencies can lead to obstacles. And force majeure—such as adverse weather conditions and strikes that affect the ability to secure materials and equipment, or to work at the job site—must be considered. And plant shutdowns or discontinuation of required products can also be constraints. Innovative new products or systems will take additional time and effort, and may have unforeseen implications on other parts of the project or be impossible to use.

The possibility of all these constraints exists at all times. But a general notion of possibilities does not permit action. The specific probability of the building blocks must be determined—using information obtained for the project. If a constraint is probable—concrete steps must be taken to ensure that the constraint can be managed, or alternate fallback positions must be included in the project approach.

Observe the Implications and Impacts of the Intended Approach

Real-world limits must be included in planning

Production Limits Must Be Checked

Job site density must be managed for productivity and safety

Job site material and personnel density affect the speed materials can move from the point of entry to the point of installation. As the job site becomes obstructed, with either material or a larger number of workers, productivity declines. There is a point where productivity nearly stops, and materials must be reorganized or moved off-site before production can continue.

A 5000 square-foot medical office building example and some guidelines

A 50′ × 100′ one-story medical office is to be constructed 15′ off one side of a 200′ × 300′ site.

Machine circle of operation

A group of machines working together will require an unobstructed work area, a circle, to achieve maximum safe productivity. The circle for a truck delivering 50′ roof joists, and a crane setting the joists is

Crane work circle with boom extended	70 feet
8-foot-wide truck on a 12-foot-wide haul road	12 feet
50′ joist	50 feet
Total circle of machine operation	132 feet
Given the building and setback:	

Building	50 feet
Building setback	15 feet
Total circle of machine operation, building, setback	197 feet

Since the site is only 200 feet wide, the 197′ listed above means only one group of these machines can operate on this side of the site. Two sets of machines would be able to operate at one time if both could and would remain in one position. In this example, if the water and sewer was being installed in the front and required no haul road, and the joists were being set from the side, two groups of machines would be possible. More groups would not be possible without severe reductions in productivity, and possibly safety.

Drawing circles of machine operation, sized to the equipment being used, on a site plan can determine the maximum number of machine groups possible.

Hand construction circle of worker operations (400–800 square foot per worker)
Materials such as framing, piping, conduit, and ceiling grid have common maximum hand-installed lengths of 8–12′.

The circle of workers' operations is

Average reach of one arm	3 feet
Average material length	10 feet
Transportation space—walkway	10 feet
Circle of worker operations	16 feet

Most rooms are rectangles not circles, so the 16-foot circle would fit in a 16×16-foot room, which has an area of 256 sf.

Maximum workers of this type in a 5000-square-foot building

Total building area	5000 sf
Permanent obstructions—walls, cabinets, plumbing fixtures	
15% of total building	750 sf
Stored materials, tools and equipment	
20% of total building	1000 sf
Unobstructed area of total building	3250 sf

With 256 sf of unobstructed work area required per worker, about 12 workers could work at once. This means about one worker per 400 sf of total building area (both obstructed and unobstructed) for perfect conditions. Obstructions, stored material, and coordination will always be less than perfect, so planning areas might be double—about 800 sf of total building area per worker.

Area for materials requiring cure time 800–1600 square foot per worker

Materials requiring cure time such as concrete floors, floor tile, and carpet have installation rates of 400–800 sf per man per day. The cure times of the materials, concrete or adhesives, require the entire work areas to be available for the entire day. Areas required are, therefore, double the circle of worker operations calculated above.

Long narrow operations limit the number of crews

Long narrow operations such as installation of pipelines or high-voltage electrical lines require a fixed group of machines and men, but encounter conditions producing variable production rates. If a crew produces rapidly and catches up to the next crew, they have nothing else to do and can only wait—with no production. To maintain maximum production, 2–5 days of buffer should be allowed between crews or the next natural break or termination point. In this case, the maximum site density is determined using a length two to five times the daily production.

For tight urban sites, temporary off-site staging and storage areas close to the site can improve timely material delivery.

Time Limits Restrict Possibilities

Limits to hours worked in a week

For continuous trade production requiring skill and judgment, 40 hours is a sustainable workweek achieving both full productivity and minimal injuries. A 50-hour workweek has productivity declines after the first week, accelerating until the end of week 6. At week 6, the productivity of the 50-hour week is the same as that of a 40-hour week, and the 10 hours of overtime is wasted. At 60 hours, productivity declines starting the first week. Incorrect work—requiring removal and rework and personal injuries—accelerates, making the 60-hour week less productive than the 40-hour week within 2 weeks.

Cure time of materials sets limits

Many installed materials involve a chemical reaction that has a fixed cure time. For example, concrete will set in several hours to ½ day, but will not be fully cured to receive adhesive-type materials or other coatings for 28 days. Painting will require a minimum of 12-hour cure time between coats. Selection of specialized products, such as high early strength cement, can accelerate these times, but not eliminate them. So these cure times must be accounted for.

Moisture reduction time management has limits and costs

Many materials have a higher presence of moisture at the time of installation than is acceptable for successive operations. For example, earthwork can be entirely submerged during portions of the earthwork operation—but must be dry before foundation installation. Concrete is a product that is made with water, but following application of coatings or paints, or installation of moisture-sensitive products such as wood doors, millwork, and ceiling tile, the partially finished product requires a far lower presence of moisture for acceptable installation and long-term serviceability.

Removal of some of this moisture will take place naturally when exposed to the prevailing weather, but further removal requires and can be accelerated by the use of mechanical heating and cooling. Minimum moisture extraction times will be at least weeks and probably months. Moisture removal time can be accelerated—at a cost—but cannot be eliminated.

Crew size can be by task requirements or for maximum efficiency

The smallest crew size suitable for a task will tend to achieve optimal productivity. Weight, length, and height of specialized pieces of equipment or operations, where workers must be stationed at multiple points, can dictate minimum crew sizes. In the absence of these specialized requirements, a crew size of 5 has frequently been found to be a common practical productive crew size. This permits an individual capable of understanding and performing the task with limited supervision to oversee a few competent individuals, and possibly one or two of less than desired competence, or trainees.

Sequence of operations—work with the normal and customary or pay a premium

There are normal required sequences of operation. When obtaining material, materials must be selected before evaluation, technical information evaluated to ensure suitability, materials ordered before fabrication, and fabricated before shipment. On the job site, digging the hole precedes the foundation, and installing the structure precedes the roof. Alteration of the normal sequences is possible in only some cases—and alteration will always require more management time.

Time to obtain materials and train personnel limits possibilities

The time to obtain the materials and equipment must be specifically determined for each building block for this project. The time for training of employees must be realistically assessed.

Training for some very limited specific tasks that require no judgment or response to changing conditions can be performed within 2 weeks—fast-food workers, for example. Training a competent individual in one additional specific skill can also be done in hours, days, or at most 2 weeks. The training time for a trade apprenticeship is 4 years. College education is 2–4 years, and some professional education requires 2–4 years after a 4-year college education. And at the conclusion of these educations, students are only beginning to learn and are not yet experienced and fully capable of working on their own.

With these time constraints, it is unreasonable to anticipate significant retraining of personnel for any specific project with the expectation of producing competent, skilled personnel capable of reacting to changing conditions with judgment. For a specific project, one must take people as they come and plan feasible training within available time limits.

Cycles of Refinement Achieve a Workable Approach

Selecting a possible project approach, counting (listing) all the building blocks, and evaluating results within a logical sequence of operation are repeated with increasing precision—using the three-step process (qualitative evaluation, counting and measuring, implication evaluation). When doing this process, one should first rule out any unacceptable options. And do not attempt to work top down. Going for the best and working down until an acceptable approach is found sounds easy, but it is easy to fall into a totally unacceptable option.

A useful decision-making aid is calculating breakeven between two possibilities. If two options are being evaluated, determine when the options have equal cost. For example, if use of a machine costing $500 per hour or hand labor costing $100 per hour is being considered, the break-even point is when the machine can produce five times as much per hour as the hand labor. If two options are close, using the more customary, normal, and comfortable will tend to produce the better results. If the break-even calculation is tremendously lopsided, the right decision is also suggested.

The cycle of selecting a possible approach, counting, and evaluating can stop when:
1.   All building blocks are within an achievable range of grade of material, time, and cost.
2.   The building blocks can be arranged in a sequence that is achievable.
3.   Every critical project constraint is under control or has an alternate fallback position planned.

Stop the cycle when new information cannot be obtained

Once a workable approach is confirmed, the process can continue to be repeated with increasing precision and will provide some benefit to the completed project. However, once no further information is available, no significant further improvement can be made. Stop talking and build it.

The Project Charter Documents the Intended Scope, Time, and Cost

The project charter documents the decisions about scope, time, and cost that will fulfill the project reason and the purpose. And a structure is established for information storage that will be maintained throughout the project. It is critical that all project participants, particularly the project sponsor (who, among other things, authorizes funding), agree on and commit to support this charter.

Construction project management performs more detailed analysis to establish the project charter than project management in some other fields. Construction involves the application of the principles of physics, chemistry, and engineering to the real world. Soil mechanics, concrete materials, refrigeration principles, and the weather have compelling impacts on construction management possibilities—but these impacts exist on all projects. So more time is spent in the initial stages defining the impacts of these physical constraints on the reasonably possible—so later improvement cycles to rule out the unfeasible are reduced.

Construction contracts also usually require inclusion of the project charter's definitions of scope, time, and cost. Most contracts include a cost determination, such as a guaranteed maximum price, and preliminary scope and time definitions. Construction project management for a fee only (not at risk) and project management in other industries—which is more commonly fee only—do not fix cost as precisely in the early project stages. These delivery systems can, therefore, have a looser project charter and more revision cycles throughout project planning and execution.

Value Engineering Seeks Cost Reduction without Altering Scope

The discussions in this and preceding chapter developed the scope, time, and cost simultaneously to develop a workable approach that fulfills the project purpose—so the cost was determined to be appropriate with no further adjustment. This process seeks to build in the optimal value starting at project initiation as defined by the charter. Yet, this balanced development does not always occur or substantial changes in condition may alter project requirements.

The construction manager has no input in project planning in "design then bid" delivery, so value engineering may be needed to manage costs late in the project development. Similarly, the design may be substantially complete in the construction management delivery system before the construction manager is asked for pricing. Or, the project owners' sudden change in business conditions or cost restrictions mandated by a lender may mandate reduction of planned costs that were previously agreed to be acceptable. The techniques of value engineering seek to obtain these cost reductions while maintaining the agreed scope.

Value engineering seeks to provide a product that fulfills the project purpose with an equivalent or higher grade of material at a lower cost. This cost reduction is obtained by evaluating alternate building systems, construction means and methods, or alternate manufacturers.

Some commonly used value engineering suggestions are listed below.

Steel vs. *concrete structural frame.* The optimal system will be governed by the prices of steel and cement, time of construction, site congestion, available steel fabricators and concrete installation vendors, fire-resistant requirements, and complexity of related miscellaneous steel attached to the structural frame. Variations in these factors can change the low-cost solution by place and time.

Wood vs. *light-gauge steel framing* vs. *masonry.* Structural system possibilities vary for the same reasons as steel versus concrete frame above, but will also vary significantly by building area and fire compartment size—producing some unexpected opportunities.

Slab on grade vs. *basement.* When unsuitable soil must be removed and replaced with engineered fill below a proposed slab on grade, frequently a basement avoids the cost of engineered fill and produces a lower foundation cost. This solution proves more successful in areas that have long haul distances and high cost of disposal and purchased engineered fill—but will probably not prove successful where the native soils are suitable for fill.

Off-site prefabrication. Off-site fabrication with uncongested work areas, superior equipment, and well-organized inventories of needed material can significantly increase productivity and reduce assembly cost. For example, for high-rise office construction with repetitive stacked washrooms, prefabricating the waste and vent trees (does require additional temporary bracing for transit) off-site and placing the entire toilet waste and vent rough-in in one crane pick can save cost and time.

Up-down foundation construction. In conventional construction, the foundation is excavated and installed followed by the superstructure installation. If extreme schedule acceleration is sought, the foundation columns and portions of the beams may be drilled and installed through the earth and the superstructure started. Excavation for the foundation and installation of the foundation walls and floors then follows at the same time the superstructure installation continues. This produces savings of finance cost of the construction loan gained by markedly shorter construction times—a savings that will be particularly pronounced in times of high interest rates.

Newer types of equipment or vendors. Equipment comparison and price shopping between conventionally competitive vendors such as Carrier, York, or Trane for HVAC rooftop units, can produce only small cost savings—this comparison has been done so often that everybody knows the drill. But introduction of new vendors previously unknown in the marketplace can produce larger benefits. For example, in the early 1980s, Fujitec (from Japan) entered the U.S. elevator market with products of noticeably superior quality. Priced below domestic competition, Fujitec became a significant recognized brand name and U.S. market player over the next 20 years. Kone (from Finland) entered the United States elevator market in the early 2000s with new technology that minimized or eliminated machine rooms and offered lower operating costs—and quickly became a recognized brand.

If these suggestions still do not achieve the needed cost reductions, the construction manager then offers suggestions for scope reductions. Since the purpose of this exercise is cost reduction, the contractor knows the architect and engineer will probably not be paid extra to make the very substantial required drawing revisions, so corners on the drawings revisions will be cut. But the additional management time and loss of field productivity to execute the incompletely redesigned work will increase cost. So, full credit cannot be provided and the work suffers. This frequently used patch-and repair technique reduces scope so is not really value engineering.

Steel truss erection *Photo 2 of 5*

Change Management Continues through Planning and Execution

Change management is the process performed continuously at regular intervals and when a change is requested or appears needed, to determine if the change is consistent with the project plan and should be approved. The real need for mid-project change due to change in technology or market conditions is extremely rare in all industries, and substantially absent from most. But arbitrary requested changes by those unable or unwilling to plan or those who want to throw their weight around to show who is boss are common.

For example, if a factory is being constructed to produce a chemical, and a previously unknown vastly superior chemical is brought online by a competitor, the project in progress must be radically changed (mid-project change) or abandoned (the original purpose of the project is no longer achievable). This could be called a change. But complete ignorance of a competitor's developments is rare, so care must be used. For example, for a high-rise condominium, the most saleable mix of one, two, and three-bedroom units is always initially a guess. What is true will be verified by presales. This is not mid-project change since the need for flexibility is a known project requirement. Late project alteration in the mix of units should have been built into the original design and project plan and not called change at all.

In either case, the change will be out of sequence so cannot be performed optimally or at the lowest cost, and removal and rework cost may add yet more cost. Reduction in scope or grade of material mentioned above is frequently offered. But reduction in cost, grade, and scope subtracts value so is not desirable change management.

In most projects, the owner and designers will have already invested substantial time and made commitments to others they can only partially reverse. Deductive change orders lead to the owner and/or the architect attempting to get money back from the construction manager, rather than not giving it to them in the first place. Not an easy job! For most projects, value engineering and change management can be minimized or eliminated with a workable purpose and a workable approach.

Change management techniques

A hard dollar lump sum project may need to rigorously limit cost changes, frequently due to committed funds—there is no money and no way to get money for cost over-runs. One approach is to freeze all changes—whatever the question, the answer is no. But this can lead to reduction in serviceability if some very necessary components were missed or designed incorrectly. And all projects, no matter how carefully designed, have some deficiencies.

Another very similar approach is to freeze the project scope in stages. Establish milestone dates when no further revisions will be considered—such as for the foundation, the structure, the exterior weather envelope, and mechanical equipment and electrical service gear. This technique can achieve significant cost management while minimizing the disadvantages of the total scope freeze described above.

An innovative project by its nature will require constant adjustment to scope. And fast-track past project delivery will establish limits on scope and cost, but continually refine and manage the achievement methods within these limits. The scope and cost can best be managed in this framework by estimating high and low ranges based on actual physical scenarios. Sketch out physical solutions for a low and high range and perform detailed and cost estimations on these ranges.

For example, for a project planned in the dry season, the excavation slopes dictated by soil conditions and safety would require 3000 cubic yards of excavation, but the project delayed into the rainy season would require excavation of 5000 cubic yards. The cost for excavating 3000 cubic yards defines the low end, and 5000 cubic yards defines the high end. This quantitative definition will permit active management—if the low end is sought, the early start date must be maintained.

This is in marked contrast to imperfectly defined cost ranges that permit no management. And arbitrary of allowances are the worst example of this abuse—in someone's mind the allowances are already spent and only need to be documented by available details. Establishing and costing these ranges is significant work, but also will produce the needed cost-effective management.

Summary

Determining a workable approach must be preceded by a workable purpose. An organizational system for fact storage must be in place early to handle the large quantity of facts the project will require—without exceeding the participants' tolerance for detail.

The workable approach is then determined by intuitively understanding the project and selecting a possible approach, counting the building blocks, determining the impact of this information, and then repeating the process until a workable approach is reached. All work items (even small items) must be identified and counted, and specific determinations of cost, time, and effort necessary to secure materials must be made.

Job site constraints of density, work hours, cure time, and moisture control, as well as constraints by politicians, major natural disasters, material, equipment, and labor availability must be identified and be determined to be within achievable limits.

The cycle of refinement continues until a workable approach that satisfies the project purpose is found. The scope, time, and cost, as well as management assumptions and planned approaches, are documented in the project charter—and the project is committed. Project planning and execution then follows.

Review Questions (True or False)

1. Designing and refining a workable approach is a circular three-step process involving: (1) develop a qualitative intuitive understanding of the nature of the project, (2) count the building blocks and obtain the facts, (3) determine the implications and impacts of this information.

2. Designing a workable approach does not start with a blank state, but rather involves selecting a project template that resembles the present project, and confirm, modify or reject this template.

3. A well-organized and detailed counting of the physical components of the building is sufficient to develop and analyze a workable approach.

4. The building blocks to be counted and measured are scope, time, and cost.

5. Constraints that must be identified and managed include information and knowledge (that are always in short supply), and obstacles and risks.

6. The site size and shape and the type of operations being performed all influence maximum productivity rates.

7. 50 hours is the maximum sustainable workweek both for maximum productivity and for minimal injuries.

8. Larger crew sizes usually produce economies of scale that reduce unit labor costs.

9. Cycles of approach refinement should stop when it is determined that: (1) all building blocks are within achievable range, (2) the building blocks can be arranged in a sequence that is achievable, and (3) every critical project constraint is under control and no further useful information is available.

10. Value engineering seeks to obtain cost reductions while maintaining the agreed scope with equivalent or higher grades of materials at a lower cost.

11. Value engineering may involve alternative structural systems and reductions in material quantities and overall scope.

12. The most effective way to manage change is to freeze all scope changes and permit no revisions of any kind.

13. Project planning can substantially reduce or eliminate the need for value engineering and change management.

Test Your Understanding

1. *Engineering News Record* magazine lists current material prices in tables near the end of the magazine. Identify one current unit price for lumber, one for concrete, and one for steel, and then find the prices for the same materials 3 years ago. Calculate the percent change for each material. (Prices are usually related to availability.)

2. For the 5000-square-foot medical office building described earlier in the chapter, discuss which of the following tasks could be scheduled simultaneously while maintaining maximum productivity:
Landscaping (truck access for black dirt and plant materials required)
Roofing (crane access for materials required)
Roof sheet metal (access by ladders only)
Bituminous parking lot paving (machine and truck access required)
Painting of building exterior (without use of mechanized man lifts)
HVAC rooftop unit start up and commissioning (ladder access only)

3. Calculate your total hours for all work or school activities during the middle of the semester. Include time spent in class, labs, discussion groups, project or paper research and preparation, study, and jobs. Then, calculate the additional time spent per week during the end of the semester when final exams are taken and all final projects and term papers are due. Estimate how long you could maintain each of these workweeks working 50 weeks per year with 2-weeks of vacation.

CHAPTER
2.5

Estimating Project Costs to Determine and Confirm Scope and Approach

Setting Carrier chillers at Trump Tower in Chicago, Illinois. *Photo courtesy: Temperature Equipment Corporation.*

Estimating Project Costs to Determine and Confirm Scope and Approach

Balancing cost with scope and grade of material, and time of construction

Cost planning and estimating manages the cost part of the triple constraint of scope, time, and cost. Planning the approach to the project, scope and grade of material, and time of construction all affect costs. The acceptable target costs in the workable approach affect the possible approaches, materials, and time. So, costing must be included in planning the approach development and confirmation process—with back and forth, and give and take between approach and costs. Costing for planning is then followed by a highly detailed cost estimate of the selected approach that is later inputed into the cost monitoring and management and control system.

Cost estimating systems are far more developed in construction than in most other industries. Construction costs are high, profit margins are low, and construction cost is frequently used as a tollgate the construction manager must pass prior to award even for service only contracts.

Large and variable construction costs can make or break a project, so early accurate costs are key for planning. Detailed cost estimates are usually best performed early in project planning. And since these construction estimates involve breaking down the work into activities that can be measured and counted, the estimating process substantially defines both the activities and the WBS (work breakdown structure). The need for early costs, estimating systems that can provide these costs, and the organizational impact of the CSI (Construction Specification Institute) system make cost estimating a significant contributor to early accurate scope definition.

Order of magnitude estimates are needed to initiate and plan the project

Before a project is initiated, an order of magnitude cost is required to determine that the project is probably feasible. There are four estimating methods used for this determination.

Expert judgment

The first, expert judgment, is guided by historical information and tempered by present conditions specific to the contemplated project. An example might be "university buildings of this approximate size cost $25–$30 million."

Analogous estimating

The second, analogous estimating, uses slightly more detailed analysis of comparable projects analyzing the size complexity and difficulty. An example might be "the last three 200 room university dormitories cost of $28 million, so this one should be about same."

Parametric estimating

The third, parametric estimating, uses measurement and a numerical multiplier. An example might be "dormitories cost about $140 per square foot, so this 200,000-square-foot building should cost $28 million."

Three-point estimates

The fourth, the three-point estimate, uses a weighted average of the most likely optimistic and pessimistic as shown by the formula:

$$\text{Three-point estimate} = \frac{\text{Pessimistic} + 4 \times \text{Most likely} + \text{Optimistic}}{6}$$

The three-point estimate provides a very rough approximation of the center of a normal statistical distribution.

These order of magnitude estimates can only be used to determine project feasibility—further drill-down analysis is not possible. Costing to plan and manage the project requires bottom-up detailed estimating as described below.

Professional construction managers must achieve accurate and precise costs

Some industries can accept preliminary cost estimates with plus or minus 50% margins of error, but greater precision is required in construction. This is partially because construction costs are large, but also because construction projects are typically subjected to the internal and external financial analysis. Well run companies will subject all projects to an internal rate of return analysis, but construction projects, that frequently require financing from external organizations such as banks or bond markets, will be subjected to a second round of financial scrutiny. This scrutiny usually involves industry benchmarks and comparable projects, which produces a narrow range of acceptable costs and rates of return. 15% variation from target cost is frequently considered a maximum for project planning.

And project execution requires more cost precision than project planning. Construction managers will usually bear financial risk for project performance—through fixed lump sum contracts, guaranteed maximum cost, or guaranteed maximum cost with shared savings. Since construction managers' after-tax profit averages 1 ½%, construction cost variation very close to this number must be achieved to preserve this profit. Some project scope changes will be legitimate and will increase the reimbursable cost of the work and therefore not degrade profit. But the portions of cost increases the project owner should not or will not reimburse are subtracted directly from profit, which makes accurate cost estimates and cost control critical. (Qualitative evaluation of fee-only construction management without risk performance will use these same quantitative standards.)

Bottom-Up Estimates Require Professional Skill and Knowledge

Estimates start with an organizational system—to see the big picture and miss nothing

Estimate preparation starts with establishing an information organizational system that contains all work items and activities. If all work items are in the estimate, but not precisely estimated correctly, mid-project feedback and control makes correction possible and success still probable. If a work item is not in this original estimate, additional management time and probably cost will be incurred later. And timely completion at the required cost will become less likely—full recovery is usually not possible.

A reusable template is required

Few can visualize an entire project in detail, and starting with a completely blank slate every time is inefficient. A reusable organizational framework for the type of project your firm builds is required. The CSI 16 section (pre 2004 version) or 49 section (nominally 50 section in the 2004 version) classification system is a common and useful framework. All 16 sections must be included in the reusable framework, even if some of the sections may not apply to all projects. Additional subsections should be added to the template for the common work items but must be limited—few will ever encounter all 10,000 subcategories in the CSI format.

The effort to make a specific determination that a section does not apply, or is not shown but maybe should apply, or is shown and needs to be counted and costed forces thought on the scope of the project. The estimate summary sheet containing the 16 or 49 sections and selected subsections should be limited to one page for small and medium-sized projects and two to three pages for the largest projects, or it becomes difficult to see how the pieces fit together to form an understandable project. (Summary items will, of course, be supported by more detailed estimates on supporting pages.)

Counting and Measuring

Component cost breakdown—labor, material, subcontractors and vendors

Once all components are identified in the organizational system, these components are measured and counted. Each component is broken down into three parts—labor (forces on your own payroll), material (you purchase directly from a supply house but not custom manufactured for the project), outside vendors (including equipment and material made to order for the job, and subcontractor costs). The three-part breakdown is useful to permit easy adjustments of the preliminary baseline unit costs—and these three categories behave differently. Labor productivity may change labor costs but not material costs. A sudden increase in material prices will not affect labor productivity or cost. Also, this breakdown resembles the way a project is contracted, managed, and paid, so this breakdown serves as the starting point of future accounting and project control. People get weekly paychecks, material vendors get paid shortly after material delivery, and subcontractors get paid at agreed times after milestones are reached. This component breakdown is also customary and is therefore widely recognized and accepted.

The components are counted in the order they are installed. This is a pipe-by-pipe, stick-by-stick, brick-by-brick count. Not square foot, ballpark figures, or plugged cost for assemblies. You cannot buy 1,000 square feet of electrical work from an electrician, so do not measure electrical work by square foot. To permit communication and help see how the parts fit together, standard unit of measure must be used. Measure square feet, not sheets, rolls, or bundles. Measure cubic yards, not truckloads or bags.

Complete and comprehensive is very important—precision is less important

The estimate is calculated in a very short time: days, weeks, or, for very large projects, months. This limits the information available and the possibilities that can be explored. The organizational system and component counts must be fully complete and make one fully possible workable approach. That is the best that can be expected during the estimate preparation. It must be a good possible way to build the project, but it may not be the best way. If, when building the project, personnel with a different point of view and more time find a faster or more efficient approach that will alter component quantities, productivities, and cost—this improved approach might be selected.

The counted and measured quantities of physical objects can and should be precise from the start—get it done right, so it is out of the way and you can move on. But the unit costs assigned will be at first very imprecise. As the estimate is completed and the time, approach, and productivity that affect costs are refined with the workable approach, precision of unit costs will increase but will still be approximate. The precision of the unit costs is limited by available information—and there is always less information than one would really like.

Labor Cost Estimating

Estimate using baseline unit costs—man-hours first, then money

Labor unit costs must first be estimated in man-hours, not money. (Cost in money is calculated by multiplying your burdened labor rates times these estimated man-hours.) Baseline labor rates from the developed cost library (cost libraries are discussed below) are entered to start. This makes the estimated cost useable for variable wage rates, in different time periods, or in different regions. Adjustments for the trade type and crew size assigned to the task can be made. It also makes it easy to adjust for job-site-specific productivity variations.

Adjust baseline costs for productivity

Job site productivity adjustment is influenced by travel time from the site entrance to the work area and mobility at the work area, as restricted by high, confined, or congested spaces. Productivity is also affected by time—the pace of the project. Productivity will increase with increased pace to a point—then decrease as the pace increases further. Productivity will decrease rapidly with project change or lack of required information. Using these considerations, estimated modifications to the project's baseline productivity are entered. Start with a productivity modifier for the entire project (125% or 75% of baseline productivity), which can be further modified for individual work tasks or later again modified for the entire project. Start with the best, but imprecise, estimate, and continue to increase the precision as the workable approach is refined. Modification to labor productivity is the largest and most common adjustment to labor baseline costs. Changing labor rates by assigning the same task to a different trade with a different labor rate is also possible.

Material Cost Estimating

Materials estimating starts with counting and measuring the physical components in standard units of measure—not money. Baseline unit costs in money from the cost library are then entered and multiplied by the measured quantities. Material cost includes the cost of the material, vendor delivery charges, and sales tax. (Initial entries are from your cost library but must later be verified for this project.) To this burdened material cost, waste factors must be added. For components that are completely divisible into any sized unit, such as earthwork or concrete that can be obtained in a ½ cubic yard unit, a percentage waste factor based on historical knowledge can be added, usually less than 5%. For components that come in standard sizes, specific knowledge of the dimensions and delivery possibilities must be known, and an appropriate waste factor used. For example, carpet typically comes in 12′ wide rolls. When carpeting a corridor that is 7′ wide, 5′ of every 12′ roll will be wasted.

Adequate precision ok for estimates—higher precision required later when ordering

The component counts are part of securing the information that will refine the workable approach. Therefore, these counts are initially less precise than the built result. For example, if a roof slopes from 12′ to 14′ uniformly, the walls under the slope will average 13′ high. Estimating 13′ high framing material is acceptable for an estimate. But since material only comes in 12′ and 14′ lengths, the 12′ and 14′ lengths must be counted when ordering the material. Specific verification of the material unit costs for the project and determination of waste factors are the largest and most common modification to material baseline unit costs.

Subcontractor and Vendor Cost Estimating

As knowledge of their work increases, adjustments to baseline costs are more limited

The construction manager is responsible for cost estimating of hired subcontractors' or vendors' work and must estimate subcontractors' work in the same manner as self-performed work—a detailed count and costing of each of their components with the labor, material, and vendor/subcontractor component breakdowns. Project-specific subcontractor quotations must also be obtained.

Detailed estimates are required first to understand the nature of the subcontractors' work and second to keep them honest and catch mistakes. Finally, their estimated labor determines the limits and opportunities for improvement of the workable approach for the subcontractors' work items. And

| Steel truss erection | *Photo 3 of 5* |

subcontractor labor can only be accurately determined by independent construction manager estimates. This estimated labor figure will also be used later to develop the project schedule.

Adjustments to the baseline subcontract costs are more limited than the adjustment possible to labor and material since you receive lump sum quotations. But this dual internal estimate and lump sum quotation approach will determine that the received quotations are good—and if not why, and what can be done about it.

After Costing of the Permanent Project—Cost the Temporary Construction and Activities

Detailed count and costing is first performed on all the components of the permanent project—the components shown by plans and specifications. Once the building is measured, counted, and costed, the activities that are not part of the permanent project and are not shown on the plans, but are required for construction, are costed. These cost items—general and supplementary (special) conditions, and soft costs—will be discussed in the next chapter.

Costing general and supplementary conditions after costing the permanent work produces the most precise costs—but many construction management contracts now require fixed general condition costs before award. (General conditions can be used as a dumping ground for the construction managers' personnel and equipment not needed on other projects—which can inappropriately increase general condition costs.) To satisfy this requirement, the general conditions must be estimated before the scope of the work is accurately defined—and the estimate focuses more on the reasonableness and saleability than on accuracy.

Making a Cost Library

Establishing baseline unit costs

Baseline costs must be internally generated from actual job experience. This is not difficult and can be done by anyone with a working knowledge of the trade. A tradesman who has never performed an estimate can begin to assemble costs from existing information gained from past experience. Labor hours worked, materials used, and equipment for the past few jobs, or the past few months, can be used to calculate a starting point for unit costs. An experienced estimator with an existing cost library moving into a new and unfamiliar area of work can use common themes to assist in understanding a new activity. For example, lineal feet of white or black pipe have the same installation costs. Installation of ¾″ conduit and ¾″ copper pipe in the same situation will have similar installation cost. Using standard units of measure, with records of productivity adjustment due to travel time to the work site and productivity in the work area, can produce quite close approximations of unfamiliar work items.

Material unit costs are determined in a similar manner. Invoices and job records from past projects can be used in times of stable material pricing. (Prompt payment discounts, such as a 2% discount for payment within 10 days, or restocking charges for returned materials, are not included in the unit baseline costs. These cost modifications are caused by good or bad management—which is a future unknown.) Job-specific material quotations are necessary in times of material price instability, and always for new or different types of work, or work in unfamiliar regions.

For vendor-purchased equipment or subcontract items, detailed records broken down into labor, material, and their sub-vendor pricing must be recorded. Occasionally, a subcontractor will perform only a single task on a project, which will show some unit costs. Other times, subcontractors will give unit cost information that can be understood, checked, and believed. As projects are executed with estimates using these unit costs, monitoring of job site productivity can continue to refine these unit costs and improve the accuracy and the completeness of the subcontractor baseline costs over time.

Making a cost library is not difficult, but it is tedious, slow, hard work. This internally generated cost information is the only method that works for estimating costs, feedback and control, and process improvement. Cost indexes, such as RS Means, can only be used for public relations and discussion purposes with the owner or for parametric estimating described above. These cost services have baseline costs that must be adjusted by multipliers for productivity, quality of construction, type of construction, and region of the country—each of which can produce 10%–20% ranges. Such broad ranges with a loose definition of terms do not produce costs anyone can take to the bank. These types of estimates also do not produce the detailed component counts needed for project planning, monitoring, and control.

Burdens Applied to Labor Costs

Allocating burdens for your own use and the project owner's acceptance

Costs that are imposed by the government or insurance companies, or internal costs that must be added to the raw cost of labor are called burdens. These include government payroll taxes such as Social Security and Medicare, insurance tied to payroll such as worker compensation, and a portion of liability insurance tied to payroll, union dues and contributions, health or pension contributions, mandated training costs, vacation and sick pay, and sometimes small tools and supplies. These costs now center in the area of 50% of gross payroll. Safer trades, such as carpet installation, will have a lower burden (maybe 40%) than dangerous trades, such as ironworkers who will have a higher burden (maybe 70%–90%).

These burdens must be allocated in a way that is easy to understand, easy to check, compatible with the construction manager's accounting system, and acceptable to the project owner. Owners will accept a burden if it is similar to the burden they see in other areas of their lives. For example, a car mechanic will charge an hourly rate, which includes labor and a fee for the maintenance of the shop, tools, and equipment. Attorneys' and accountants' hourly rates include the expense of their time plus expense for administrative support and the maintenance of their offices.

At least some actual cost figures are typically presented to the project owner at some time for most projects. Even if methods of allocating burden costs are entirely justifiable and supportable, the owner will take severe exception to certain types of burden allocation and readily accept the same burden presented in another manner. Tell the truth, but tell them what they want to hear, the way they want to hear it.

Checking the Estimate During Preparation

Estimate the way you build—do not be satisfied until it makes sense

Since estimating is a process of building the project mentally and on paper, components should be counted in the order of installation. For example, estimate clearing the site, digging the hole, installing the foundation, installing the structure, and then installing the roof. Estimate plumbing sanitary waste, vent, and then water. The process will be real and make sense. Nothing will be missed, and items missing from the instructions received from others will be noticed. When performing a count of components by system in order of installation, questions such as "What holds this up?" "Where does this water drain?" and "How is the equipment powered?" will emerge. Questions should continue until the complete project makes sense.

Comparing expected results with estimated results—make sure estimates are reasonable

Early completeness—making sure everything is counted—rather than high precision was emphasized. Very close to right, but imprecise is good—not right but very precise is not. Completeness can be checked for reasonableness. This is done by constantly comparing expected values with estimated values.

For example, ratios of material to cost of labor by component, component percentage of the total project cost, component cost per square foot, component man-hours per square foot, or man-hours as a percentage of the total project cost, and historical values from past project to the estimate for this project are all used to spot unusual patterns or deviations. Errors in the estimate will be discovered, or unusually expensive or inexpensive materials, unusually high or low labor usage, or usually large, heavy, or numerous components will be identified and analyzed. This both produces an accurate estimate and gets to "know the job," which materially aids analysis of scope completeness.

The estimate is then used to assist planning, and monitor and control costs

For both the construction management and the lump sum hard bid delivery systems, the estimate is used to establish the initial contract sum—to "get the job." After contract award, the estimate then has other valuable uses. Labor man-hours and costs, material quantities and costs, and subcontract costs are exported to the job costing system to monitor and control cost and schedule performance. And the labor hours can be exported directly to the schedule to calculate task durations. (Task durations can be determined from estimated man-hours and the number of workers assigned to the task.) The well constructed estimate will make these critical exports a routine clerical task that is either fully or partially automated—both saving time and ensuring accuracy and credibility.

The estimate can also be similarly used to increase the accuracy and speed of job site planning. The estimate's detailed quantities—cubic yards of concrete, tons of structural steel, and board feet of lumber—broken down by installation location can assist selection of hoisting equipment such as tower cranes, buck hoists, and mobile material handling equipment for the project. Proper flow and storage of materials can maintain an unencumbered job site that increases productivity and safety.

For construction management delivery systems that require value engineering and significant costing of alternatives, multiple pricings of similar work items and revisions to previously priced work items can become time consuming and confusing to the construction manager and owner. If the well organized structure and methodology of the original estimate is used for the changes as well, these difficulties are minimized. The structure, format, and information of the original estimate used for costing of changes speed costing and provide consistency that makes the result credible and acceptable to the owner.

These multiple uses—getting the job, developing the schedule, influencing project equipment selection, monitoring and controlling costs and schedule, and effective pricing of changes that can assist scope management—make the estimate a critical project management tool. And the construction project manager will be the only project team member with the skills, information, and diligence needed to produce an estimate that can be used for these multiple purposes.

Summary

Estimating develops the cost part of the workable approach. An organizational template for your type of project must be developed to ensure every component is counted and costed. These components are broken down into labor, material, and sub vendor components, and then measured and counted. Baseline unit costs for these components from your cost library are applied. Adjustments to the library unit costs for waste, productivity, market and regional variations, and risk are made.

The estimating organization system and the information it produces is the start of project planning, costing, scope verification and cost monitoring, and control.

Review Questions (True or False)

1. Order of magnitude estimates are needed to initiate planned project. Identical methods are used to estimate costs and to estimate time.
2. Detailed bottom-up estimates are needed to establish a firm price for contract.
3. Each project is unique, so project estimates must be unique as well and cannot effectively use reusable templates.
4. Bottom-up estimates, which are a pipe-by-pipe, stick-by-stick, and brick-by-brick counting and measuring, estimates labor, material, and outside vendors separately since these categories behave differently.
5. Estimates are calculated in a very short time—days, weeks, or, for large projects, months. Completeness is essential but a lesser, but achievable, level of precision is acceptable.
6. Labor costs are always estimated first in currency to ensure maximum accuracy.
7. Field personnel may use the quantities in the estimate without alteration to order materials.
8. Work by subcontractors and vendors must be estimated in the same manner as self-performed work. This helps understand the nature of the subcontractor's work, keeps them honest and catches mistakes, identifies opportunities for improvement of the workable approach, and can later be used to develop the project schedule.
9. Costing of the general and supplementary conditions is best performed after costing of the permanent building work. However, some construction management contract forms require estimating and fixing the general conditions before award.

10. The cost library, which is an essential component of bottom-up estimating, is tedious, slow, hard work that must be prepared by professional consultants outside the construction management firm.

11. Estimates are best performed in the order of actual installation of the work and must continually compare expected with estimated results to spot unusual patterns or deviations, unusually expensive work items, and "get to know the job".

12. Estimates are used to establish the contract sum that "gets the job", to monitor and control costs, and for job site planning such as selection of hoisting equipment.

13. Estimates can assist in value engineering and can be used as a basis for pricing of change orders.

Test Your Understanding

1. Using a copy of RS Means unit costs, note the following:
   The structure of the estimate (crew size, material units, and equipment)
   The methodology (described in the front of the Means book) used to prepare these costs
   The modifiers (described in the back of the book) used for regional and project type differences
   The format for calculation of costs such as general conditions and overhead and profit
   (Note that although the RS Means cost is not an example of bottom-up estimating, the explanation of methodology is short and clear, and can assist understanding.)

2. Discuss the use and types of estimate for project planning, establishing contract costs, accounting, field engineering, and change order pricing.

3. Project estimating templates, cost libraries, and detailed records of cost performance from completed project are a construction manager's assets. Discuss how a firm that self-performs significant portions of trade work could have higher quality information that produces a competitive advantage over a CM that subs out all trade work.

CHAPTER
2.6

Estimating to Achieve Target Project Costs

Setting Carrier chillers at Trump Tower in Chicago, Illinois. General condition costs were needed to build temporary protective enclosures around the chillers to minimize the possible mechanical damage from the other surrounding heavy construction operations. *Photo courtesy: Temperature Equipment Corporation.*

Estimating to Achieve Target Project Costs

If everyone can count and measure the same, why do prices differ?

The previous chapter discussed order of magnitude and bottom-up estimating—counting, measuring, and costing the components of the permanent building. Although all bidders can count, measure, and cost the same, their prices differ. Why? The answer is that pricing is not just a collection of calculations, but refining costs to achieve targeted pricing—either the owner's statement of the price that fits his purpose or the bidders' assumptions of the price needed to get the job. Temporary work is required to build the permanent work. The nature and scale of this temporary work is determined by the approach selected. Assumptions, expectations, market forces, and risk affect the approach to both the permanent and temporary work—and therefore costs. A back and forth process of refining the approach and assumptions and adjusting the costs continues until the target cost is reached.

Temporary Work Is Required to Build the Permanent Work

General and supplementary (special) conditions must support the chosen approach

General and supplementary conditions are the terms customarily used to describe work required to complete the project—but not included in the finished work. These work items are not shown on any blueprints or specifications—experience must determine what is required. So, the approach heavily determines the scope of general and special conditions.

Also, the general and special conditions are more affected by time than the permanent parts of the work. Supervision and equipment rental incur costs every day they are on the job, regardless of what is accomplished. Additional expenditure on general conditions, such as more or bigger cranes, hoists, and haul roads, can vastly increase productivity and the speed of permanent construction—but at a cost. So, the development of the workable approach continues with an estimate of the general and special conditions—and possible revisions to the productivity and time of the permanent project construction. The permanent and temporary estimating methods are the same: a reusable template is reviewed for each project. All components are measured and costed using the labor, material, and subvendor breakdowns—and adjustments for productivity and time are made. Costing temporary work as a percentage of construction should be avoided—or used only for the last few very small items, as described below.

Job site supervision and management—a large cost critical for project performance

Job site personnel working only on the site—but not directly installing the permanent components of the building—are general condition costs. These include site managers, supervisors, project managers, superintendents, project engineers, foreman, and safety personnel. These costs are estimated using each of these personnel's unit cost and their estimated duration on the job site.

Temporary structures and facilities—are determined early and influence productivity

Temporary structures and facilities—such as roads, retention walls, hoisting such as cranes, and temporary elevators, storage sheds, and job site office break and change rooms, and safety barricades, and utilities—such as power, water, light, heat, and toilets—are temporary facilities or services. These are estimated using the same method as permanent work—not as a percentage of construction.

150

Equipment, vehicle, and small tools—are important management decisions

Equipment costs for large equipment intensive projects—such as road or dam construction—will be a significant portion of the total project cost. Individual pieces of equipment will be costed the same as supervision—unit cost and anticipated time of use, plus the maintenance and servicing costs times time. In addition, the costs for set up and removal must be added.

Even for work where the equipment costs are small, such as carpet laying, a calculated equipment cost should be made. The common practice of calculating equipment costs as a percentage of work is misleading, inaccurate, and troublesome. A percentage cost can be added to the material or labor portion of each work item, but differences in labor rates or material costs will make these inaccurate. (Cheaper labor does not use less equipment. More expensive carpet does not take more equipment to install.) A percentage could be added to the entire project or a cost can be included in the project overhead. The last two burdens typically tend to raise owners' objections—who view an increase in overhead as an increase in profit. Also, if they see certain tools and equipment that are not in constant use at all times on the job site, they have an emotional reaction that a credit is due for every moment that the tool is not in operation.

Some sample general condition categories and work items

A reasonably comprehensive list of general and supplementary conditions work items is shown below. Not all items will be needed on all projects—only about 10% of these items may be needed for an interior tenant improvement project. And larger or specialized projects will need additional items. Review and analysis of such a comprehensive list on each project—and then elimination of unneeded items—will help ensure everything is considered and nothing is missed.

Site Management and Supervision	
Office management/engineering	**Outside services**
Project manager	Engineering
Assistant project manager	Architectural
Project engineer	Equipment maintenance/repair
Assistant project engineer	Building maintenance/repair
Estimator	Janitorial
Cost engineer	Landscaping
Scheduler	
Office engineer	**Site office equipment**
Safety engineer	Office furniture
Subcontract engineer	Copy machine
Technical aides	Fax/printer
Secretary/clerk	Blueprint machine
	Plotter
Field supervision	Computers
Project superintendent	Fire extinguishers
Architectural superintendent	
Civil superintendent	**Site office supplies**
Electrical superintendent	Stationary and office supplies
Mechanical superintendent	Engineering/drafting supplies
Structural superintendent	Outside blueprint costs
Equipment superintendent	
Assistant superintendent	**Site office utilities**

Field engineer	Water hookup and supply
Technical aides	Power hookup and supply
Secretary/clerk	Gas hookup and supply
	Telephone hookup and supply
Administrative	
Office manager	**Other site office costs**
Accountant	Photographs
Bookkeeper	Travel expense
Timekeeper	Permits and license
Secretary/receptionist	
Clerk/typist	

Temporary Construction, Facilities, and Services

Temporary buildings	**Temporary barriers and enclosures**
Site offices—staff	Temporary air barriers
Site offices—owner	Temporary dust barriers
Change houses—craft	Temporary noise barriers
Toolsheds	Temporary barricades
Warehouse	Temporary fencing
First aid	Temporary protective walkways
Fabrication shop	Temporary security barriers
Fuel and repair facility	Temporary security enclosures
Temporary controls	Temporary telecommunications
Temporary erosion and sediment control	Temporary water
Temporary pest control	Temporary sanitary facilities
Temporary environmental controls	
Temporary storm water pollution control	
	Temporary utilities/other
Vehicular access and parking	Gas systems
Temporary road access	Compressed air systems
Haul routes	Welding power systems
Temporary parking areas	Telephone systems
Temporary roads	Telecommunications systems
Traffic control	Dewatering
Staging areas	
Temporary bridges	**Hot weather protection**
Temporary decking	Fans and ventilators
Temporary overpasses	Tarps and plastic
Temporary ramps	Shelters
Temporary runarounds	Ice plant
Project identification	**Cold weather protection**
Temporary project signage	Unit heaters
Temporary interior signage	Tarps and plastic
	Enclosures
Construction aids	LP gas/oil

Temporary elevators	
Temporary hoists	**Cleaning and waste management**
Temporary cranes	Progress cleaning
Temporary scaffolding and platforms	Site maintenance
Temporary swing staging	Construction waste management and disposal
Temporary ladders and stairs	Final cleaning
Temporary utilities	**Outside services**
Temporary electricity	Material testing
Temporary fire protection	X-ray and other locators
Temporary fuel oil	Authorized inspector
Temporary heating, cooling, and ventilating	Testing and inspection
Temporary lighting	Survey and site layout
Temporary natural gas	

Vehicles, Small Tools, and Equipment

Equipment, company owned	**Equipment, rental/leased**
Equipment service vehicles	Company rental
Cars	Company lease
Vans, pickups	Outside rental
Light trucks	Outside lease
Heavy trucks	
Equipment-operating expense	**Equipment supplies and services**
Fuels	Small tool purchases
Lubricants	Tool man
Repair and maintenance	Load and haul equipment
Operations labor	Cartage
Oil	Repair and maintain equipment
	Job mechanics
	Oiler

Insurance, Bonds, and Insurance

Insurance	**Permits**
Builder's risk	Sidewalk and curbs
Fire, extended coverage	Driveway
Earthquake	Street
	Overhead canopy
Bonds	Water
Bid	Sewer
Payment and performance	Inspection fees
Material supply	Occupancy
Subcontractor	Highway
Employee	Storm water management
Installation warranty	Impact fees
Contractor license bond	

Fees and Soft Costs Increase in Variability and Cost

Permits are now granted and costed locally

Building permits, permits such as for road use, and dump fees vary widely by area, change frequently, and are only limited by the imagination and greed of politicians. These must be specifically calculated by permit type and checked for each project.

Until the mid-1990s, permit fee calculation methods were specified in the then BOCA (Building Officials & Code Administrators International, Inc.) code which later changed to International code. This methodology was used by most cities and tended to produce permit fees under 1% of building cost. Permit fee schedules are now customarily determined by each municipality and vary hugely—from a fraction of 1% to over 10%—and further impact and tap fees may be added as well.

Project-specific insurance not tied to payroll must be managed and costed

Bonds such as payment, performance, permit and street use, and insurance such as some types of liability and builder's risk that are project-specific mandates by the owner or government have costs obtained using project-specific quotations from the insurance agent or carrier.

Office Overhead and Profit Must Be Costed and Presented Carefully

Same as temporary construction and supervision but at a different location

Office overhead and profit must be added to the cost of all work items. Home office overhead includes some components of tools and equipment, home office vehicle expense, and insurance not included in the direct cost of the work as described above. In addition, it includes the office employees, including project engineers, estimators, clerical support, shop labor, and home office rental, utility expenses, office services and supplies. Profit is what is left over after all costs are paid. It is the payment the market will bear for the risk of the project.

The project owners, however, emotionally cannot help but view office overhead (a real cost) and profit as the same thing. Further, owners tend to think that their and their designers' instructions for the project are completely self-evident and can be executed by robots on autopilot. Therefore, for most owners, it is important to minimize office overhead as a line item. This unfortunately results in relocating costs that are legitimate office overhead (for the work the project owners require and demand) to the labor and material direct cost of the work. This clouds the clarity and the use of the estimate information, but may be necessary to sell the job to unsophisticated owners.

Costs Must Be Both Flexible and Complete

Supporting line item costs can vary when conditions change, but the total costs remain fixed

Estimating the cost impact of the intended approach

Companies executing large projects well know the size and importance of temporary work. A mine, refinery, or power plant constructed in the wilderness can require marine structures to accommodate ships, haul roads, temporary utility plants and fuel storage, and temporary housing and support structures—which can take years to construct before work on the permanent project can start. The man and material hoists and tower cranes for construction of a high-rise can cost 6% of the total project cost—but are the lifeblood of the project—determining pace and productivity.

The facts gained in preparing a detailed component estimate increase knowledge of the project. At the conclusion of the counting of all the components, the order of magnitude of the project and each of the components is known. Probable range of costs for each component, and the total project, and the range of probable construction times are known.

Steel truss erection   *Photo 4 of 5*

A minimum amount of temporary work is required for a project. Above the minimum, additional temporary work can be effectively added if the cost of the additional temporary work is exceeded by the decrease in cost through increased productivity, or shorten construction times. Although this cost–benefit trade-off is known to large contractors, it also applies to all efforts larger than a repair job where a tradesman can carry all the tools and materials for the job in his hands.

Every firm has one speed and will visualize only a small range of possible approaches. Large firms may spend more time, effort, and money mobilizing for a small project than a small firm will spend completing the project. A small firm will not grasp the temporary work required for a large project and will fail to complete the project, or even start it well. Although each firm must work near its normal range, expanding the range even a little can increase productivity, reduce time, reduce cost, and produce continuous improvement.

Big or small, the approach is the same: estimate an approach, cost the temporary work required by the approach, review the cost of the approach vs. the benefit of increased productivity and shortened schedule, and continue to refine until the targeted costs and schedule is obtained. Small firms can expand the possibilities they explore by realizing that there is not just one way. Spending money on temporary work can have a greater cost reduction in productivity and schedule savings. Larger firms can also increase their range of possible approaches by reviewing these cost–benefit trade offs.

Again, the triple constraint: approach to the scope affects both time and cost

The temporary work determines the range of construction times possible—and time determines much of the cost of the general conditions, and temporary construction. So, the approach and time—which determine general conditions and temporary construction—must be adjusted and revised until the owner's targeted cost and time is reached. This cycle of revising approach and time is similar to the cycle of approach and cost.

Everyone and every firm have one speed—and reputations are persistent. So, a firm's ability to rapidly change approach to build projects faster and more efficiently (and therefore get lower subcontractors pricing) will not be believed immediately or without heavy explanation. Either long-term gradual change or immediate selection of alternate vendors—whose only speed is faster—can be sought to achieve the required improvements.

Estimating the costs of the permanent project discussed in the previous chapter and estimating the costs of the temporary work discussed in this chapter would, in a stable and rational world, produce bids from comparable contractors that are far closer than are achieved in the real world. The world is not stable, and people are not rational, so further modifications to costs occur.

The Irrational Modifies Costs

Assumptions about materials affect grade and cost

Owners seldom know what they really want, and architects, engineers, and owners seldom completely mean what they say. Specifications for model numbers that do not exist, from companies that have gone out of business, with grading systems that are no longer used are normal. Architects and engineers "borrowing" or buying canned specifications produce these errors. This may mean that no one has seen or knows anything about the specified product.

Further, there are regional conventions that, even though clearly stated, are assumed to be incorrect. For example, a painting specification for one prime coat and two finish coats is widely accepted to mean one prime and one finish in some regions—"everybody just knows". Each installer will have certain standards. Either they will know code and manufacturer's requirements, or they will have their own standards superior to the specifications—"we do it this way because we want to be proud of our work and we don't want any call backs".

These assumptions will produce different interpretations of materials to be used. These assumptions can range from "this is the code conforming, best, accepted way" to " they didn't tell me what they want so I will just give them this" to " they told me what they want, but they don't really mean it". All of these are good faith efforts to do the right thing, but produce different material selections. Outright cheating "I know what they want, but I will give them something less" also occurs.

Expectations influence reality

Each type of project will be known to have certain acceptable rates of productivity, risk, and cost—and these become self-fulfilling prophecies. For example, an apartment building will be a far less expensive project than a college dormitory, even though the completed results may be similar. The cost difference is greater than the cost of generally increased grade of material that exists in a college dormitory. This is true because everyone knows apartments have to be cheaper to get the job, and this expectation produces a certain level of effort and urgency. This would be similar to the productivity an employee might achieve Monday through Friday at their job, and achieve a much lower productivity for work around the house on the weekends. Same person—different expectation and results.

Risk modifies cost

There is also the risk of unexpected events. These include government interference—such as restrictions on transportation to the site. For example, use of public highways to and from the site may be completely legal and customary, and have been used for years—but a specific project may produce neighborhood or political objections that make far longer and therefore more expensive haul roads necessary. Weather is an unforeseen condition only when it is significantly worse than the normal weather for that location at that time of year. (The impact of normal seasonal variation is not unforeseen and should be included in the estimated costs.) Another risk in this category is nonpayment by the owner. The greatest single risk is unanticipated changes in productivity due to owner's activities. Failure to provide correct information when required, frequent changes in the work, or scheduling their vendors to work concurrently with the construction of the building can all cause massive reduction in productivity.

These risks can cause either an increase in the unit labor cost due to lower productivity, and increase in temporary work and office overhead due to extended time, or an increase in the profit for these risk premiums.

Market boom and busts (another risk) affect cost and prices

Construction continually moves through periods of boom—where the demand for material, skilled labor, and available vendors exceeds the available supply, and bust—where firms will take drastic measures to keep busy. This will affect the costs (expenditures to achieve a result) and prices (the charges to achieve a result, regardless of the cost). Costs and prices, which usually are closely related, can temporarily disconnect in times of boom and bust.

Different regions of the country and different countries will also have variable or opposite ups and downs. Project types will not move up and down at the same times. Single-family residential housing may boom, while electrical power plant construction is non-existent for years. The type and location of the project will affect the construction types customarily used, which will affect the materials and labor skills required.

In times of boom, the costs will increase because factories and field labor are stretched beyond their limit. Some overtime can be used—for additional cost, or lesser skilled labor can be added—who will produce less. If factories, contractors, and shipping companies are all at their limit, many will raise prices farther above their costs than usual to make quick profits.

These swings in cost and price are sudden and temporary, and the causes are too complex for anyone to understand. (Demand for structural steel in China may outstrip the capacity of the new steel mills in India, so the cost of structural steel in New York rises.) The practical answer is first to have a general understanding of the global forces that affect the materials and labor used for your project type so you can know the possibilities for change. Then, specific determination of the cost and availability for all ingredients for your specific project must be made in the project planning stage. These specific costs and delivery times must be included in your estimates for your workable approach.

Finalizing the Cost Estimate—the Number of Useful Revisions Is Limited

Repeated revisions produce diminishing returns

Order of magnitude cost estimates to determine that a project is feasible and worth pursuing were discussed in the previous chapter. Frequently one, but no more than three, estimate is needed to make this determination. If more estimates appeared required, probably the scope or possibly the time are imperfectly defined and should be revisited and refined—or the project abandoned.

Revisions to bottom-up detailed estimates are limited both by information available and by contractual expectations and customs. Once the estimate costs all needed line items and reflects the intended approach, if no further useful information can be obtained to clarify future uncertainties, further refinements of the estimate will produce no additional value. (Multiple scenarios may have been considered and costed to determine this estimate.) One carefully crafted, analyzed, and reviewed estimate is usually sufficient.

Project management in other industries finds project long revisions to this baseline costs acceptable—construction does not. Construction project management fixes this initial budget and later modifies the costs of select line items only—by change order. Most contract forms—lump sum, construction management with a guaranteed maximum price (with or without shared savings)—include a hard cost or at least an extremely critical budget as the contract price. This initial cost then becomes a fixed cost. Large or numerous change orders that increase this cost are usually perceived as evidence of poor project management and possibly project failure. Therefore, change management in construction focuses heavily on resistance to unwanted change.

One apparent exception to this resistance to change orders might appear to be fast-track construction—which can produce thousands of change orders as the design is completed in phases. Yet these change orders are not new unexpected work but are rather refinements and confirmation of previously anticipated and budgeted work items. So these change orders (as long their aggregate value remains under the budgeted cost) are administrative and accounting documentation, not changes in scope or cost.

This attitude toward change management is accentuated by the sequential nature of construction. Revisions to the completed work are extremely costly and difficult to implement—installed foundations are difficult to remove or alter. Such late project revisions are rarely contemplated or performed.

Summary

Once the work of the permanent project is costed, the necessary temporary work is costed. Estimating the temporary work is similar in approach and method to estimating the permanent work. It differs first because nothing is drawn or written to show you what to do—requirements and possibilities must be known from experience.

Temporary measures also are more heavily related to time—causing costs by the time in use, and shortening or lengthening the construction time of the permanent project. Permanent and temporary costs are modified by irrational assumptions, expectations, risk, and market forces—which requires further revision to approach (cost, grade, and time) to reach the targeted costs.

Review Questions (True or False)

1. After a detailed bottom-up estimate is performed, these resulting costs are refined to achieve a target price that fits either the owner's purpose or the bidder's assumption of the price needed to get the job.
2. General and supplementary conditions, which describe work required to complete the project but not included in finished work, are shown on blueprints and specifications.
3. General and special conditions, which are heavily influenced by the chosen approach, are heavily affected by time regardless of the physical work accomplished.
4. Temporary facilities and structures are estimated using the same material, labor, and subcontractor estimating procedures used for permanent construction, and large equipment is estimated the same way as supervision: unit costs and anticipated time of use.
5. Costing general conditions as a percent of the cost of the work is another acceptable estimating method.
6. Fees for building permits, road use, and dump fees, as well as project-specific bonds and insurance vary widely in cost and specific prices must be obtained for each project.
7. Some portion of home office overhead expense may be legitimately costed to the project, but a careful and correct presentation of these costs is required to overcome contractual requirements and owner objections.
8. Temporary work has a cost but can produce the benefit of increased productivity and therefore lower cost of the permanent work. This cost–benefit analysis is used to evaluate the impact of different approaches.
9. Once an acceptable cost for an acceptable approach is determined, the resulting time must be accepted.
10. Imperfections in specifications and regional customs can cause very different bidder interpretations of materials to be used.
11. Expectations of probable acceptable cost for a project type may influence bidders to assume higher level of productivity, and lower grade materials and workmanship.

12. Each bidder will have a different appetite and capacity for managing risk and therefore will perceive the project risks differently and add different risk premiums.

13. Up to 10 revisions may be needed to fine-tune the estimate.

14. A large volume of change orders and significant cost over-runs must be anticipated when using fast-track project delivery.

Test Your Understanding

1. You are to build a 20-story office building for a single tenant who has critical time constraints and seeks the earliest possible completion, but cannot accept a significant cost premium. Discuss which approaches, and general and special conditions work items you could explore to achieve the needed schedule acceleration with minimal cost increase.

2. You have a contract with a restaurant chain to build 300 restaurants throughout the United States. The owners try to make each restaurant (and the cost) as close to identical as possible, but you know costs will vary. Discuss which general and special conditions and technical work items will probably be most variable and then discuss approaches to managing this variation.

3. For the same restaurant example, discuss how cost (and cost variation) information can be most effectively organized and persuasively presented to the restaurant owners (who expect no cost variation at all).

CHAPTER
2.7

Time Is Continuous and Has Costs and Impacts

Mass grading operations are increasingly assisted by global positioning systems that can control grade elevation and location.

Time Is Continuous and Has Costs and Impacts

The measure of time, the cost of time, lost opportunities, and momentum

Time is the most difficult element of the triple constraint to communicate effectively

Time is always passing. It cannot be "requested" or stopped. It is not purchased like other resources, but it does have costs and impacts. Since it is "free" but has "costs", time is measured both directly and by its impact.

Time is measured and managed directly with scheduling, and the direct cost impact is measured with cost management. But since time is an element of the triple constraint (scope, time, and cost), and a change in one element changes the other two, time has indirect costs as well. And it is these indirect costs that are most difficult for project participants, particularly project owners and designers, to understand.

Earned value, which integrates cost performance with schedule, can help bridge this gap for those are comfortable with this technique—but most owners and designers are not. The impact of lost opportunities and the productivity increases caused by momentum may have to be explained for each case with cost-benefit analysis—explaining the integrated effects may not be convincing. Other techniques such as using scheduling milestones as freeze dates to force decisions and restrict future changes may also be attempted.

Time Periods Must Suit the Project and Project Participants

Standard time measurement units are recognized by all—but....

Time is measured directly using conventional standard units such as seconds, minutes, hours, days, weeks, months, years, decades, centuries, and millennia. Just like a ruler, this is an objective counting of time. These standard units of time measure are objective facts that are recognized by all. But they give no meaning or purpose to the time measured.

Conventional time measurement periods—for a purpose

Conventional time periods group the standard time measurement units for a purpose.

Examples of conventional time measurement periods:

Employee pay periods—Daily, weekly, bimonthly, monthly. The length of pay periods is customary by country, time, and industry. Once established, these periods strongly affect how productivity is measured. Labor cost information by pay period will be used unless there is a reason (and foresight and money) to measure labor another way. These pay periods have meaning to the employee, personnel managing the project, and accountants.

Accounting periods—Weekly, monthly, quarterly, and annual accounting periods are established by custom, accounting regulation, corporate law, and tax law. The start and end of each period is fixed and will not change for any project. The accountant will know the costs by accounting period, and the project personnel will know work executed by time periods defined by the project tasks. Management effort is required to reconcile costs expended by accounting period and work executed by project time periods. If this reconciliation is not done, the accountant's report will tend to get more attention by the company owners, even though the report does not accurately represent the status of the project.

Seasons—Weather conditions change by season: extremely high heat, freezing temperatures, extremely dry conditions, heavy rains, and high winds are familiar to all who work outside (although not to many office personnel). The seasons will dictate the desirable and possible times to perform activities and become another system of measuring time that is very meaningful to those doing the work.

Time periods that have meaning to multiple project participants should be sought

An accountant may choose a customary period, such as a financial quarter, and state, "This is the answer—I know I am right—I checked my work and the books balance." The field personnel who installed the work may state, "I was there—I know when we started and when we finished." Both may be right for their own purpose, but because common time periods were not used, communication does not occur.

The weekly period is the longest time period that is common to both the accountant and the personnel doing the work. It is, therefore, the period that should be used by all so that communication happens. The accountant should not try to communicate with quarter or year-end figures, nor the project personnel with seasonal or project task completion figures. Using the week will permit both to agree on single objective facts. Agreement on a collection of facts, discussed in project schedule below, is then possible.

Relevant Time Periods Established by Project Participants

Drop-dead dates

"Drop-dead" completion dates exist for projects that are definitely fixed in time. Projects to serve the Olympics, a political election, or part of a war are examples that have no use or value after a specific time. Most projects with drop-dead dates really mean, "We need it done by this date as long as you will not charge me anymore." These often cease to be drop-dead dates once costs are known.

Project funding dates

Project funding will have time both for the funding review process to start and to complete the funding process once started. Both governments and companies will have fiscal years (usually different than calendar years) and authorize a fixed expenditure at the beginning of that year. Financial lending institutions will adjust lending policies one to four times per year, and loan committees will approve specific loan applications every week, 2 weeks, or month. (Very small loans may be approved by a loan officer with no committee approval.)

Project schedule dates

The project schedule is a statement of the intended sequence and duration of activities to complete a project, at an acceptable time and cost. The objective time periods that each project participant use must be summarized into project milestones. Milestones describe events that have meaning to all but do not exactly match any participant's conventional time periods. Examples of milestones are project start, structure complete, weather enclosure complete, heating and cooling complete, climate-controlled environment achieved, and project complete. This requires an effort to prorate fractions of weeks to match the exact dates of the milestones.

| Steel truss erection | *Photo 5 of 5* |

The Cost and Value of Time

The "cost in money" directly caused by time

Time causes costs—personnel and equipment cost money every second they are assigned to a project. The personnel could be assigned to another project or terminated—and the equipment could be assigned to another project or sold.

The owner of the project will also incur costs continually—both on the cost of their personnel involved with the project and on the continual interest cost on their construction loan. Cost will also occur because of the "lost opportunity" cost of not receiving the income and benefits of the completed project.

Lost opportunities caused by time—not to decide is to decide

Each sequence of activities such as designing, obtaining required manufactured products, and constructing a building takes a minimum amount of time. If selection of an approach is started sufficiently early, all options are possible and can be considered. Passage of time will progressively eliminate possible options. For example, an innovative new custom design is possible with unlimited time, but as available time is progressively reduced, a custom but uninnovative design, or reuse of a previously completed design, may become the only available options—by default. And the more rushed options may be both less desirable and more expensive.

Increasing momentum increases productivity

Every activity has an established pace and feel. For construction projects, the fastest pace that the cure times of materials permit and that can be maintained without causing a loss of productivity is usually the most desirable pace. The reason this is true is that the personalities attracted to construction want to move—to get things done. They want to see a lot of material in place fast. Give them this satisfaction, and they will be more content and have fewer problems and expressed dissatisfactions—which increases productivity.

High-productivity expectations increase momentum

High-productivity demands and expectations increase productivity. The saying "if you want something done fast, give it to a busy person" illustrates that once productivity is high, it tends to stay high.

Attention of project participants is focused on fast-moving projects. If there is no time to wait and see what others do, they act—not react. Full attention is devoted to the job. A few repetitions of "Too late it's poured" and "Get moving or we will bury you" focus the mind on rapid execution of essential tasks.

Speed also permits focus on only the important and relevant, avoiding entirely the trivial and unimportant. Petty nonessential grievances and disputes that would have occurred if there was more time than necessary to complete the task never materialize. Communication is improved, the number of items requiring consideration is reduced, and disagreements are minimized. Momentum increases productivity, reduces cost, and improves communication.

These elementary time concepts are the foundation of time management

The concepts discussed in this chapter seem at first elementary and obvious but are the foundation of scientific measurement needed to produce comparable data sets. Believable comparable data sets permit analysis and comparison between different departments and companies analyzing time and cost. The use of these elementary concepts in the time management and scheduling techniques discussed in the next chapters makes success possible. The very common failure to use these techniques precludes this success.

Summary

Time is the most difficult element of the triple constraint to communicate effectively—particularly to project owners and designers. Methods such as cost-benefit analysis for each work item or decision, and establishing milestones that force and confirm decisions may be needed. This communication of the direct and indirect impact of time is particularly critical—time is always passing—so full mid-project recovery of mistakes related to time is seldom possible.

Time should be measured with standard units and in standard periods that permit communication among project participants. Measuring the value and cost of time, the cost of assigned personnel and equipment, the lost opportunities caused by passing time, and productivity increasing momentum can all benefit the project. Management of time can only bring these benefits when started in project planning and continued through execution and control. These "time basics" discussed in this chapter must be integrated into the very powerful techniques of schedule planning and management discussed in the following two chapters to maximize the benefits of these techniques.

Review Questions (True or False)

1. Time has costs and impacts managed and measured with scheduling and cost management.
2. The time impacts of indirect costs are readily understood by the project owners and designers.
3. Time units to measure periods must use both conventional standard units such as days, weeks, and months, and periods that have relevance such as employee pay periods, accounting periods, and seasons.
4. The weekly time period is the longest period common to both accounting and project personnel.
5. Drop-dead dates occur for most projects and must be included in project planning.
6. Financial institutions usually make funding decisions related to project financing once each calendar year quarter.
7. Milestones such as project start, structure complete, weather enclosure, and project complete are frequently effectively used to communicate schedule progress to the owners of the project.

8. The construction management firm performing the project will have time-related equipment and personnel costs, and the owner will also have personnel costs, financing costs, and the lost opportunity cost of delaying the income or benefits of the completed project.

9. Large approach or scope changes can be accomplished anytime in the project if cost can be increased.

10. A fast-paced project that increases momentum also increases productivity and reduces cost and improves communication.

Test Your Understanding

1. For a six-story speculative office building with no committed tenants at the time of construction start, which of the following time constraints would apply: drop-dead dates, project funding dates, or project schedule dates?

2. You wish to complete a 4-year college degree in 4 years earning only the credit hours required. No cost or schedule over-runs are acceptable. With these constraints, when will the opportunity to change majors be lost: second term of the sophomore, junior, or senior year?

3. You are building a project and the project owner has no theoretical construction management knowledge or experience. Which of the following tools could be effectively used to communicate the impact of time on the project: milestones with freeze dates, cost-benefit analysis of select work items, earned value analysis, careful presentation of indirect costs, and the time value of these costs, or a detailed explanation of the impact of the triple constraint.

CHAPTER
2.8

Scheduling and Time Planning also Adjusts and Confirms the Scope and Approach

Large earthwork operations have huge hourly equipment costs. Equipment capacities, and cycle times, and work flow must be planned to optimize productivity.

Scheduling and Time Planning also Adjusts and Confirms the Scope and Approach

Planning an approach that can be made to work

Time planning must look first at the scope and global forces affecting the scope

A rough idea of project timing must be established to determine feasibility prior to project initiation. This involves a higher-level view of the triple constraint and analysis of global forces working on this constraint.

The nature of the scope may establish time constraints—such as a classroom project that must be completed for a new school year, or a factory for new manufactured product that must be launched in the fall. Most projects seek to balance timing and cost and to some extent scope—the needed scope and a very narrow range of acceptable costs frequently (but not always) make time the balancing entry of the triple constraint. The priorities of the triple constraint will be different for each project and must be established early in the planning stage.

Global forces affecting time must then be identified. Cost and risk management analysis can identify innovative design complexities, difficult government approvals, scarce trade labor, long lead equipment orders, and possible strikes or material shortages that may restrict timing possibilities.

Project planning and evaluation requires order of magnitude time estimates

Time planning then must seek order of magnitude time estimates—and these estimates are similar in nature but less quantitatively precise than the order of magnitude cost estimates.

Expert judgment

Expert judgment is guided by historical information tempered by present conditions specific to the contemplated project. An example might be: "university buildings of this approximate scope require 6 months to design, 3 months to obtain permissions, and 18 months to build."

Analogous estimating

Analogous estimating uses more specific comparable projects to estimate time. An example might be: "The last two similar projects were completed in an average of 2 years 4 months. The similar project now being planned should be scheduled for 2 years 2 months."

Parametric estimating

The third, parametric estimating uses measurement and a numerical multiplier. An example might be dormitories are built in about 3 weeks per floor, so this 10-floor dormitory should take about 30 weeks.

Three-point estimates

The fourth, the three-point estimate, uses a weighted average of the most likely optimistic and pessimistic as shown by the formula:

$$\text{Three-point estimate} = \frac{\text{Pessimistic} + 4 \times \text{Most likely} + \text{Optimistic}}{6}$$

The three-point estimate provides a very rough approximation of the center of a normal statistical distribution.

The more quantitatively precise estimating techniques used for cost are rarely used for time. This is true because cost estimating techniques in construction are well developed, and job costing, with the oversight of the accounting department, subjects the achievement of these estimates to extreme scrutiny—producing large credible historical data sets. This accounting oversight could be achieved with earned value for time evaluation, but rarely is—so detailed historical time data sets rarely exist. Also, external factors such as strikes, equipment manufacturing delays, and material shortages have a greater impact on time than on cost—making meaningful project comparisons difficult.

Once feasibility has been determined and a project is initiated, time management begins to use scheduling to plan, execute, and monitor the project.

Building the Schedule to Implement and Communicate the Plan

Scheduling is a tool using graphs and numbers that shows if the estimated decisions together achieve the workable purpose. Scheduling also takes the activities (and their resources established in the estimate) and specifies their relationships—to produce the estimated project duration. Some refer to scheduling programs as project management software, but this is not correct. Scheduling programs focus on time and the integration with the triple constraint. But time management is an important, but only one, aspect of the entire project management process.

Scheduling in construction occurs after cost estimating to use the very detailed activities and resources identified by the estimate—but it is not an afterthought. (Project management in other industries that lack the sophisticated estimating capability of construction performs the schedule before the estimate.) Scheduling is not a separate activity occurring late in the project development process to answer the question: "we know what we want to build, now how long will it take?" Also scheduling will not "keep a project on schedule"—people do that—by determining and managing a workable approach. Scheduling identifies resources and a sequence of activities to be altered to achieve priorities of cost, time, grade of material, and use of limited resources.

Scheduling used to be done by hand (or on a mainframe computer), but such handwork exceeds the patience of most project personnel. So scheduling was given to a specialist—removing the activity from the management mainstream of the project—and thereby losing much of its usefulness. Scheduling tools on personal computer programs now make multiple evaluations of alternate scenarios feasible within the usual time and effort limits—making more widespread participation possible. The discussion below assumes, (without specifically discussing) the use of personal computers in scheduling.

Define all activities and arrange to improve communication

Activities are actions with assigned resources (e.g., personnel, equipment, and cost) and resulting durations and are the basic building blocks of the schedule. All work activities identified in the estimate—installation of the physical components of the building, but also including permissions, administrative work, engineering, and material procurement—must be included in the schedule. The WBS (work breakdown structure) used in the estimate greatly helps define activities, but additional subdivisions are needed to enhance communication and monitoring and control.

Every project participant must be identified and have at least one activity. If a purchase order or a subcontract is issued, even for equipment delivered in a single day, it must be identified in the schedule—so nothing is missed, and to answer the question: "Where's my stuff?". And except for long lead equipment and material fabricated off site, activity durations should be 2 weeks or less to permit effective monitoring and control.

Summarize activities to show relevance to other activities

Because all activities are related to other activities, they must be summarized in a form that has meaning to both the installing party and to others.

For example, when pouring a sidewalk the activities consist of:
1. Propose concrete design mix, obtain design mix approval.
2. Fine grade, install forms, install reinforcing mesh, pour concrete, finish concrete.
3. Strip forms, concrete cure, apply sealer.

These should be summarized to:
1. Concrete Design Mix Determine. (Requires interaction between concrete contractor and engineer.)
2. Sidewalk Install. (Requires prior completion of utility work below sidewalk.)
3. Sidewalk Cure. (Makes area inaccessible to full-weight equipment until cure completion.)

The greater detail excluded from the summary is important to the installer, but not to others.

Every activity has a beginning (predecessor) and an end (with one or more successor(s))

Once all activities have been identified, they are set in order by specifying their relationship to other activities. The project has one starting point and one ending point, and every activity has one or more preceding and one or more succeeding activities. There can be no "orphan activities" that do not have both a predecessor and a successor.

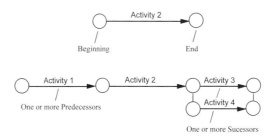

All activities identified in the schedule are necessary for project completion. So, they are broadly related. But "everything is related" does not show the importance of the relationships. The skill and the art of specifying relationships is to show all necessary relationships, by specifying only the most important ones. Nothing can be missed, but the fewest relationships possible will best communicate the meaning and importance of these relationships.

The activities should first be listed in order by system, exactly as the installing contractor will install them. Listing in installation order, but not yet specifying predecessors and successors, will speed the processes and maintain common sense. (This shortcut is limited by the number of activities in sequence one can keep straight in your head.)

Then, the relationship between all activities in all systems is specified and connected. For example, in a single-story building, the earthwork, concrete, steel, and roof installers will dig the hole, install footings, install foundation walls, backfill, install concrete slab, install structural steel, and install roof. The plumbing contractor will install underground rough in, above grade rough in, and later (after finished walls and materials are installed) install fixtures and trim. The relationship between activities in both systems becomes: dig hole, install footing, install foundation walls, back fill, install plumbing rough in below grade, install concrete slab, install structural steel and roof, install above grade rough in, install finished walls and materials, install plumbing fixtures, and trim. Showing listed activities by system "builds the installer's work mentally and on paper." Connecting the activities in all systems "builds the whole project mentally and on paper."

Diagram 2

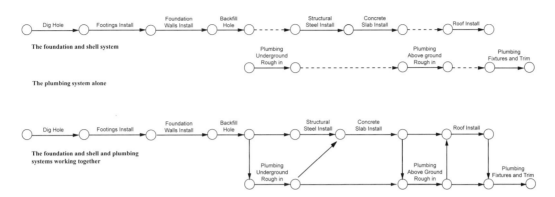

Start and finish relationships must be real and manageable

The connection of the activities described in the previous section can occur in four ways as described below.

Finish-to-start

The start of a successor activity depends on the completion of the predecessor activity. An example might be "complete first floor, then start second floor." This is by far the most common relationship used in construction scheduling. Many simpler schedules are constructed with this technique alone.

Finish-to-finish

The completion of a successor activity depends on the completion of the predecessor activity. An example might be "complete piping loop suspensions structure, then complete piping on this structure." This technique can be used to express some necessary relationships but makes use of lead and lags described below and schedule adjustments trickier.

Start-to-start

The start of a successor activity depends on the start of a predecessor activity. An example might be "notice to proceed, then multiple succeeding activities." This technique is technically possible, but the possibly clearer and more rigorous scheduling technique would identify notice to proceed as an activity with very short duration—that all succeeding activities would follow, thus creating a finish-to-start relationship.

Start-to-finish

Completion of a successor activity depends on the start of a predecessor activity. An example might be "leak test tank, authorize tank testing." Since this technique is confusing and can be more clearly expressed with other techniques, it is seldom used.

The finish-to-start relationship is used for most construction scheduling relationships. After activities have been identified, the preliminary determination of relationships is almost always shown as a finish-to-start relationship. Addition of leads and lags, as described below, can reflect real-word realities and management's preferences.

Lead, lag, and float can adjust the schedule and absorb shocks
The skillful can build a robust schedule that seldom needs adjustment

For all but the smallest projects, multiple trades work on multiple tasks for most of the project duration. Many finish-to-start relationships can be overlapped—successors start when the predecessors are only partially complete. The length of this overlap is called the lead, and can be used both to reflect the way projects are efficiently run and to accelerate the schedule. But care must be exercised so that leads do not compromise chemical cure times or produce congested work sites that reduce productivity.

In contrast, a lag delays the start of a successor activity. Lag can adjust a schedule for constraints or potential problem management such as likely bad weather, probable congested work areas, or subcontractors unlikely to make their scheduled commitments. Lag can be used to strategically inject float at potential problem areas.

A sequence of activities that defines the total project duration is called the critical path. Each and every duration change of any activity on this path produces a commensurate change in the overall schedule duration. Multiple sequences could tie in length, and all ties would be critical paths.

All sequences not on a critical path will have float. Float is the length of time a noncritical sequence can increase before becoming critical. Float, therefore, acts as a shock absorber for these noncritical sequences. And a carefully constructed schedule will strategically locate the float in the areas of highest risk to produce a robust schedule. Multiple adverse performances on the noncritical sequences can produce no adverse effect on the overall project schedule.

Resources Assigned to Activities Can Show the Impact of Time on Cost

Resource driven schedules are a powerful management tool

Resources are executers of an activity, usually in the same form as the estimate: labor, material, equipment, and subcontractors. These resources and estimated quantities from the estimate are transferred to the activities in the schedule. For all controlled activities, the estimated quantities and the resources assigned determine the activity's duration.

Structural steel and bar joist erection—The Wheaton Bible Church structure used structural steel framing and bar joists and deck. Since the structure had multiple roof levels, both pitched and flat, the erection sequence had to be carefully planned and scheduled. For each section of the building, structural steel was placed, then racked to plumb and square, and then connections welded and high-strength bolts torqued to specification. The order of these operations must be planned for each section of the building, and for all sections together. This planning requires a working knowledge of structural engineering   *Photo 1 of 4*

Working calendars define and limit resource availability

Establishing durations for individual activities must be proceeded by establishing a working calendar for the project—showing the number of hours to be worked for each day of the project. This is an annual calendar for the specific project location that specifies the number of hours to be worked per week (5 8-hour shifts totaling of 40 hours per week), and nonworking time due to seasonal weather, holidays, and other nonworking time observed such as hunting, fishing, farm planting, and harvesting.

One Normal Work Calendar

S	M	T	W	TH	F	S
				1	2	3
4	5	6	7	8	9	10
11	12	13	14	15	16	17
18	19	20	21	22	23	24
25	26	27	28	29	30	31

8 hours per day, 5 day work week

8th is fishing opening day, so 8th and 9th are not worked

30th is a National Holiday and not worked

19 day x 8 hours = 152 man hours

Total man hours: 152 per month

Diagonal line means not a work day   Blank means work day

One More Agressive Work Calendar

S	M	T	W	TH	F	S
				1	2	3
4	5	6	7	8	9	10
11	12	13	14	15	16	17
18	19	20	21	22	23	24
25	26	27	28	29	30	31

10 hours per day, 5 day work week

4 hours per day, Saturday

Same days off as above except since the 8th and 9th are fishing days, noone will work on Saturday, the 10th

19 day x 10 hours = 190
3 days x 4 hours = 12
Total man hours: 202 per month

Many more calendars can be developed for the work hour and nonworking customs for the project—but they must be real. These calendars must show what all project participants will do—not what one would like them to do. The farming, hunting, fishing days, and other holidays employees assume are not worked in the project area must be shown as nonworking on the calendar. If the calendar requires overtime or shift differential pay, this additional cost must be included in the estimate.

Labor is the resource that most commonly drives the schedule

The most common assigned resource is labor of the required skill and capacity. The man-hours for an activity from the estimate and the number of workers assigned will determine the duration of the activity. For example, if an activity is estimated to take 40 man-hours to complete and one man is assigned (working 40 hours per week), the task will be completed in 1 week. If five men are assigned to the same activity, the task will be completed in 1 day.

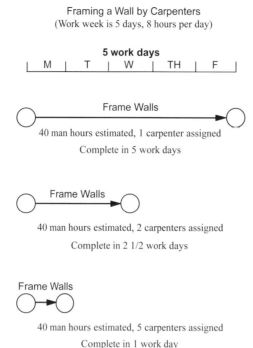

Framing a Wall by Carpenters
(Work week is 5 days, 8 hours per day)

This example shows how estimated quantities and assigned resources determine the duration for controlled activities. In the real world, the job site density produced by 5 additional carpenters must be determined to not reduce productivity, and thus increase duration and cost. Such common sense and practical knowledge must be used at all times. The schedule must reflect building a real project, not a numbers game.

Equipment, if critical and scarce, can also drive the schedule

Scarce equipment can be another assigned resource. For example, if a high-cost specialized paving machine for which no identical machine can be obtained in time for the project is needed, the resource of one paving machine, the hourly production of the machine, and the estimated quantity to be installed determine the activity duration. Small tools and equipment, which are almost never scarce, are not assigned as resources.

Material is rarely an assigned resource

Material can be, but is not frequently, an assigned resource. Assigning material as a resource makes sense when it is sufficiently large or heavy to make transportation to the work area limited by the available transportation means. For example, if 10,000 cubic yards of a material were required, but the haul road could only handle 1,000 cubic yards per day, material might be assigned as a resource. (Treating material procurement—purchasing, engineering, fabrication, and delivery—as an activity, not a resource, is common and used on most projects.)

Cost is frequently an assigned resource, but rarely drives the schedule

Cost is another resource that can be, but seldom is, used to determine duration—at least obviously. If the owner's money to pay for a project is only available at certain intervals, the project can be scheduled so that the dollar value of construction completed is always slightly less than the money available. This is very seldom used obviously, but can be used as a management tool if the owner has intermittently available funds. Assigning money as a resource—not to determine duration but to project cash flow needs—is frequently done.

It should be noted that resource assignment requires detailed knowledge of the estimated resource for this project at this time. This can only be obtained efficiently and precisely from the estimate.

Schedules made with only intuition and general historical knowledge of past projects without project-specific information cannot predict time, evaluate allocation of resources, or help manage a project. Such schedules, however, are common and of little value.

Time for controllable activities can be adjusted for schedule improvement

The desired time of each activity and the total project is estimated during the development of the workable approach. However, in scheduling, the real time of the activities and the project is determined as the result of the resources assigned to activities. If this resulting time proves unacceptable for your purpose, it must be altered by changing resources, or predecessors and successors as described below. Arbitrary assignment of durations to controlled activities has no basis in fact, and is wishful thinking—but not prediction and management.

Time for uncontrollable activities be managed by adjusting related activities

Activities controlled by the owner, outside vendors, chemical cure time, or weather will have specified dates or times. For example, a school remodeling will start after the year's last day of classes, and be complete before the start of the next school year. Some products will have a production date set by the manufacturer. Some excavation and all landscape planting cannot be done in frozen ground. Some of these fixed dates are unavoidable. But when a fixed date is specified, all ability to manage that activity is gone. So, fixed dates should be avoided whenever possible—and this includes most subcontractor/vendor activities.

Group Activities into Bite-Sized Pieces to Aid Understanding and Monitoring

Job site activities should have maximum durations of 2-weeks

Every job site activity scheduled must have a duration of a maximum of 2 weeks to have reality to most people, and permit monitoring during construction sufficiently early to take necessary corrective action. When a longer activity must be subdivided into 2 week durations, use readily identifiable breaks, such as "Pour concrete floor level 2 northwest," not "pour ¼ of concrete floor." The 2-week maximum duration does not apply to off-site wait times controlled by others. For example, if equipment is to be produced on a specified date 3 months in the future, the 3-month activity need not be broken into 2-week segments.

Subprojects and milestones help define activity groupings

Similar to the 2-week maximum duration for on-site job activities mentioned above, breaking a longer schedule into bite-sized pieces of grouped activities increases understanding and eases monitoring. Subprojects are grouping of activities that have a natural relationship. Groupings by a team or crew of people, at the same time, at a specific location, or working on a shared task help people recognize: "Oh! There I am, that's my work."

Milestones designate the start and end of a subproject, or other groupings that have a natural relationship. The milestones for these groupings must be unmissable and should be identified by an event that takes no special knowledge or information. Examples might include activities such as "permanent electrical power on," or "permanent conditioned air delivered."

Four useful subprojects are
1. Permissions, such as permits, and project-specific licenses.
2. Preparation such as finance, project specific insurance, and design completion.
3. Material order, engineering, fabrication, and delivery.
4. Job site construction.

Subprojects for the construction portion of a building construction might be

1. Site preparation.
2. Foundation and structure.
3. Weather enclosure.
4. Interior construction.
5. Final site work.

In all cases, all activities in the whole project are still related as if no subproject existed, but the grouping will aid in understanding and later monitoring.

Activity groupings meaningful to work groups can add clarity

Predecessor and successor relationships link all tasks in a meaningful way, but graphically grouping the tasks in areas of the schedule that roughly correspond to work groups and responsibility can greatly aid understanding. One such group is permissions (which are mostly secured by office personnel—and started in preconstruction), material order and fabrication (which can be started in preconstruction by office personnel with the assistant of field supervision—including review of shop drawings and submittals by both office and field personnel), and on-site construction (which involves continuous field supervision and frequent project management oversight).

Arranging groups in the sequence of execution graphically communicates the past sequences—which also aids in understanding. Many other such groupings segregating on-site and external activities are possible and can increase schedule relevance to all project participants.

Production Limits Must Be Observed

Scarce resources, maximum job site density chemical cure time all limit possibilities

All projects have production limits, either absolute production limits determined by scarce resources or chemical cure time of materials, or desirable production limits to achieve maximum job site productivity. The scheduling tool will show the cumulative effect of all the individual decisions made when determining predecessors and successors and assigning resources to activities, and determine if all decisions together exceed the production limits.

Critical path—the production limit for the project

The critical path is the series of activities from the start to the end of the project that determines the project duration. For each day one of these activities changes, the overall project duration changes by one day also. The critical path, therefore, forms the production limit for the entire project, given the selected approach, and the estimated and assigned activities, relationships, and resources. This path will be critical only for these predecessors, successors, and resources. If any of are changed, an entirely new set of activities could form a new critical path. (For very technical scheduling, the critical path weighted and driven by resources is called the critical chain. But the critical chain is more commonly also referred to as a critical path.)

Does the Approach Work? If Not, How Can it Be Corrected

Reports from the schedule show the impact of previous decisions and assumptions

The schedule tool will produce reports that summarize all of the decisions made for each resource to show man power, material, equipment, and money used for all activities for each unit of time—hour, day, week, month. Although the assignments and decisions were made when assembling this schedule, the cumulative effect of all decisions was not immediately apparent. With these reports, over allocations of specific resources can be determined, so necessary actions can be taken.

Structural steel and bar joist erection   *Photo 2 of 4*

Carpenter Allocation Report

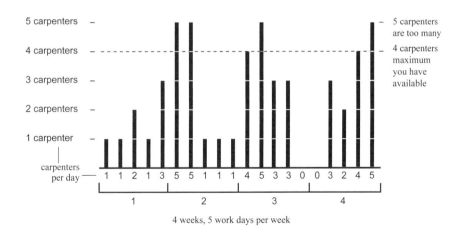

4 weeks, 5 work days per week

Carpenter allocation is produced by the decisions made about estimated quantities, assigned resources, sequences of activities, and the working calendar. This report shows the cumulative result of all decisions made for all activities. There is no other way (within the normal limits of time and patience) to show the effect of many decisions made at and for different times.

If there are only four carpenters of the required skill available for work on the project, or four carpenters is the maximum for the project area without loss of production, changes must be made. If a constant steady crew size is desired, changes are also required. Changes to activity sequences, assignment of activities to other parties, change in resource quantity assignment, or change in working calendars are a few ways to level the carpenter allocation. The scheduling tool allows you to instantly try these adjustments and see the results.

The scheduled project duration must match the planned approach

Scheduling is usually thought to be about time, "How long will the project take?" But scheduling is not just lines drawn on paper. That is only wishful thinking. As described above, time shows the results of the decisions made when developing the workable approach. It is not, "How long will it take?" but, "With the known facts and assumption made, what is the resulting time?" This will either confirm that that the workable approach achieves the required duration or show the problems and opportunities for correction.

Adjustments for Schedule Improvement can Impact Cost and Quality

If the resulting schedule does not achieve the required duration, minor modifications can make improvements, while staying within the limits of your planned approach as described below.

Overlap activities—adjust lead and lag times

The predecessor and successor relationships were first specified as end-to-end relationships—one cannot start until the other is finished. But this is not how things work in the real world. Frequently, some of the succeeding activity can start before all of the preceding activity is completed. For example, a wall cannot be painted until it is built, but some walls can be painted before all walls are built. This overlap of predecessors and successors can accelerate the schedule, but must recognize the real-world and project-specific production limits. Practical knowledge of how things are done also limits the overlap. A minimum of a 3-day head start (3 days of work available for the succeeding activity) is also a practical management limit.

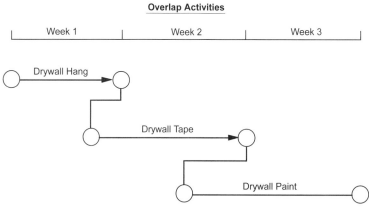

You can not tape drywall until it is hung. But, you can begin taping some of the hung drywall before all drywall is hung.

Fast-track scheduling uses leads to accelerate the schedule

Most schedules have some leads, but fast-track construction adds additional leads or increases the length of existing leads to accelerate the schedule. One common example would be to design, permit, and start construction of the foundation before the completion of the superstructure design and costing.

Fast-track scheduling has higher risks, can produce higher costs, and requires careful analysis of construction means and methods and job site density limits. Schedule compression can increase job site density beyond productive limits that can both increase the cost of labor and decrease quality. And since needed information is by nature incomplete when needed in the fast-track method, additional management time is needed to fill in the blanks—assumptions will be used and mistakes will be made.

Resources can be added—but there are limits

Additional resources assigned an activity will shorten the activity duration. Resource assignments up to the maximum available, while still within the job site density production limits, can be added without increased cost. Another possibility is to assign a different resource to the same task (a different trade or an outside vendor).

Resource leveling can manage scarce resources, job site density, or achieve desired crew sizes

Scheduling typically seeks to manage activities and resources to optimize efficiency and achieve a target completion date. Maintaining a scarce resource or an assembled work force continually on the project can ease management and increase productivity. Resource usage reports can identify times of over or under allocation, and assigned resources can be adjusted (leveled) to achieve the desired constant usage. Leveling may be necessary and desirable for the construction managers but should be communicated carefully to the owner to avoid the perception that the construction manager is placing their interests before the owner's.

Crashing the schedule—throwing additional resources at the problem

When fast-track scheduling still does not achieve the desired schedule acceleration, more resources, usually manpower (in the form of additional manpower per shift, additional shifts, or use of overtime), can be added. Crashing almost always increases cost and decreases quality—so is only used when timing is so important that cost and quality can be accepted as balancing entries.

Predecessors and successors—consider other possibilities

Assigned predecessor and successor relationships were the best planned choice, but not always the only choice. For example, for interior construction wall rough in, the plumber (who has larger pipes that must slope to drain) should work before the electrician (who has smaller conduit that does not slope). With coordination and good tradesmen, however, the electrician could work first. Such a change can change the critical path and the whole project duration.

Working calendar can be altered—a big decision that probably will affect cost

Working calendars can be changed to work more hours per week to shorten the project duration. The ability to achieve these improvements without additional cost is governed first by the work and compensation practices in the project area. Shift pay premiums, overtime costs, and supervision and utility cost for extended work hours all impose additional costs. The work limits per man per week that can be worked without loss of production and increase in errors is another limit (about 50 hours per week).

Critical chain project management

A mechanistic application of CPM without considering limiting resources usually fails disastrously in the real world where resources are limited and constraints abundant. This chapter describes use of CPM with applied resources and real-world buffering techniques to produce a resilient and achievable schedule. This integration of resources and addition of buffers to achieve an optimal real world solution is formalized in the process of critical chain project management. Critical chain management developed in the late 1990s using tools and techniques to achieve the optimization this chapter describes.

Summary

Some idea of required time is needed to determine feasibility and initiate a project. Order of magnitude time estimates similar to cost estimates, but less quantitatively precise, provide these approximations.

Scheduling is the graphic and mathematical tool that shows the time that results from the estimated workable approach. Itemization of activities, relationship between activities, and resource assignment produce a schedule that can be made to work. Resources assigned to activities relate the planned time to planned cost. And graphically grouping activities in the schedule to roughly resemble the responsible workgroups aids clarity and communication. The next chapter describes how to make this workable schedule work well in the real world.

Review Questions (True or False)

1. Project planning and evaluation requires order of magnitude time estimates that can be obtained by expert judgment, analogous estimating, or parametric estimating.

2. Scheduling is a tool using graphs and numbers that shows if the estimated decisions together achieve the workable purpose.

3. Scheduling in construction is performed before the cost estimate to identify resources and sequence of activities to achieve the priorities of cost, time, and grade of material.

4. The schedule should identify activities with maximum 2-week durations that show relations and relevance to other activities.

5. Every activity has a beginning (with a predecessor) and an end (with one or more and successors).

6. Activities may be related by finish-to-start, finish-to-finish, start-to-start, or start-to-finish with start-to-finish being by far the most common.

7. Leads, lags, and float, if carefully managed, can adjust the schedule, absorb shocks, and produce a more robust and achievable schedule.

8. The working calendar must include the quantity, wage rates, and premium time wage differentials (if any) of the labor included in the estimate.

9. Labor, material, equipment, and costs are all frequently used as resources to drive the schedule.

10. Subprojects and milestones can help define meaningful activity groupings and add clarity.

11. Scheduling tools can be used to identify and manage resource usage and develop cash flow projections

12. Crashing the scheduled and changing working calendars can accelerate the schedule, usually at no cost.

Test Your Understanding

1. If a predictable, achievable schedule that requires minimal mid-project revisions is sought, what tools and techniques will be most useful, and which must be avoided.

2. Schedule acceleration with little or no cost increase can be achieved by which of the following:
   Fast tracking
   Adjusting leads and lags
   Adding resources
   Resource leveling
   Crashing
   Alternate work calendars

3. Make a precedence diagram (sequence and relationship of activities but without durations) to make a meal consisting of a hamburger and a can of soup. Include acquisition of materials (ingredients) assembly of equipment (dishes, pans and utensils), cooking and cleanup. Schedule so that cooking the hamburger and soup are finished at the same time.

CHAPTER
2.9

Construction Project Delivery Methods Continue to Change

The water truck's distribution of water can both control dust and manage the soil moisture content for workability and strength.

Construction Project Delivery Methods Continue to Change

Increasing distribution of knowledge alters responsibilities and relationships

A single master builder—an old delivery method phased out by technical progress

From 1900 to 1950, the architect was the master builder—designing the building, its structural system, piping, and electrical systems. These buildings were constructed with basic materials and methods, and employed much on-site fabrication. Concrete, plaster, and paint would be mixed on site, and millwork would be built in place.

On-site assembly could be done by three contractors: a piping contractor, an electrical contractor, and a general contractor. Trade skills to manipulate these generic materials were extensive and inclusive. For example, a "trowel tradesman" would place and finish concrete, install block, brick, cut stone, and plaster. Specified performance and installation precision were below today's expectations. For example, the old plaster on clay tile wall construction accepted straightness variation of 3/4″ in 10 feet, but present drywall construction seeks straightness within 1/8″ in 10 feet.

Knowledge became increasingly distributed after 1950

Knowledge became increasingly embedded in products. Assemblies designed and fabricated off site frequently included patented components and processes. Smaller and more economical microprocessing devices were installed in many components—such as hot water heaters, HVAC units, fire alarm systems, and security systems. Proprietary patented chemicals improved concrete mixes and surface treatment, and coatings on architectural surfaces such as curtain walls. And roofs became "roofing systems"—with all detailing and connection details engineered and specified by the manufacturer.

This distribution of knowledge produced increasing specialization, with accompanying specialized channels of distribution. Manufacturers sought to position their proprietary product as the "premium solution" and therefore jealously guarded their detailed technical information—which limited the architects' possible knowledge and design confidence.

At the beginning of this evolution, large format design drawings were supplemented by specification books that added more precise quantitative data and installation instructions. But if the bidding vendor for a proprietary product also designed that product, they had already written the specification. This self-serving circular arrangement made specification books for proprietary or contractor designed products less necessary. Although boilerplate generic technical data could still be bound in a specification book, the selection of a manufacturer's model and features determined what would be built. (Some government and private organization procurement policies prohibit specific product selection and require generic specifications. Clever manufacturers circumvent this requirement by writing specifications that appear generic but require features that their product alone can provide.)

This distribution of knowledge and design responsibility required more collaboration and cooperation among the architect, contractor, and material vendors. But this collaboration could not be just a talking shop—someone had to lead the project. And who could and would lead was determined by the parties' capacity, temperament, and credentials, as described below.

Who Can and Will Take Responsibility and Lead the Project?

What a party can do, wants to do, and thinks they should do limit possibilities

Needed capabilities are developed slowly and with effort

Projects live on cash flow, which can come from either equity or credit. Paying for mistakes requires money. Absence of both equity and credit prevents assumption of risk and responsibility for many project activities, such as cost control.

Also, there are established channels of distribution for products, which take years to establish properly. Establishing accounts and credit can be done in months, but proper ordering of materials does take knowledge and experience, which takes years to learn. And trust must be established before the distributor will release needed portions of the proprietary information. This process cannot be rushed even by very large and well-capitalized buyers. The buyer may be big and rich, but the product sales firms are often (not always) small and have one speed—usually cautious and slow.

An assembled workforce is required for optimal results. This includes individuals with certain skill sets, knowledge, talents, and shared cultural values. This again cannot be assembled quickly. An impromptu pickup team will not perform as well.

Temperament must be appropriate

Some may have the pioneer spirit with the motivation, drive, appetite, and capacity to bear the risk necessary to push and lead. Others think and talk about things that others must make happen. Others may seek to avoid all risk—and perform an advisory role. People also see themselves as suited to a certain type of work—professional or trade.

The project management process in construction involves much repetition. This includes both trade work—such as a block layer who lays 400 blocks a day, 5 days per week, for a 30-year career—to cost estimators who count and measure millions of times or schedulers who integrate vast amounts of job cost data into a scheduling program. Those who are unwilling to do this type of work cannot participate in the cost and scheduling parts of the project management process.

Credentials are mandated by regulation and law

The architects' credential, which consists of a prescribed education followed by relevant experience, and a test, is the strongest design credential for building construction. It is a government granted license to design, supervise, and certify building and structural work, and to supervise mechanical and electrical designs. This credential is usually legally required for commercial and industrial projects. Licensed interior designers have made inroads into the residential and portions of the commercial design in some states.

Contractors are legally entitled to rely on the architects' design. Obvious errors must be identified, but independent verification of the adequacy of the design is not required.

Engineers have a similar credentialing system but focus on a more narrow discipline—such as mechanical engineering, electrical engineering, structural engineering, and the diverse branches of civil engineering. An engineer's license may substitute for an architect's on civil or strictly industrial projects. And an engineer may take the lead on industrial projects, such as power plants or some manufacturing facilities, with an architect performing a supplementary role for design of the building portion.

General contractor and subcontractor government licensing requirements—and value of the license—vary hugely by governmental unit and location. Some require an extensive course of study followed by a test, others just a test, some just a background check, and others require only a signature on a form at the building department. This license is required to operate as a general contractor and obtain building permits.

Factory certification of installers for specific components or systems is increasingly common. Training usually consists of less than 2 days of instruction, but can include instruction of up to 3 months. This can be required for coating products, roofing systems, door hardware components, and mechanical/electrical components and systems. A firm must have these factory-certified employees on staff to receive a factory certification of an installation—or even to purchase material.

Design Now Involves Many Specialists

Distribution of knowledge is an accelerating force

The AIA once enforced a fixed design fee structure

Some of the forces distributing design responsibility are described above, but there were two major events that accelerated this trend. Before 1978, architects' fees ranging from 7% of construction cost for a small commercial building to 18% for a complex building—such as a hospital—were fixed and enforced by the AIA(American Institute of Architects). These fees included architectural, structural, civil, and mechanical/electrical design, as well as field inspection and administration throughout construction. This relationship also required that the architect establish building cost budgets. If the bid costs were over this budget, the architect had to redesign the project with no additional compensation. This resulted in cost consciousness and cost estimators on staff.

Also prior to 1978, the AIA manual of practice prohibited architects from having any financial interest in construction. This prohibited direct participation in design-build project delivery.

This monopoly was broken in 1978

In 1978, the U.S. Supreme Court determined that this ban on price competition constituted illegal price fixing under the Sherman Antitrust Act. Entering a recession that lasted until 1982, the architects did not fight back—and repackage services to maintain fees and value. Instead, they drastically cut fees—some from 7% to 2% of commercial building cost.

To achieve this severe cost reduction, architects began giving up responsibility for everything except programming and artistic aspects. Architectural college education required technical courses in strength of materials, structures, and building environmental technology, and mechanical and electrical systems were reduced to less than 15% of the curriculum. An architect who showed any aptitude or interest in technical details was (basically) barred from promotion to the highest levels of the firm—and was the first to be let go in a downturn. Responsibility for site inspection and contract administration was greatly reduced, and responsibility for cost containment was abandoned.

"Scope drawings" forcing the rest of the design and engineering on the general contractors and subcontractors resulted. At first, many coasted on their previous knowledge—"do it like we did it last time"—but this was an inadequate mid and long-term solution. Contractor design skills for specific tasks increased.

These reductions in responsibilities and competencies reduced the architects' meaningful contribution to parts of scope definition. All cost and schedule management aspects of project management were abandoned by the architects. But an excellent design idea that cannot be executed at the owner's required time and cost cannot be used.

Also in 1978, an architect whose membership in the AIA was suspended for design-build violations sued for and won reinstatement. This dimmed the previously bright line between design and construction and made design-build and other forms of distributed design more accepted and common.

Design leadership was then up for grabs

Distributed design responsibility compromised the architect's traditional leadership of the design process. But design and project leadership is still required and will happen either on purpose or by default.

Suggestions about a tipping point of control from other fields help illustrate when control is lost. After World War I, the defeated Ottoman Empire began reordering into new countries. Calouste Gulbenkian, an Armenian with a 5% stake in the area's oil industry, was able to substantially influence the government and industry development in that area for decades. The ability to introduce or block resolutions and agreements had a much larger effect than the 5% ownership would suggest.

The Security and Exchange Commission, which regulates stocks and securities and corporate governance structures and financial reporting, has established that 7% ownership of a company constitutes control. And when military theorists try to determine the portion of a nation's population that must be destroyed by nuclear war to defeat the country, a figure of 20% is common. At this point, the connections and relations between people and organizations necessary to make the country run stop functioning.

The percentage of the construction value designed by each party for 63-story retail, office, and residential high-rise designed from 1979 to 1981 and constructed from 1981 to 1984 illustrates the design responsibility distribution after 1978.

| **Project Work Items Costs (without fee)** | | **Percent of Total** | **Engineering by** | |
CSI Div.	**Work Description**		**Contractor**	**Architect**
1	General conditions	5.08%	5.08%	
2	Demolition	0.01%		0.01%
	Excavation	1.50%		1.50%
	Dewatering	0.06%	0.06%	
	Sheeting/Shoring—Bracing	3.36%	3.36%	
	Caissons	2.60%		2.60%
	Earthwork—Hand	0.06%		0.06%
	Lawns & Seeding	0.05%		0.05%
	Parking Lot Striping	0.01%		0.01%
3	Concrete Structure	8.71%		8.71%
	Reinforcing Steel	9.18%		9.18%
	Concrete Walks & Curbs	0.14%		0.14%
4	Masonry	1.17%		1.17%
	Granite Curtain Wall	10.11%	10.11%	
	Travertine (Interior)	0.41%		0.41%
5	Structural Steel	2.15%		2.15%
	Metal Deck	0.45%		0.45%
	Miscellaneous. Metals	1.16%		1.16%
6	Finish Carpentry	4.33%		4.33%
7	MembraneRoofing, Accessories	0.92%	0.92%	
	Membrane Waterproofing, Damp Proofing	0.22%		0.22%
	Metal Flashing—Thru Wall	0.10%		0.10%
	Safing Insulation	0.09%		0.09%
	Window Wash Track	0.58%	0.58%	
8	Glass & Glazing Curtain Walls	6.85%	6.85%	
	Glass Entrances, Doors	1.12%		1.12%
	Aluminum Canopy with Canvas	0.05%		0.05%
	Hollow Metal Doors and Frames	0.30%		0.30%
	Revolving Doors	0.38%		0.38%
	Rolling Doors & Shutter	0.05%		0.05%
	Finish Hardware	0.43%		0.43%
9	Gypsum Drywall	6.75%		6.75%
	Acoustical Ceiling	0.09%		0.09%

	Ceramic Tile	1.20%		1.20%
	VCT Floor	0.07%		0.07%
	Carpet	0.07%		0.07%
10	Specialties	0.59%		0.59%
11	Residential Appliances	1.00%		1.00%
13	Swimming Pools	0.20%	0.20%	
14	Dock Leveler/Bumper	0.01%		0.01%
	Elevators	6.25%	6.25%	
15	HVAC	6.70%		6.70%
	Plumbing	4.26%		4.26%
	Fire Protection	2.32%	2.32%	
16	Electrical	8.86%		8.86%
	TOTAL	100.00%	35.74%	64.26%

The items indicating engineering by contractor only list items that were entirely engineered by the contractor. Items that were partially engineered, such as the electrical switch gear, or that were models selected from a catalog, such as residential appliances and dock levelers, were left in the architect engineering column. Adjustment for these partially engineered items would increase the portion engineered by the contractor.

With the contractor engineering over 35% of the project, by any measure described above—5%, 7%, or 20%—the tipping point has been passed and the architect has lost design control. Since there is no incentive or trend to regain this control, this new reality must be recognized in both contractual (or at least formally recognized) distribution of design responsibility and selection of the appropriate project delivery method.

Major Participants Have One Nature
Recognize and work within these limits

Architects see the project as a part of a global picture

Architects have a global, outward looking, generalist view of a building—and its relation to the building's surroundings, current building fashions, and impact on posterity. This view is essential to produce a building that meets the needs of the user, community, conforms to governing laws and codes, and has pleasing aesthetics. But for project delivery, if this outward looking view is not managed, it will persist throughout the project—much to the detriment of focused project scope management. A constantly changing scope will produce cost over-runs, schedule extensions, and frequently project failure.

Architects have an essential credential, no capital, little appetite for risk, and a decreasing technical knowledge or interest—particularly in mechanical/electrical. Big name rock star architects can seek to maximize cost (since fee can be billed as a percentage of construction cost, and higher grade materials, even if unnecessary, may be chosen) and are little concerned with schedule management. "Real world" architects may be conscious of the owner's cost requirements, but lack the knowledgeable personnel and information to actively manage project cost and schedule.

Engineers solve defined problems

Engineers are similar to architects in many respects, except will focus more on detailed execution of the specific task rather than a continual outward looking view. Mechanical, electrical, and civil engineers for buildings tend to seek an optimal solution from the viewpoint of their specific discipline, but this may conflict with the optimal cost and schedule requirements of the project.

And seeking a carefully researched design, engineers are frustrated when vendors refuse to provide needed product information. Abandonment of that part of design frequently results.

Engineers performing civil engineering work unrelated to building work with well understood generic materials frequently have an excellent grasp of the technical execution of the work, as well as cost and schedule.

Contractors get things done

Contractors focus on execution and results. This move from the big picture to the specific is the opposite of the natural tendency of the architect who best views the big picture. Contractors are motivated by continuing new work volume, new challenges, and money. They have capital, appetite for risk, but little or no conceptual architectural design aptitude. A very few can think conceptually, permitting involvement from the project start, but input for most usually starts no earlier than when the concept design is in progress.

Technical knowledge and credentials vary hugely. Some may have on-the-job experience but no formal training. Others may have extensive education and professional engineering credentials sufficient for full legal design responsibility for specific tasks. Careful selection is required to match contractor qualifications and capabilities to project needs.

Material and equipment vendors use their knowledge and skills to maximize sales

Vendors of basic materials and methods such as lumber, concrete, and nonproprietary supplies are "minding their store"—taking and competently processing orders and focus much of their efforts on relations with customers.

Vendors of proprietary products seek to distinguish themselves from a commodity and position their product as a preferred solution. Excellent technical knowledge—and writing the specifications and provision of drawing details that the architect can represent as their own work—reduces competition. Some may have big picture cost and schedule knowledge, but this should not be expected normally. Vendors of propriety products are frequently part of international conglomerates with capital sufficient to bear all reasonable associated risks.

Project Leadership and Risk go Together—Decide Who Gets It

With leadership comes responsibility—the buck must stop somewhere. Every decision has cost and schedule consequences, and mistakes will be made. Only the project owner, GC(general contractor)/ CM (construction manager), and some subcontractors and vendors have the capital to bear cost risk.

The owner hires the project team to transfer some portion of this risk. One-project owners usually do not have the temperament, appetite, or skills to manage much risk—and may seek to transfer as much risk as possible. Multi-project owners may seek to retain and manage much more risk. The CMAA (Construction Management Association of America) finds that automotive, chemical, energy, food processing, health care, military, municipal, and gas and oil owners all retain more than 60% of the project risk. The CM/GC and hired subcontractors and vendors must directly assume the rest of the risk—and must lead the project to manage the risks of all parties.

The project leader must manage scope, cost, and schedule at the same time

Successful project management requires simultaneous management of the triple constraints of scope, cost, and schedule. This management must start when a potential project is analyzed for feasibility and continues through every step of the project until completion and closeout. Since the CM/GC has sole responsibility for cost and schedule, early and continuous involvement is essential. This involvement, plus the capacity to bear risk and a "can do" temperament, makes the CM/GC the most frequent project leader of choice.

| Structural steel and bar joist erection | *Photo 3 of 4* |

Present Project Delivery Systems—an Evolving Work in Progress
The owner's desire and capacity to manage and the need for early design completion influence possibilities

Design-Bid-Build

Bids for cost and schedule only—proposals add qualifications and suggestions

Bids provide a cost and a time of completion only. Qualifications, exclusions, and suggestions of even the most minor nature may require rejection of the bid. Bids are used on hard bid unit cost and hard bid lump sum delivery methods.

Proposals also include the cost and time of completion but accept modifications and welcome suggestions for improvement, and alternate means and methods that provide cost, schedule, or quality advantages. Proposals are used for construction management and design-build delivery methods.

Hard bid unit costs that are totaled to form hard bid total costs

With this system, the project scope and transportation distances are identified and the design engineer establishes work line items with quantities. The contractor bids unit cost for each line item, and the extended costs are then totaled to form one lump sum bid. Final quantities are measured, and compensation is adjusted at the end of the project.

This system is used successfully for road construction. Since well known basic materials and methods are used, the design engineer—with supplemental laboratory testing—can fully design and engineer the project. The owner's staff supplemented by consulting engineers and the contractor with the usual education, credentials, and experience effectively manage this delivery method. The contractor's variables are a skilled workforce, equipment, material and transportation cost, and knowledge of the project's soil and moisture conditions.

More complex projects—that include proprietary equipment and contractor-furnished design—render this system infeasible in the United States. The British use this method for costing of entire commercial buildings. But British architects demonstrate and value knowledge of building technology more than their American counterparts. For example, British design competitions include categories in technology—a practice unknown in America. However, British surveyors (the British term for cost estimators) who have immigrated to the United States suggest adoption of their system does not promise improvement.

Lump sum hard bid

For civil projects that still consist primarily of basic materials and methods, such as locks and dams, lump sum hard bids still may be feasible. Projects such as multifamily residential where low costs are valued over quality or schedule may also use this delivery method. However, contractor input into the constructibility of the design is becoming increasingly important—and extreme long lead material order times make early contractor involvement desirable. But this system, which delays contractor input until after design completion, bid, and contract award, prohibits such early involvement—which limits the range of projects suitable for this delivery method.

For decades, lump sum hard bids for building construction have been recognized as unfeasible for projects that seek to optimize the triple constraint of scope, time, and cost at the same time—because of the significant contractor performed design work that will be furnished after the bid. When this system fails, it lays the groundwork for massive claims for extras, schedule delay, disputes, lawsuits, and an inferior product. Although still mandated for some government and private projects, building owners are exploring ways to opt out of this system—seeking more suitable project delivery methods.

Value engineering is used as a patch and repair technique for troubled lump sum bids, with limited scope alteration achieved, reduced quality, and mediocre success. The AIA document system focuses on this delivery method. The AIA recently introduced a pilot contract model for collaboration, but it will only be fully tested through decades of use followed by court challenges.

Lump sum bid delivery is administratively easy—a fixed sum of money is exchanged for a fixed scope of work. This minimizes discussion, analysis, and documentation. Owners who do not have the knowledge, skills, time, or interest to actively manage a project may choose this delivery system. And contractors who lack the basic verbal, written, and numerical skills required by other delivery methods may be utilized—which expands the pool of possible bidders. These contractors may provide marginal or deficient quality after the desired time, but at a low price. Projects that have much repetition, prize low price, and are indifferent to quality and schedule, such as multifamily housing and hotels, favor lump sum delivery. (However, if the project becomes more complex and less repetitive, such as a hotel with a convention center, restaurants, retail, and a parking garage, the lump sum delivery system frequently fails.)

Multiple primes (separate trades) lump sum hard bid

Under the multiple prime system, the architect/engineer completely designs the project and then separate general and subcontractor trades bid directly to the owner. This system attempts to make the CM assume responsibility for the low-bid subcontractors—but someone has to lead! Since lines of communication, responsibility, and payments are between the subcontractors and the owner, no allegiance is owed to the CM. This matrix structure of many chiefs and few reluctant indians rarely works well. Anyone who has had even one bad subcontractor on a project can readily see that this system is destined for trouble. And this legalistic determination of the work packages eliminates all more desirable work package arrangements—and hugely limits possible improvements.

This system is mandated by the New York State 1918 Wickes law, which requires all public projects valued over $50,000 to receive separate bids from general, plumbing, HVAC, and electrical contractors. The state later exempted the school authority, which permitted quantitative evaluation of this method. It was found that multiple primes cost 13% more and took 60% longer than single prime project delivery.

The primary benefit of the multiple prime systems is that it allows the government to pass out more favors directly to more parties. And vendor listing and preapproval processes can further limit bidding competition and influence contract awards—to steer work to favored parties.

CM for fee with no risk

When the owner cannot or does not want to assume project leadership, such as multiple prime delivery, a CM can be engaged for the task. The CM is an agent of the owner for fee and bears no project cost or schedule risk. A legalistic bureaucratic management style is used, so adequate management of the ordinary may be achieved, but process improvement and excellent achievement of the triple constraint cannot be expected.

CM for fee is also used for projects such as road construction for which there is also a general contractor. The CM first oversees testing and documentation—the massive logs of weather, soil and concrete testing, and material deliveries that document quality control and appropriate payments. The CM also acts as a public relations project spokesman on matters of budget, schedule, public noise, dust and congestion complaints, and accidents—so the career government employees can avoid adverse notice.

The Architect, Engineer, and Contractor May Develop the Project Together

Design officially by the architect and engineer but actually also by the contractor

CM at Risk

In the CM at risk system, the GC/CM involvement early in project development provides constructibility advice, cost and schedule management, and guidance on optimal proprietary systems. Enhanced analytical skills and more frank communication, including proprietary information, are key. For the construction phase, the general contractor functions in the usual manner but with more communication and documentation.

The project owner will be actively involved in key project decisions so must have the motivation, knowledge, authority, and time to review and analyze large quantities of technical information at the pace the schedule requires. The triple constraint can be optimized with this delivery method, which is a huge benefit. But this method can only work well with the needed owner involvement.

In most cases, the general contractor is at risk. Under systems such as a guaranteed maximum price (with shared savings), the contractor retains liability and cost risk for the construction. In a variation of this system, the CM is the owner's agent for a fee, and not at risk. The owner retains all the risk, which many find undesirable.

The AGC (Association of General Contractors) and the CMAA have long-established administrative and contractual document systems for each CM project delivery methods. The AIA also has a CM document system. But it was adapted from their "design-bid-build" forms and lacks the project delivery methodology detail of the AGC and CMAA systems.

Fast-track construction

This is a variation on the CM process used when the product or service to be provided by the building is urgently needed—so aggressive schedule acceleration is required. This is accomplished by overlapping activities that are optimally performed in sequence. This accelerated overlap increases risk and management time and effort.

The design and construction are done in small work packages, and the construction chases the design. For example, the foundation may be designed and construction started before the superstructure on the foundation is completely designed. This system accentuates the need for communication and excellent cost controls to protect the owner's interest.

One firm can integrate engineering and construction for some industrial projects

Projects such as power plants and refineries are frequently performed by a single integrated engineering and construction firm. This is desirable first because some major equipment components have extremely long order times—1 to 3 years. And there may only be a few, sometimes only one or two, vendors in the entire world capable of providing the components.

The on-site construction of the project can easily take 3–7 years, so fast-track construction—material order and construction start before all design work is completed—may be considered. This can accelerate the schedule by years.

This system can work well because the owners of such projects have technically oriented sophisticated staff who can better describe performance requirements and can conduct ongoing quality review. Although this system is nearly identical to design build described below, the term *design-build* is seldom used for this system.

Design-build for commercial buildings

Here the design is completely under the control of the contractor, and the designing architects may even be employed by the contractor. Scope, cost, and schedule are developed simultaneously, which produces controlled and predictable project delivery.

However, definition of the grade in the initial scope will favor the design-builder's "normal and customary", which may not match the project owner's needs or expectation. Unsophisticated one-project owners, unfamiliar with construction terminology, may find—late in the project when correction is economically unfeasible—that they are receiving surprise compromises. Cost and schedule are frequently satisfactorily achieved, but scope and quality then become the balancing entries.

Traditionally, this delivery system has been used for private repetitive projects such as office warehouses and owner-occupied offices. Although this delivery system frequently has a reputation for lower quality finished product, this does not necessarily have to be so. The Design Build Institute promotes this delivery method and has developed the required administrative and contractual structure.

This delivery method makes the contractor responsible for design liability, which is different from the hard bid and CM systems described above. This profoundly changes risk, liability, and the insurance responsibilities and contractual requirements—a change that requires careful analysis and necessary action.

The CM as owner, either permanently or temporarily

Some project owners act as their own CM. Single-family residential construction firms almost exclusively perform their own construction, and some retail and high-rise mixed-use owner firms use this method as well. These firms then must perform real estate, land development, finance, marketing, and possibly facility operating and maintenance functions, so the construction department must compete for importance and authority. Repeated performance of the same project type for the same owner can limit innovation. And if the firm does not have a constant construction work volume, staff levels can fluctuate significantly, limiting continuity of shared knowledge.

A similar delivery method is "build, operate, and transfer" where a construction management firm delivers a finished building to the owner. The CM will be responsible for land acquisition and development, design and construction, and finance of the project until turnover. In some cases, the CM will retain ownership of the project, and the owner will commit to an extremely long-term lease.

This delivery method can permit an owner to obtain the facility without following their own internal regulations of finance, hiring, and purchasing. It can also be beneficial when the owner does not have, or does not want to commit, the management resources to manage a construction project. Public–private partnerships may use this method.

Where we are now

A CMAA survey of present delivery types by number of projects found:

Combined Building and Nonbuilding Projects	
Design-bid-build	56%
Design-build	16%
CM at risk	15%
Multiple prime	12%

Building Projects by Type					
	Design-Bid-Build	CM at Risk	Design Build	Multiple Prime Contracts	Other
Retail	81%	6%	6%	7%	0%
School (other)	69%	16%	2%	14%	0%
Hotels	64%	10%	16%	10%	0%
Medical clinics	60%	17%	17%	6%	1%
Religious	60%	17%	12%	9%	1%
Office	58%	18%	16%	8%	0%
Multifamily residential	56%	17%	9%	18%	0%
Recreational	54%	15%	21%	10%	0%
Auto/garage services	54%	15%	21%	10%	0%
Dorms	51%	21%	21%	6%	1%
Transportation terminals	48%	16%	25%	11%	0%
Warehouses	45%	4%	41%	10%	0%
Government building	41%	25%	12%	22%	0%
Hospitals	40%	41%	7%	11%	0%
College/university	35%	34%	2%	28%	0%
Schools K12	35%	34%	2%	28%	0%
Manufacturing	34%	13%	39%	13%	1%

Nonbuilding Projects by Type					
	Design-Bid-Build	CM at Risk	Design Build	Multiple Prime Contracts	Other
Bridges	75%	0%	16%	9%	0%
Streets	79%	2%	9%	11%	0%
Sewer	59%	6%	25%	10%	0%
Water	70%	2%	18%	11%	0%
Electric/power/gas/ communication	55%	10%	21%	14%	0%
Dams/harbors/etc	77%	0%	15%	8%	0%
Nonbuilding—Other	53%	15%	19%	13%	0%

(This CMAA survey of 2,500 projects recognized and attempted to correct the possible bias toward CM projects.)

Where qualitative and quantitative performance for buildings is not valued and the projects are smaller and shorter, the administrative ease of design-bid-build is favored. Retail—which some consider a "box for selling" with a short life span—is one example. Civil projects, where a detailed prebid design is still possible, also favor design-bid-build. As project size increases and performance is more valued, such as manufacturing and hospitals, CM and design-build are more favored.

What is next? Direction of resolution

Continued improvement in construction material and method technology will continue this trend toward specialization and distribution of design responsibility. The benefits of improved products are too compelling to permit reversal.

At the present time, the legal system and the accepted contract documents—with the exception of the design-build system—still assume that the architect is the controlling design authority for the entire project. Yet, although we all pretend this is true, it is not. Design is now—and will continue to be—more distributed.

Some inroads have begun, such as municipalities allowing contractor HVAC, fire protection sprinkler, wood truss, and precast engineers, to seal drawings for permit without supplemental architectural review. The legislators and the courts have yet to complete this catch-up so that the laws reflect what people are actually doing. Resolution might come in 10–15 years, if no roadblocks are raised.

The Design Build Institute and CMAA—as their names imply—already have identified what they believe to be the optimal delivery system. The AIA and AGC have different, and more flexible, positions. Conflict between these groups will slow final resolution.

Although final resolution is distant, understanding the underlying assumptions, strength, weaknesses, opportunities and threats of each of the present delivery systems aids intelligent use. And use of different delivery methods for different project types and owners may be required to produce the best results.

Summary

Technical innovation—and the required specialization—has distributed knowledge and design responsibility. This alters management structures and project delivery methods. But project delivery methods—and related administrative and contractual arrangements—have not quite caught up with this reality.

When selecting a project leader and distributing risk and responsibility, one must recognize the character and capacity of each party and work within their strengths and weaknesses. Forcing a project delivery system on the incapable or unwilling cannot produce success.

There is not a single best project delivery system for all project types and owners. Engineer-led unit cost lump sum bids may continue to work well for road construction—until increased use of proprietary products and systems distributes design responsibility. Lump sum hard bid is still used for repetitive projects, such as multifamily residential, that prize low cost over quality or schedule. CM-led collaboration with architects is now the delivery system of choice for commercial building projects that seek to optimize the triple constraint—but optimization and formalization of the parties' responsibilities is still a work in progress. And single-firm CM/engineer delivery may continue to work well for large industrial projects such as power plants and refineries—when the project owners have experienced technical staffs capable of defining project scope during early project planning.

Careful choice of project delivery methods is required for project success. Full recovery from a poor choice is rarely possible.

Review Questions (True or False)

1. Prior to 1950 when buildings were constructed with basic materials and methods employing much on-site fabrication, the architect would design the building and structural, piping, and electrical systems.

2. After 1950, sophisticated proprietary products and microprocessors in many building components distributed knowledge and increased specialization.

3. This distribution of knowledge and design responsibility required more collaboration among the architect, contractor, and material vendors, which increased the architect's project leadership.

4. Motivation, appetite, capacity to bear risk, willingness to perform detailed repetitive work, and established channels of distribution all influence project leadership possibilities.

5. Licensed credentialed designers are legally required for commercial and industrial and some residential projects. Architects design most commercial buildings, engineers design some civil and industrial buildings, and interior designers have made inroads into some commercial design in some states.

6. Architects routinely provide detailed cost estimates of the work they design.

7. Before 1950, architects were responsible for design of all building components, but this design responsibility became distributed to CMs, subcontractors, and vendors. Clues about the tipping point (the percentage of design work that can be performed by others before the architects lose full design control) may be between 5% and 20%.

8. Project leadership requires assumption of responsibility and the capacity and willingness to bear risk.

9. The project leader must carefully manage scope but can delegate management of cost and schedule to others.

10. Both a bid and a proposal provide a cost and schedule in response to detailed instructions, and a proposal adds qualifications and sometimes suggestions for improvement.

11. Hard bid unit cost delivery can be effectively used when the design engineer has excellent knowledge of all basic materials and methods.

12. Multiple prime lump sum hard bid delivery reduces costs and shortens schedules.

13. The CM as agent for the owner with no risk can be used to oversee testing and documentation, manage administrative procedures, and act as the owner's public relations spokesman.

14. Fast-track delivery can be used when the design is completed later than required, and the CM is then required to accelerate the schedule.

15. With the design-build delivery system, the design is completely under the control of the contractor, and scope, cost, and schedule are developed simultaneously, which produces controlled and predictable project delivery. This system may tend toward the design-builder's "normal and customary," which can limit scope possibilities considered.

16. When an owner acts as its own CM, the design and construction activities must compete with real estate, land development, finance, and marketing. Further, uneven work volumes make stable staffing and therefore continuity of knowledge challenging.

17. The design-build-transfer delivery system requires ongoing owner involvement in design and construction.

18. Although the design-bid-build delivery system is used for the majority of all buildings, it is not used for the majority of select project types.

19. Because of legal purchasing restrictions, all government projects are performed using the design-bid-build delivery.

Test Your Understanding

1. Visit 10 construction projects in progress in your area. Based on the information in this chapter, suggest the probable delivery method for each project. How does the observed percentage by delivery method compare with the CMAA survey?

2. A manufacturer must construct a new building for a recently developed new process to produce a new product. The scope is critical because the process is new and the design may not yet be refined, time is critical because of the urgent market needs for the new product, and cost must be reasonable but is not critical. The owner has sophisticated personnel knowledgeable about the processes but unfamiliar with design and construction. Which project delivery system would be best?

3. Which of the skills listed below are (1) essential, (2) desirable but not essential, and (3) not needed for (a) lump sum hard bid delivery or (b) CM at risk. (Skills may be needed for one or both delivery methods.)

   Cost estimating capability

   "What if" alternate costing scenarios

   Job cost controls

   Monthly cost reports with explanations for variation from planned

   Scheduling capability

   Scheduling/cost controls such as earned value

   Well developed public speaking and verbal communication capabilities

   Multipage, well reasoned report writing capabilities

CHAPTER
2.10

Negotiating, Bidding, and Buying the Job

As excavation operations near completion, removal of haul roads must be planned and management of the ratio of loading to hauling equipment must be adjusted to maintain needed productivity.

Negotiating, Bidding, and Buying the Job

CM contracts, subcontractor work packages and contracts, and project documentation are all used

Contracts document precise agreements, so the contract and all documentation leading up to the contract must be highly accurate. Spelling, punctuation, capitalization, and dates and names all determine winners and losers in later disputes. Every document must be sufficiently precise so that a disinterested person can reliably select the exact described document out of a pile of papers. This critical but tedious attention to detail can be performed mainly by clerical personnel, but always requires project management oversight. A well-constructed project with unusable documentation will be judged a failure by regulatory agencies, finance companies, and many project owners.

Contracts Define the Parties' Agreements about the Project

What will be built, how it will be built, and limits and conditions

CM–Owner Contracts Deal with Execution of the Entire Project

Construction management contracts document a CM–owner meeting of the minds to achieve a specified scope, at an agreed time and cost—using agreed rules and procedures. Lawyers will be involved, but the contract should not be a rigid structure that has no relation to the parties' meeting of the minds and normal business customs.

A portion of this triple constraint can be defined initially with hard technical data, but a portion also must be defined and refined during the course of the project. Shared understanding and some trust and flexibility are needed for this refinement and resolution.

A construction contract must work within the constraints of existing laws and accepted conventions and practices in the project area. Enforceable contract provisions may be defined by statute (laws passed by legislatures) or contract. But statutes are altered by case law (concluded litigation that serves as precedents for future cases), so definition of what is legal is not fixed and constant.

A contract term that requires a party to perform an illegal act is unenforceable. And contract terms that are impossible or grossly inequitable or attempt to transfer all liability are considered unenforceable by many, but not all, judges. And the interpretation of both statutes and case laws is unevenly enforced—prevailing conventions in an area may take precedence over formal laws. "We've always done it that way" or "everybody knows that" may be accepted by businesses, lawyers, and judges. Unreasonable contracts can be ignored, can be worked around, or can cause arguments and costly and time-consuming litigation.

The Kansas City walkway disaster—an example of contractual overreach

The Hyatt Regency walkway disaster that occurred in Kansas City, Missouri, on July 17, 1981—killing 114 and injuring over 200—illustrates resolution of contract ambiguities. The hotel had a four-story atrium with walkways crossing the atrium at each level—the fourth floor walkway was positioned over the second floor walkway. The design specified a single continuous threaded steel rod for the full atrium height—with a bolt supporting each walkway. The threaded rod would support the weight of both walkways and each bolt would support only a single walkway. This design would require very long multistory threaded rods and, without couplings, would require bolts to be screwed up from the ground floor to the fourth floor walkway.

The structural steel fabricator altered the design on its shop drawings to use a single-story threaded rod to support the fourth floor walkway, and then another offset two-story threaded rod to support the second floor walkway below from this higher level. This meant that the fourth floor walkway bolt would support not just that walkway, but the second floor walkway as well, which doubled the load, which was not envisioned or accommodated in the original design. The shop drawing showing this alteration was submitted to the architect and reviewed without noting and demanding correction of this deviation. After occupancy, these walkways collapsed while heavily occupied.

During the resulting multi-decade litigation, the architect argued that the contract transferred design responsibility to the contractor through shop drawings. The court ultimately found that the design professional could not transfer all design responsibility by shop drawing approval. The version of the model contracts provision that was used for this project was then deemed unenforceable.

Other common examples of burdensome one-sided contract terms

"The contractor has constructed several projects of this type and has knowledge of the construction and finished product." This clause is intended to force the contractor to correct all architect errors and omissions for free.

"If any of the work is not on schedule, the contractor shall immediately advise the owner of proposed action to bring the work back on schedule. The owner will require the contractor to work overtime, including Saturdays, Sundays, and holidays at no additional cost to the owner." This makes the contractor financially responsible for owner or architect caused delays.

"If the owner and contractor are unable to agree on the amount at any cost changes, the contractor shall promptly proceed with such changes, and the cost or credit the owner should receive will be determined on the basis of reasonable expenditures." In other words "Do the work and we will tell you later what, if anything, we will pay you."

Other clauses may unreasonably attempt to make the contractor responsible for all concealed and changed conditions, and to perform independent design analysis of the structure the architect and engineer designed. Attorneys often seek to delete the negotiation, mediation, and arbitration dispute resolution requirements, which leaves litigation—which provides the highest attorney profit.

Construction managers are not lawyers and should not attempt clever legal subtleties. Although there is no indisputable correct way to execute bombproof contracts, seeking what is legal, normal, and customary and well accepted in the project area, and balanced and fair to all parties, as described below, promises the best results.

The Elements of the Contract

Parties to the agreement

The contract parties, the owner and construction manager, must be identified with their proper legal names and street addresses. This can be as simple as their usual business names, but frequently project-specific entities, which can have significant implications, are created. Owners of development projects may create a new legal entity for the project, and construction managers may create a joint venture for the project. Assets, or relationships to firms with assets, must be verified to determine that these entities are not simply empty shells incapable of completing their contractual and financial obligations.

Project identification must be accurate, but not highly precise

The commonly recognized project name and location identify the project. The project name can usually be established from the initial owner or architect documentation and then can continue to be identified by this common name. A street address and, for multi-building campuses, a building designation, and for construction within a multistory building, a floor number define the location. If a street

| Structural steel and bar joist erection | *Photo 4 of 4* |

address has not yet been established, descriptions of cross streets, highways, or monuments "commonly known as" must be used.

These definitions define the project area in general, and the more precise architectural and engineering documents included in the document register described below add more precise refinement. This two-step project identification—first an imprecise common name, then more definitive engineering documents—is a well-accepted method of project definition.

Scope—Both the Permanent Work and the Means to Achieve It Are Defined

Documents for the permanent work, and shared understanding with guidelines for temporary work

Definition of preconstruction work is done mainly by the construction manager

Construction management services may be broken down into preconstruction work and administration of the contract (construction of the building)—which may be awarded as contracts to separate firms—or a combined contract to one firm. Model construction management contract templates can serve as the starting point for preconstruction work definition, but much more project-specific detail must be added, and is developed principally by the construction manager, with input from the owner.

Documents by the architect and engineer define the permanent work

The permanent work is defined by design and engineering documents. A document register lists all the documents included in the agreement. These typically include drawings, possibly specifications, soil engineering reports, surveys, environmental reports, and agreed work descriptions or defining narratives. It is critical that all documents that were reviewed and included in the scope are included, and that no irrelevant documents are added.

Each document must be accurately identified, including preparer, title, number (for drawings), and the latest revision date. There may be many, sometimes hundreds of, document revisions, so accurate dating of documents is critical for accurate scope definition. This is one of the most critical, but frequently overlooked, tasks in contract preparation. Document registers listing drawings with no dates or "current edition" are all too common—with disastrous results. This careful document identification may be mainly performed by clerical personnel but remains a critical project management task.

Either specific work in place or performance achieved may be required

Most construction contracts specify work in place—a configuration of materials of a specified grade installed in a specified manner. There is no insurance that this completed assembly will satisfy the owner's needs or requirements.

In contrast, a performance specification defines the capabilities and output of specific parts of the project, such as purity of chemicals delivered or characteristics of electrical power distributed. These performance requirements tend to exist on technical or industrial projects and are not found on most commercial projects. Commercial projects sometimes have more limited performance criteria, such as determining project approval by receipt of a certificate of occupancy issued by the authorities having jurisdiction—which is only partially within the construction manager's control.

Project owners frequently seek performance guarantees, but unless a specific guarantee is appropriate to the project type, discussed, understood, and agreed, the construction contract should deal with working in place—not performance achieved.

General conditions in the specifications defines responsibilities, limits, and rules

There is no widely recognized definition of "general conditions," so the term confuses even those with decades of experience. Yet, general conditions are one of the crucial driving factors affecting project quality, cost, and time.

General conditions are similar in concept to sports rules, which are fixed for a sport, level of play, and an association, such as a league. The rights and responsibilities of the teams and players, the rules of the game, regulations of competition, and procedures for termination such as rain delay or team forfeit are established and remain unchanged for the season. These fixed rules allow season-long planning and minimize discussion for each contest. The general conditions seek to establish the same clarity for construction projects.

The general conditions in the specifications of the model contract form first define the parties and their responsibilities. This includes the construction manager, project owner, and their consultants, such as architects and engineers and owner-hired subcontractors and vendors. Rights and responsibilities of each of these parties and their authority to order starts, stops, and changes in the work, and render determinations are specified. The rules of payment, schedule, and project termination and warranties are also defined. There will be general descriptions about the owner's and architect's access to the project site to inspect the work, but detailed descriptions of temporary construction measures are specifically avoided in the architect's or engineer's general condition specification—which produces a huge scope definition gap.

The tables of contents for AIA (American Institute of Architects) and AGC (Associated General Contractors) general conditions are compared below to show the similarities between the two document systems.

	AIA Document A201		AGC Document No. 200
	Table of Articles		Table of Articles
1	General provisions	1	Agreement
2	Owner	2	General provisions
3	Contractor	3	Contractor's responsibility
4	Administration of the contract	4	Owner's responsibility
5	Subcontractors	5	Subcontracts
6	Construction by owner or by separate contractors	6	Contract time
7	Changes in the work	7	Contract price
8	Time	8	Changes

9	Payments and completion	9	Payment
10	Protection of persons and property	10	Indemnity, insurance, and waivers
11	Insurance bonds	11	Termination of the agreement, suspension, and notice to cure
12	Uncovering and correction of work	12	Dispute resolution
13	Miscellaneous provisions	13	Miscellaneous provisions
14	Termination or suspension of the contract	14	Contract documents

General conditions also include construction that is not part of the permanent building

The construction manager is solely responsible for design, execution, and maintenance of the "construction means and methods"—procedures and temporary measures needed to build the building. Architects and engineers deny any responsibility and even avoid any knowledge of construction means and methods to attempt to limit their liability to the permanent work they designed.

General conditions consist of all temporary construction measures needed to erect the building. This can include temporary roads, drainage structures, hoisting mechanisms, ramps and stairs, and temporary heat, light, power, and communication. The cost of management and supervisory personnel, professional engineering services, tools, equipment and vehicles dedicated to multiple tasks, and some types of insurance is also included.

These general condition items are a large part of the overall building cost budget, easily 8% or more, but are nowhere specified or described in any meaningful detail on the drawings or in the specifications. Different construction managers' concepts of how the project will be managed, and therefore general conditions to be included, can produce huge ranges in cost, schedule, and quality. Further, since there is no description, communication with the architects, engineers, and project owners about the benefits of alternate general condition possibilities is a daunting construction management task, and a time-consuming portions of contract negotiation.

Supplementary conditions: project-specific insurance, regulation, and administration

In contrast to the general conditions, which seek to be uniform for many projects, supplementary conditions specify requirements unique to one project. Bonds, insurance, prevailing wage, minority participation, security requirements for partially owner-occupied sites, and project documentation requirements mandated by regulatory or funding agencies are specified. Supplementary conditions may grow to become extensive boilerplate for some government agencies, but are entirely absent on many private commercial projects.

Cost (Initial) Is Usually Clearly Defined

The cost for a lump sum contract will be a lump sum, possibly supplemented with alternate costs or unit costs.

A construction management contract will define markup percentages and a fixed fee or fee structure. The construction cost may be guaranteed with a GMP (guaranteed maximum price) or a cost plus agreement with no fixed limit. Increasingly, the general condition costs (which can frequently experience large cost over-runs) are now itemized and capped with GMP. In addition to a guaranteed maximum cost, allowances for specific line items that are difficult to quantify, such as building permit fees and other permissions, may be included—along with a specified mechanism for cost adjustment.

Unit cost contracts have itemized unit costs with unit quantities that extend and total to the project cost.

Although future adjustments to the initial cost can be controversial and become a significant management task, the initial cost included in the contract is seldom controversial.

Time is Frequently Defined Arbitrarily without Project-Specific Verification

Time is described in the contract, but it is the element of the triple constraint that gets the least detailed serious attention. Time is commonly identified, as the number of calendar days needed for completion after the owner issues a "notice to proceed." If all parties of the contract are capable of executing the contract promptly, actual start and end dates may be used instead.

The time of the contract can be extended by conditions (itemized in the contract) beyond the construction manager's control, such as natural disasters, labor disruptions, war, and acts of God. Extension of time for other reasons, such as the owner's or architect's changes in the work or failure to provide complete information when required, can also extend the schedule—but proof is contentious. For this reason, bonuses or penalties for early or late completion are avoided for most private, but not for public, projects.

Suites of Forms Standardize Legal Documentation to Achieve Wide Acceptance

Construction managers are not lawyers and should not attempt to develop new contracts from scratch. It is better to use suites of contract documents jointly developed and reviewed by owner, architect, engineer, and contractor associations and their legal advisors that are tested by use and litigation. These suites include the full range of documents needed for the administration of the contract: construction manager–owner contracts, architect–owner contracts, construction manager–subcontract agreements, change orders, and final completion documents.

The AIA provides one such long recognized suite of documents (originally developed for the design, then bid delivery system). These documents were developed in conjunction with the AGC and were subjected to extensive legal review before finalization. The forms require entering pertinent information such as owner, construction manager, project, cost, scope (document register), and time. The balance of the contract is standard boilerplate. But even with these careful efforts, legal acceptability must still be verified by litigation—and the first test case may not conclude for 10 or more years after a contract version is finalized and placed in use. Further, these model contracts are national, but litigation about property and cost (the most common contract litigation in construction) is conducted in county courts that have highly variable interpretations. Sample AIA contract documents are shown in the appendix.

This boilerplate strives to reflect real-world practices fair to both contract parties, so that the contracts can be confidently reused for new projects with minimal discussion and revisions. These documents are carefully crafted and extensively cross-referenced so that alteration of the document itself is impractical. No seasoned construction attorney attempts such alterations. Other project-specific agreements are best handled by a rider describing supplemental or modifying agreements, which is appended to the contract. The less changed, the better.

The AGC has a very similar document suite that places the construction manager in a more central role, starting with early involvement in the preconstruction services. The AGC documents may be more appropriate for a full-service construction management delivery system. This delivery system may envision the construction manager performing portions of the construction work, at least general conditions, with their own forces, or may be a "for fee" advisory-service-only agreement. Sample AGC contract documents are shown in the appendix.

The CMAA (Construction Management Association of America) also provides similar documents for the construction management delivery system. Their system focuses on construction management services for fee (sometimes, but not always, at risk). This construction management system envisions the construction manager performing little or no construction work with his own forces.

The Design Build Institute, U.S. Army Corp of Engineers, GSA (General Services Administration—an agency that builds and manages Federal Government buildings), the American Consulting Engineers Council are a few of the other more specialized entities offering a suite of documents. Serious efforts to merge some of these suites into "consensus documents" have been underway for decades, but no project-ready documents have yet been produced.

These suites consist of different packages for project sizes and delivery methods. For example, the AIA has the "document families" of Conventional (for all project sizes) including A101 Owner–Contractor Agreement Form—stipulated sum; A105 Owner and Contractor Agreement Form—residential or small commercial project; A132 Owner–contractor agreement form—CM advisor; Owner–Contractor Agreement Form—CM Advisor; and A133 Owner–Contractor Agreement Form—Cost of Work plus a Fee with a GMP. There are also agreement forms for interiors, international, and design-build. The AGC has a similar range, but started placing the construction manager in a more central role than the AIA, so has been more extensively tested in the marketplace and courts for the CM delivery system. These variations produce hundreds of documents. But a construction manager performing a few types of project size, with a few delivery methods, only needs to master about three suites.

Very large and sophisticated construction managers develop very clever and detailed contracts. This sophistication focuses on avoiding risk and liability, particularly defects that could be claimed under warranty. Unless the owner of the project has matching sophistication, this approach cannot work well. Almost all projects use one of the suites of contracts—filling in the necessary blanks and adding riders for specific agreed changes.

Work Packages: Allocation of Work Tasks, Management, and Risk

Construction manager leadership: what can and should be done

The construction manager leads the project first by establishing and communicating scope, time, and cost. Then, assigns components of this scope to the subcontractors and vendors most capable of executing the work consistent with project requirements. The project manager then directs and monitors the project with feedback and control.

Construction managers must be able to manage projects as a generalist, including understanding innovative unfamiliar tasks. Quick systems thinking and the perseverance to handle unfamiliar poorly defined and unpleasant tasks that others cannot or do not want to handle is one of the project manager's key competencies. Construction managers know a lot about project management and a little about everything else. Every subcontractor must have superior knowledge and capabilities for their specific task or they have no value—the construction manager could more economically and effectively self-perform the work.

Construction managers also should perform portions of the general conditions that benefit many equally. Temporary roads, parking lots, elevators, tower cranes, shared project offices, sanitary facilities, and rubbish removal that benefit many each day should be installed and maintained by the construction manager. Attempting to make each party provide their own facilities or charging back a prorated share is an inefficient operation that can lead to variable quality and a large administrative burden.

General condition work that benefits only one party can usually be best delegated to that single party. For example, hoisting of heavy and large mechanical units and demolition and removal of a replacement unit can require specialized cranes, and is best delegated to the installing mechanical contractor. And haul roads solely for the benefit of the earthwork contractor should be installed and maintained by that contractor.

How subcontractors and vendors can best add value

Subcontractors and vendors have an assembled organization consisting of administrative support staff with established procedures, an assembled work force, necessary equipment, and a network of loyal vendors with valuable technical knowledge and shared values. The subcontractor will have specific trade knowledge and possibly control of patented procedures, materials, or unique sources of supply.

These subcontractor capabilities can increase quality and productivity, and lower cost. Each subcontractor will identify themselves by these capabilities and feel a type and range of work is normal and customary. This higher comfort level will assist their effective management of higher levels of risk.

Conventional, accepted work task groupings are specific to the project type and area

Packaging work to conform to the comfort zones of three or more bidders in the project area will produce optimal quality, productivity, and lowest cost. If subcontractors are forced to solicit major sub-bids because of uncomfortable work packages solicited by the construction manager, the results will be poorer. The subcontractor will not feel ownership of the subcontracted work, may have insufficient knowledge to adequately supervise, and will also charge a markup on the subcontracted work—causing poor management, lower quality, and higher cost.

Some common successful work package decisions that can be selected

Parking lot replacement—consisting of asphalt paving, concrete curbs and walks, drainage structures, and landscaping—may be sought as a single lump sum bid for the convenience of ownership, but may be more effectively delivered by breaking the work into three or four conventional work packages.

In some project areas, structural steel fabrication and erection are performed by one firm, but in others the firms are separate and require a very different management character. (The fabricator may have detail-oriented technical and shop personnel and sophisticated certified equipment. The erector may be more oriented to high productivity under challenging conditions.)

Roofing and sheet metal are usually performed by a single contractor for conventional commercial and industrial flat roof construction. However, complicated decorative sheet metal or multiple very different roofing systems (such as wood, slate, clay tile, or copper) on a single project may be better performed by multiple subcontractors. (The maintenance of single source responsibility for roofing warranty must be carefully considered in this work package choice.)

Interior wall systems consisting of light-gauge framing and drywall, acoustical tile ceilings, and painting may be performed by a single subcontractor—but there are seldom three or more subcontractors with these multiple capabilities in the project area. This work is more commonly performed by separate wall, ceiling, and painting subcontractors. So it is better to accept proposals for one or more of these work items from each subcontractor so all competent subcontractors are considered.

HVAC contractors tend to be stronger in either sheet metal or piping, but the separation of these two trades increases the construction manager's coordination burden. The relative volumes and complexity of the project's sheet metal and piping, as well as the comfort zone of the subcontractors available in the project area, influence optimal HVAC work packages. HVAC contractors are accustomed to and frequently comfortable with use of a number of subcontractors such as pipe insulation, temperature control, and test and balance. This is a common successful exception to the principle of avoiding forcing subcontractors to subcontract work.

Similarly, electrical contractors may be strong in some but not all of the categories of power and light, site lighting, site power distribution, and low voltage and signal. Multiple electrical work packages for the project area is usually the optimal solution.

The optimal work packages must be designed so that three or more competent subcontractors in the project area consider the package normal and customary and will perform installation principally with their own forces. The construction manager will maintain the risk for performance of the common good, and each subcontractor will be at risk for its own performance. This is consistent with the principle of allocating risk to the party best able to manage it.

But unsuccessful work packages are common as well

Some very common but unsuccessful work package arrangements are listed below.

The use of four work (bid) packages for general construction, plumbing, HVAC, and electrical was originally mandated by the Wickes law (A New York State law mandating multiple primes for certain public project types.). To provide the missing leadership, construction managers were then added, effectively adding a fifth work package. This matrix management structure increased cost and extended schedules.

Some "paper" construction managers seeking to minimize both their own risk and their self-performed trade work structure work packages for their own convenience. Work packages as limited as a specified number of subcontracted man hours per week for general cleanup may be attempted. This both forfeits management leadership and establishes work packages that rarely achieve the needed performance.

Sending drawings and specifications with no descriptive request for proposal instructions let the bidding subcontractors furnish proposals for the work items they desire. This essentially transfers the establishment of a work packages to bid negotiation, which gives a construction manager wide latitude that can be perceived as arbitrary and unfair to other bidders.

These arbitrary organizational structures for work packages must be avoided, and work packages that organize the contribution of subcontractors and vendors that is normal and customary in the project area must be sought.

Frequently Used Contract Terms and Conditions

Terms that sound conventional can have large unexpected impacts

Benefit of the bargain is a theory that holds that if a party's contract is unjustly terminated, they are entitled to all the overhead and profit they would have received by completing the contract. This is a claim in contract disputes that will usually be hotly contested—but is a strong motivation to terminate rarely, and then justly with strong cause and proper notification.

Enrichment is a theory that holds that the construction manager is only entitled to additional compensation for changes that enrich the owner. Corrections of errors and omissions by third-parties, such as architects or engineers, or concealed conditions do not entitle the construction manager to additional compensation. This clause is found mainly on public projects and can create the undesirable incentive to leave defective work in place without needed notification or correction.

Final completion is the event that defines the conclusion of the construction manager's ongoing project responsibility. Events defining final completion are specified in the general conditions and most commonly include a certificate of substantial completion followed by completion of all "punch list" (identified incomplete or deficient work) items, and submission of specified documents such as warranties and as-built drawings. Delivery of a certificate of occupancy and final subcontractor lien waivers may also be included. A certificate of final completion can be, but frequently is not, executed.

Force work account. If additional work must be urgently executed to maintain critical schedule dates but agreement on the cost of the work cannot be reached sufficiently early, this contract provision can require the construction manager to perform the work and resolve the cost later. The uncertainty of the fairness of the costs must be managed to avoid poisoning relationships between the affected parties.

Force majeure. This means "major force" and the general conditions define the occurrences such as war, acts of God, flood, strikes, or labor disruptions that constitute the agreed grounds for schedule extension.

Liquidated damages are the cost per day to be subtracted from the construction manager's contract for failure to complete work by an agreed date. Although technically not a penalty but rather a prespecified amount of the economic harm the delay will cause the owner, the liquidated damages and a penalty will have the same impact on the construction manager's profit. Liquidated damages are, therefore, viewed by the construction manager as a penalty.

Notification is almost always required to be in writing and marks a milestone for defining contract events. Examples include notice to proceed, stop work or terminate.

No damages for delay is a clause frequently found in public contracts that bar the construction manager from receiving additional compensation for owner interference or delays that reduced productivity or extended the schedule. This clause is enforceable only if applied without exception—including schedule extension caused by additional requested work.

Notice to proceed is the formal notification, usually in the form of a letter, to begin the project. Notice to proceed can be in two stages, first to mobilize and install temporary facilities, which does not start the calculation of contract time. And a second notice to proceed to begin the work, which does begin the calculation of the contract time.

Pay when paid. This clause obligates the construction managers to pay the subcontractors only when they receive payment—thus forcing subcontractors to assume part of the risk for owner payment. Since construction managers do not have sufficient capital to pay subcontractors without receipt of corresponding payments from the owner, "paid when paid" is the usual system for private construction.

Prompt payment requires construction managers to pay subcontractors, and subcontractors to pay vendors within a specified time, usually 30 days after receipt of their progress payments. This clause is usually found on public projects.

Quantum meruit is the theory used in disputes that argues that the construction manager is entitled to the amount of benefit they provided to the owner—which may be far in excess of costs expended, thus increasing profit.

Substantial completion is the event documented by a certificate of substantial completion that marks the end of on-site work, except deficient or incomplete items identified on the punch list. Unless otherwise specified, substantial completion turns the project over to the owner (making them responsible for maintenance security and utilities) and begins warranty periods, and defines the end of the scheduled work. Substantial completion is one of the most important defining milestones—usually more important than final completion.

Warranty is the period of time during which the construction manager must replace or repair defective work or components. A one-year warranty for the entire project, with longer warranties for select items such as roofs and compressors, is commonly specified, but laws in the project area may actually mandate a much longer warranty period. Caution must be used in subcontract negotiations to ensure warrantees start at substantial completion rather that the time a component was placed in service, so gaps of months or years in warranty are avoided.

Bidding and "Buying the Job"
"My deal is your deal" where possible, abbreviated forms where not

The formal "bid" or less formal "proposal"
A bid is a precisely structured response to an exact set of instructions, and is used for the design-then-bid delivery system. Bid forms are provided to bidders, and each blank must be precisely filled in and all required documents, such as bid bonds, attached. Any omission or alteration, no matter how minor, is grounds for disqualification. And the bid forms must be submitted in the specified envelopes at the specified location and time—not 1 minute late.

In contrast, the proposal (used for construction management delivery systems) welcomes voluntary alternates and identification of possible document errors and omissions. Some of these may be legitimate and substantive, such as identification of discontinued components or suggestions for improvement, and others may state that the contractor cannot or does not wish to perform the work as requested. The proposal may also contain qualifications and résumés of key personnel and is used to start contract negotiations.

The forms for bid and proposal solicitations and preparation are:

Less formal
RFP (request for proposal)

Formal
The Invitation to Bid specifies the project type, size, location and due date, start and completion date, location of documents and requirements such as bonds, and minority, prevailing wage, or local participation. Possible bidders can then decide if they can perform the work at a competitive cost.

The Instructions to Bidders specifies the due date, directions for bid or proposal completion and delivery, and the time and method of award.

Bid forms
Contract forms (blank specimen forms only)
Contract documents consisting of
  • General conditions
  • Supplementary conditions
  • Drawings
  • Addenda
And the sequence of proposal preparation and award is:

Prebid conference/site walk-through (for many, but not all projects)
RFIs and responding addenda to answer questions and provide clarifications
Proposal preparation
Proposal delivery
Proposal evaluation, which can include negotiation, and revision
Comparison of completing proposals
Contract award

Proposals are developed and modifications made with some gamesmanship

Proposal preparation is not just a mathematical exercise with careful completion of forms but is rather a process to gain advantage that produces the winning proposal. Requests for information may be used not just to secure needed clarifications, but rather to produce an addendum that casts the project in a less favorable light for the competing bidders. Subcontractors and vendors may, before bids are finalized, submit and later withdraw unreasonably high proposals to drive up other bids. Some vendors, particularly electrical supply houses, will continue to revise their proposals until minutes before bids are due—to produce confusion that leads to hasty commitment.

Proposals are then analyzed for completeness and accuracy

In the design-then-bid delivery system, the conforming low bidder must legally (with a little wiggle room) be awarded the work. The construction management delivery systems reviews proposals more qualitatively.

The following factors are reviewed to determine that the subcontractor has prepared a competent responding proposal and is ready, willing, and able to perform the work as required.

The completeness of subcontract proposals is assessed by asking select questions that establish the categories of work covered and quantities of some work items. Comparing the subcontractors' quantities for cubic yards of concrete, lineal feet of wall type, and roof area can produce a feel for the competency of their estimate and also confirm that major work items have been adequately addressed.

Refinement of the dividing line between frequently ambiguous work items must then be probed. Gas piping by the plumber or fitter, starters by the HVAC or electrical contractor, and miscellaneous steel support for large light fixtures from the miscellaneous steel contractor or electrical contractor are common examples. This process continues until both qualitatively and quantitatively the completeness and accuracy of the proposal and elimination of double counts are resolved.

Inclusion of work items for the common good must be verified. The earthwork contractor's provision of temporary roads and clean up of surrounding streets is one common example. Inclusion of temporary electrical service and temporary lights by the electrical contractor, temporary water by the plumbing contractor, and temporary heat by the HVAC contractor are other common examples.

And a feel for the subcontractors' intended cooperation—whether they will work harmoniously with others or hog the site and perform work at irregular inconvenient intervals—must be assessed. Questions such as "Have you included partial truckload deliveries?" "What is the required size of your staging area?" and "What is the anticipated crew size for each phase of the project?" will confirm facts and provide a feel.

Financial capacity to perform the work is determined by review of the subcontractor's financial statement—usually the previous year, but occasionally 2 or 3 previous years. And recently completed projects of similar size and character can be evaluated. For larger subcontracts, lists and résumés of key project personnel may be requested.

In all cases, the needed project values are compared with the subcontractor's intended value. This means that the construction manager must have performed a competent detailed cost estimate and project schedule prior to start of the subcontract interviewing process. Subcontractors will not provide all helpful information, such as their estimate. And even if they did, it would usually be in a nonstandard form difficult to evaluate. Asking probing qualitative and quantitative questions based on the construction manager's detailed knowledge of the project cost estimate and schedule will get the subcontractor talking and reveal the needed information.

Rigid standards may undesirably limit possibilities

Some construction managers or owners, such as government entities and large rigid corporations, cannot or will not accept any deviations from the requested specifications, and will reject any proposal with the slightest irregularity. Other private owners may find both cost and quality benefits in carefully evaluating and "leveling" the bids (making cost allowances for differing quantities or qualities) so that the most advantageous, although possibly not the lowest, proposal may be selected. This can be a careful exercise to optimize value or it can make a favored bidder appear more competitive. A skilled construction manager can make almost any proposal appear low and provide convincing documentation to sell his recommendation.

The form of construction manager–subcontract agreement will differ by the sophistication of the subcontractors and the size of their work package. For the largest subcontractors, the usual principle is "my deal is your deal"—each and every requirement the owner imposes on the construction manager will be in turn imposed on the subcontractor. And one of the construction manager–subcontractor documents from the model suite of contracts, or the construction manager's standard form of subcontract agreement may be employed. The approach for construction manager subcontract agreements is the same as the owner–construction manager contract described above: fill in the blanks, and add riders that document discussions and agreements reached, but leave the boilerplate alone.

These model contract forms may not be economically possible for smaller subcontractors with work of limited scope and duration. High insurance limits, long waits for release of retention, and burdensome documentation requirements including attendance at project meetings may be impossible for some to provide at a reasonable cost or at all. A construction management purchase order or a contract form of more limited scope may be used. Simply signing a subcontractor's proposal is an undesirable choice that adds ambiguity and inconsistency to project administration, and should be avoided. (Rigid enforcement of uniform contract provisions for even the smallest vendors is sometimes mandated by government and rigid private firms. Subcontractor firms will be developed to respond to these requirements, but their performance may be suboptimal and their cost 500–1000% over market.)

Summary

Owner–construction manager contracts confirm previous agreements and decisions about scope, time, and cost. These contracts cannot require anything illegal, impossible, or excessively burdensome or one sided, and must instead seek fairness for both parties. Widely accepted principles and well-known rules and procedures permit planning and minimize disputes.

Because wide general acceptance of very complicated legal principles is needed, established accepted suites of "fill in the blank" contract forms are generally used. These forms include definition of the relation between the parties, changes in their work, starting or stopping, and termination. Similar suites of contracts are used for the construction manager–subcontractor agreement, with some exceptions for small or less sophisticated subcontractors and vendors.

The construction manager should retain the most poorly defined, difficult, or difficult-to-manage work tasks. Subcontractors who bring an assembled work force, management structure, equipment, and sources of supply can be effectively used for specific tasks. These tasks must be assembled into work packages that are normal and customary for the project area, so that a minimum of three qualified bidders will be available.

Review Questions (True or False)

1. Contract document accuracy is highly important. Spelling, punctuation, dates, and names can all determine winners and losers in later disputes.
2. A construction contract must work within the constraints of existing laws and accepted conventions that have been altered by case law, so what is legal is not permanently fixed and constant.
3. Contracts can transfer all liability if properly worded.
4. Burdensome one-sided contract terms, even if enforceable, may not optimize project performance. It is preferable to seek what is legal, normal, customary, and well accepted in the project area and is fair to all parties.
5. Project owners may create a new legal entity for the project, and construction managers may create joint ventures. These entities must be examined to confirm they are not empty shells incapable of completing their contractual and financial obligations.
6. The document register defines the scope of the permanent work and itemizes all relevant documents including preparer, title, drawing numbers, and latest revision date.
7. Performance specifications that define the capabilities and performance of specific parts of the work are more accurate and comprehensive and common than specification of work to be performed.
8. General conditions in the specifications of model contracts define parties and their rights and responsibilities, rules of payment, scheduling, project termination, and warranty, as well as the owner and architect access to the project site.
9. The general conditions in the specifications also specify construction means and methods and define detailed characteristics of temporary facilities.

10. In a construction management contract, the scope and therefore cost of the general conditions is difficult to define and communicate definitively and can be a source of cost over-runs and disagreements. It is, therefore, increasingly common to itemize and establish a fixed cost for general conditions.

11. AIA and AGC model contract forms are substantially identical and may be used interchangeably for lump sum hard bid and construction management contracts.

12. Construction managers can best perform portions of the general conditions that benefit many parties equally.

13. Packaging work to conform to the comfort zones of three or more bidders in the project area will produce optimal quality, productivity, and the lowest cost.

14. The construction manager should always seek to reference the terms "enrichment," "no damages for delay," and "quantum meruit" in the subcontract agreements.

15. The terms *substantial completion* and *final completion* can be and frequently are used interchangeably.

16. It is essential that the construction manager perform a detailed quantity survey and cost estimate of all work items before attempting subcontract award negotiations.

17. A bid is a precisely structured response to an exact set of instructions, but a proposal may encompass voluntary alternates and identification of possible errors and omissions.

18. Asking probing questions to verify the completeness of the subcontractor's proposal and gain understanding of their intended approach to the project produces a qualitative and quantitative understanding of their suitability.

19. "My deal is your deal," making construction manager–subcontractors responsibilities the same as owner-construction management responsibilities, should be sought as much as possible, even if not achievable in all cases.

Test Your Understanding

1. You are about to enter into a construction management contract that has many preconstruction responsibilities. Compare how the AGC and AIA model contract forms in the appendix each addresses these preconstruction services and defines the relation between the construction manager and architect and owner.

2. In the same model contracts, review how disputes are resolved and the parties that participate in the dispute resolution.

3. Using the principle that the construction manager should retain responsibility for general condition items that benefit many equally, and subcontractors may best be responsible for general condition items that benefit them alone, suggest who—construction manager or subcontractor—can best handle the tasks listed below.
General rubbish removal
Temporary toilets
Temporary parking lots for tradesman
Temporary power and light
Hoisting electrical switchgear requiring special cranes
Occupancy permit costs
Tower cranes, and material and man hoists
Truck crane to set parking lot light poles
Safety rail with toe board, intermediate rail and top rail around the build perimeter, and interior openings
Hanging scaffold for the mason consisting of guardrail system and double overhead protection

Introduction Part III
Building the Project Is a Continuation of Starting the Project

Although some believe that building the project is the "meat" of construction project management, it is really a continuation of all the previous activities. The essential knowledge and skills about people management, scheduling, risk management, communication, and monitoring and control for both quality and cost start in project planning and continue in execution—with project closeout as an essential last step.

Project execution must be seen in the context of construction rules, regulations and business practices, and the purposes and needs of the owner. Hard skills and tools must be learned and used. But performing construction management in this broader integrated context is the defining characteristic of professional project management and project leadership.

CHAPTER
3.1

Human Nature, and the Capacity and Bias of People and Companies Must Be Recognized

This internally braced sheeting to allow construction of the 10,000 cubic-yard elevator bank foundation for the Trump International Hotel & Tower in Chicago, Illinois, was installed by Hayward Baker. The exterior sheeting is driven into the unexcavated earth, and then internal bracing is placed as the excavation progresses. Careful coordination of the temporary bracing with the permanent building foundation can maximize the salvage value of the bracing and the productivity of the foundation installation—producing large cost savings. Extraction of the sheeting, which is possible in some but not all situations, can produce further cost savings. This type of retention system can be installed in most soil types. *Photo courtesy of Hayward Baker Inc.*

Human Nature, and the Capacity and Bias of People and Companies Must Be Recognized

Peoples' tendencies, strengths, and weakness must be included in project planning

Construction management is a people business. Although the final result is a physical product, a project is built by the knowledge, skill, and effort of people. Success, failure, opportunities, and problems focus on the nature, character, and capacity of people. The owners of the project must overcome their egos and commit to a workable purpose. The managers of the project must overcome their egos also and perform the work necessary to develop a workable approach. The trade personnel must know what they are supposed to do, know if they are doing it, and know when they are done.

Most failed projects are caused by a failure to define either a workable purpose or a workable approach. Most cost over-runs are caused by low trade productivity, not material or equipment problems. "Watch your labor" is a "given" for experienced managers. Failure to understand human nature and work with it "as it is" is a cause of many of these problems. Expectations and demands that cannot possibly be achieved with the people available will result in failure.

The discussion of people applies equally to companies. All companies are composed of people and develop a collective company personality. This is accentuated in construction companies that are typically small and have a very flat organizational structure—one or a few individuals can set the tone. So, this discussion applies to human resource management very broadly to include the construction management firm's personnel and the subcontractors engaged for a project.

This chapter looks at the nature of people and how they can be managed well within the project constraints. This is a fundamental first step that must be included in the planning stages of the project and continued through selection of project delivery methods, procurement, and project execution and control.

This chapter also briefly reviews the attitudes and biases the surrounding union vs. nonunion construction. The nature and regional differences of these biases must be recognized for effective project planning and management.

Work is part of people's identity—they need to be proud of their work

Work occupies the largest part of workers' waking hours. It partially defines what they are. And if they are to feel good about themselves, they need to feel that their work is worthwhile. People need to see that their part of a project fits into the whole, and have a natural tendency to see their part as the indispensable contribution that makes the whole possible. People need to feel they are part of something big and important. But not all contribute to the effort equally.

5% understand how a project works and can and will make it happen.

10% understand how the project works, but just watch and do not make things happen.

75% want to be part of the project and feel proud. They may understand their portion in great detail but do not understand how the whole project works, or even quite how their part fits with the whole.

5% are bad actors, troublemakers, and a drag on the project. Maybe this job is not right for them—maybe no job is right for them. Get rid of them or contain them in a job where they cannot affect others.

Character is unusually important in construction

Character in construction is more critical than in many other industries. This is so because the project starts with many undefined conditions and will encounter other unforeseen conditions. It is impossible to specifically define each and every condition and activity with precision at the start of a project. Only a shared understanding of how one can and should behave in reaction to these changed conditions—character—will permit successful execution.

Character has the following attributes:

1. Principles matter more than their personal gain. They must see themselves as part of something bigger than themselves.

2. They feel personally responsible for their actions.

3. They understand a deal—and will honor a contract.

4. They will stick with it when the going gets tough.

For our purposes, character is focused on the activities at work, not necessarily at home. Although people of moderate habits tend to possess the desired character more frequently, gamblers, skirt chasers, and two-fisted drinkers may possess character, while deacons in the church with religious pictures in their office, may not.

Natural tendencies—how they relate to people must be recognized

Some people like to work with people and need to work around people and in groups, and do not work well independently. (Working with people must be distinguished from very people-oriented operators, such as politicians and some self-serving sales people who really only see people as placeholders in a power relationship. If one person leaves a position, their replacement will fill the place just as well for the people-oriented operators).

Other people work with things, numbers, or written documents and do not feel the need or desire to relate with people continually.

How People Figure Things Out

Things or ideas—visual, verbal, and number people all have a preferred way of thinking

An important distinction about most people in construction is that they work in the world of things, not ideas. They must see, touch, and move things around to understand them. Talking about them, writing about them, and making counts of them are not the first natural way construction people figure things out. (Architects and engineers tend to be more on the opposite end, working in the world of ideas, drawings, numbers, symbols, and quite frequently cannot even recognize the things they are describing when they see them in the real world.)

All people make decisions in the way that works and is more comfortable for them. Some are visual thinkers. Others are verbal thinkers, number thinkers, or symbol thinkers. (Symbol thinkers are found in mathematics and philosophy and are rare in construction.)

Speed of decision making varies by person and company and cannot be changed easily or much

People make decisions at different paces. Some people can only decide quite rapidly, and if they linger over a decision, their thinking becomes muddy. Others have to think about it, sleep on it, think about it a different way, and continue for days or even weeks before reaching a comfortable decision.

Steeple erection—Construction of the steeple at the Wheaton Bible Church involved foundations, structural steel, miscellaneous steel, masonry, skylight panels, and church ornaments. Coordination of these trades to maximize both productivity and safety requires careful planning. Planning starts in shop drawing review where careful selection of connection details later permit higher productivity partial assembly on the ground with fewer lower productivity connections in the air. Hoisting and personnel access equipment must be carefully planned as well. If the steeple construction takes place when earthwork grades are near completion, a wide range of equipment may be considered. However, if the steeple is constructed earlier when the earthwork is uneven with some steeper slopes, rough terrain equipment with greater leveling capacity must be used. Note this integration of connection detailing, hoisting equipment selection, assembly locations, and scheduling in the following sequence of photographs.   *photo 1 of 15*

Time horizons vary also

People have natural time horizons, which are nearly impossible to change in the short run and very difficult to change at all. For example:

- Immediate (time horizon)—some workers can only understand the task that they are doing at that time and have no concept of what might come next.

- 2–4 hours—these workers understand their tasks and the forces that are required to do their task, such as parts or systems from other people.

- 1–2 weeks—these workers understand their tasks and how they fit with related tasks.

- Entire project—these workers know how projects in general should work and how this specific project will work.

- Their career and longer—understand larger principles and possibilities that are not apparent from the immediately available facts and can undertake tasks and project types that have never been done before.

A 2-week minimum time horizon is required for any management position, such as a foreman or an assistant superintendent. Time horizon of an entire project or longer is required for management positions that are attempting continuous improvement.

Change Is Possible—But Only a Little and Slowly

Everyone has one nature, tendency, and speed. People can make decisions usually in one way, sometimes in a couple of ways. No one is good at everything. All decision-making processes work well for some activities and not for others—but all are necessary for some part of a project. For example, a detail-oriented accountant would not be a good superintendent and vice versa. Similarly, people working in the world of things cannot be compelled to keep detailed paperwork records or to write long reports. And an office person might be completely useless at field tasks. Recognize the natural tendencies of the people, use them where their talents will produce the best results, and do not plan for unreasonable expectations—given their tendencies.

Capacity is part talent and part training and experience

The skills, knowledge, talent, and training to do a specific assigned task is, of course, critical. This usually receives proper attention and focus. However, it is frequently the only item receiving any attention at all—excluding character, natural tendencies, and time horizons.

Motivation is usually there but must be cultivated and encouraged

Some people cannot be motivated at all. Posters, incentives, and cheerleading sessions will be wasted on people who have no tendency or need to be proud of their work. Fortunately, the vast majority of workers need to be proud of their work and can be motivated if they see their efforts are part of a bigger picture. Recognition is always appreciated and is an effective motivator. Management has to genuinely believe that all tasks are really important and show this belief in their actions. A pat on the back and some nice words will not fool them—management must believe it and show it with their actions.

This trust does not happen naturally in the workplace—but can be developed with effort. It will take weeks, months, or years to build the trust, and a system of feedback and control where the workers will really believe that they are part of something good and big. It can also be destroyed in a single event, lasting even minutes.

Bias Affects All People, Companies, and Projects
Manage prejudice, put experience to work

Bias is the influence of instincts, previous experience, and purpose on the execution of a task. All human beings are biased in some way.

On a business level, people are biased against hostile and unpredictable superiors who may withhold benefits or fire them. The same is true with suppliers and vendors who have not performed as promised—be they inferior goods, late deliveries, or changing prices. On a job site level, people may have a preference for a particular brand and model of tools because of superior productivity, less downtime, and a comfort level produced by past use.

Bias can be viewed as good if someone is "experienced," or bad if someone is "prejudiced." Prejudice is experience that fails to recognize that a point of view may have been a little wrong—or changed conditions now make it a lot more wrong. Prejudice also fails to recognize that although one viewpoint is right for one purpose, a different viewpoint may be equally right for a different purpose.

The person who claims to be unbiased has not identified or recognized his/her bias—and therefore cannot manage it. Such a person is inexperienced, uninformed, or an arrogant fool—poised to make the next big mistake. The task here is to identify and admit bias, then manage it—use the experience well and control the prejudice.

Everyone Has One Nature, Motivation, and Direction

Everyone is biased
If you are a hammer, everything looks like a nail

Everyone sees their world through the lens of their previous experience and present purpose. This determines the point of view from which all observations are made. Achievement of the purpose is evaluated by incentives, and personal satisfactions and dissatisfactions. A concrete cement finisher is judged by how many square feet per day are finished at an acceptable quality. A project manager/estimator is judged both by estimates that gain the contract and by completion of the project at a cost less than the estimate.

Incentives are hard quantifiable goals and rewards: production targets to be met, job retention, or bonuses to be received. Satisfactions are the reasons one is doing the job to start with—liking to work with your hands, to build things, to be outside, and to do new things, or liking the coworkers. Dissatisfactions are the things one complains about—meaningless paperwork, arbitrary changes, bosses who will not listen, or inadequate tools.

Incentives, satisfactions, and dissatisfactions are mixed together in the real world—production goals are met, the job is kept, pride in work well done, and the boss does not interfere too much—all at the same time. To clearly recognize bias, the incentives, satisfactions, and dissatisfactions must be evaluated one at a time. Incentives—how is the purpose defined, how will success be measured, and the reward for success. Satisfactions—"Why am I doing this job?" "What do I like about it?" and "What makes me proud?" Dissatisfactions—"What do I want to minimize or avoid as much as possible?" Once each is recognized, and then mixed together, management becomes possible.

"Follow the money"—how people get paid (or profit) is often identified as the main motivator and influence on a person's point of view, but this is seldom true. People have one nature and one speed. "I do it because this is what I am," "I feel this is the right thing to do," "I have always done it this way, and it works"—all matters of personal pride and satisfaction—usually come before money. People act the way they want to act as long as they can make enough money to continue acting that way.

Managing the Bias

Recognizing bias—to control it
Recognizing bias is the first and largest step toward managing it. Questions such as
> "What tasks take up most of your day?"
> "What gives you satisfaction with your job?"
> "How is your work evaluated?"
> "How are you rewarded and paid?"

help understand your point of view.

These questions also help understand that someone spending their days on very different tasks, with different satisfactions and rewards, will have different points of view and bias that are valid for their purpose.

For example, if the pouring and finishing concrete floor slabs require and are evaluated for high production levels, the foreman will tend to be focused on rapid installation of the largest, easiest parts of the slab. Missing electrical conduit that should be embedded in the slab will require costly rework or boxing out portions of the slab—requiring uneconomic comebacks. But a foreman's bias toward high production might make him actually believe that he is 95% complete, but rework and comebacks make the job far less complete. A project manager who is motivated to finish not just the concrete but the entire job for less than the estimate will be very sensitive to the costly rework. He will manage his potential bias—because he recognized it.

Manage the bias with another viewpoint
Two heads are better than one

After the bias is recognized, the next step in managing the bias is to have another person—with a different bias—evaluate the same situation.

A common business example is the requirement for two signatures on a check. This simple act of two people thinking "is this payment right?" helps avoid incorrect payments and fraud.

The same idea is used if a foreman—biased to show lots of production—reports the labor hours expended, while an estimator or project manager—biased to show low costs—reports the amount of work executed. The agreement of these two that the concrete slab is acceptably complete can be further reinforced by the agreement of others—the plumber and the electrician agree that all the required items are embedded in the slab—and the acceptance of the slab by the floor-covering contractor.

Human resource management of people and companies must start in project planning

The earlier chapter on construction industry players describes the industry organization and distribution of knowledge and capabilities that limits selection of optimal project participants. Many subcontractors and vendors are much larger than construction management firms and many control proprietary materials and processes. Since these companies are so powerful, their nature and tendencies must be recognized and included in project planning.

Chapter 2.9 on project delivery systems identifies yet other constraints. Lump sum hard bid delivery systems require a lower level of planning, analytical, organizational, and communication skills. But these same skills must be highly developed for successful construction management or owner agent delivery systems. Availability of people and companies with the needed skills must be checked and the resulting costs and time included in project planning.

A new project is not a blank slate with no restrictions—human nature and market realities must be understood and accepted. This chapter provides some of the essential aids to understanding needed to plan and execute human resource management planning effectively within these multiple constraints. The decisions made early carry through the entire project and are difficult or impossible to correct later—so proper execution of this first step is key. The next chapter builds on this knowledge of human nature and discusses organizational structures to manage human resources for the project.

Biases for Union or Nonunion Construction Are Regional and Pronounced
Construction labor is now mostly nonunion, but biases die hard

The union membership as a percentage of the workforce is shown below.

Union Affiliation of Employed Wage and Salary Workers 1930–97

Union members in the workforce (%)

1930	11.6
1935	13.2

1940	26.9
1945	35.5
1950	31.5
1955	33.2
1960	31.4
1965	28.4
1970	27.3
1975	25.5
1980	23.0
1985	18.0
1990	14.9
1995	14.9
1997	14.1

(The statistics are approximations since the Bureau of Labor Statistics methodology for counting the workforce changed in 1980. And some workers who are not members of unions are employed in a workplace covered by a union bargaining agreement. But the trend is clearly a rise then a decline.)

Union or nonunion superiority for quality and cost has not been established

The total compensation package of wages and benefits is lower for nonunion workers. And the non-union workforce does not have work rules that restrict the type of task that a worker may perform or the number of workers required for a task. This flexibility can enhance productivity.

Traditionally, nonunion firms, with few or no apprenticeship programs, struggled with training and quality assurance. And each nonunion worker was required to perform multiple trade specialties and did not always reach the quality levels of specialized union tradesman. A greater number of supervisors per nonunion worker are needed to compensate for these variable skill levels. But this historic gap in union and nonunion skill levels has been eliminated in some areas of the country.

The nonunion workforces claim lower hourly cost, and the union workforces emphasize higher quality. There is no known study establishing the superiority of either type of workforce for both cost and quality of work together. So nonunion market share continues to increase for projects that value low cost over high quality, and unions struggle to maintain market share for projects that require high quality. But as the union–nonunion difference in quality erodes, the market share of union contractors erodes as well.

Union and nonunion increasingly work together

Some areas in the south and southeast are predominantly or exclusively nonunion. Unions can enforce all union projects in some larger cities in the west, midwest, and northeast. And Davis–Bacon for some federally funded projects mandates that "prevailing wages" must be paid, which practically (but not completely) requires union labor. (Union contractors may legally pay lower wages to apprentices, but nonunion contractors may not on Davis–Bacon projects.)

Union or nonunion construction managers with a mixture of union and nonunion subcontractors are increasingly common. Mechanical electrical subcontractors are the most common union subs for these projects.

Unions continue to attempt to enforce all union projects but achieve only partial success. Union plumbing and pipe fitting trades and to a lesser extent electrical trades are willing to work on otherwise nonunion jobs. The teamsters (truck drivers) attempt to do their part to enforce union-only jobs by refusing to deliver to a nonunion project or projects with picket lines.

Attitudes and traditions are ingrained and die hard

Unionized labor still has a feeling of the "brotherhood" and pride in the craft. An attitude that the labor-management struggle is ongoing still exists with some. But since most needed wages and benefits and working conditions improvements were won by struggles in the first half of the 20th century, union members today did not experience this effort, and this attitude enjoys declining legitimacy and support.

Nonunion construction, particularly championed that the ABC(Associated Builders and Contractors), values individual responsibility, self-reliance, personal integrity, opportunities for merit advancement, and free enterprise. This struggle to gain legal acceptance is ongoing and very real for companies and craft workers, and frequently has a patriotic feeling.

These different origins and attitudes of union and nonunion construction produced regional differences affected by emotion as much as objective facts.

Labor conditions for each project must be included in project planning

Labor-management harmony can have a huge effect on project schedule and cost. Labor regulations and traditions vary regionally and can be further affected by the supply of labor at a project location. And labor regulations and conditions, particularly with respect to union and nonunion labor, are continually changing. To manage these variables, labor conditions for each project must be analyzed.

Summary

Construction is a people business, and people have different strengths and weaknesses. Trade skills such as carpenters, plumbers, and electricians are usually recognized—but character, and method and time of decision making are less frequently recognized. The human time horizons are frequently overlooked. And since longer time horizons are required for higher management positions, promoting someone with a short time horizon can guarantee failure.

Recognizing bias and putting measures in place to manage it are extremely important. A slight adjustment in attitude can increase communication and understanding—and help avoid costly mistakes. Once the negative aspects of bias are controlled, the benefits of the positive aspect of bias—experience—can be put to work. Talent, training, and experience—if controlled—can produce the judgments and intuition necessary for success.

Companies consist of people, and companies and people can change only a little and slowly—usually not in time for the project. Match people and companies as they are to the task needed. The culture of the company, training, and experience can improve the person but not completely change their nature. Companies with the needed characteristics for each project are scarce, and project delivery methods further limit choices. This integrated human resource approach manages these constraints but must start in project planning.

Review Questions (True or False)

1. Most unsuccessful projects are caused by failure to define a workable purpose or workable approach, and most cost over-runs are caused by low trade productivity.
2. All people have a natural tendency, and since companies are composed of people, companies also have a personality and culture.
3. The majority of project participants must have a comprehensive view of the project and long time horizons, or the project cannot succeed.
4. Because every project starts with imperfectly defined scope and will encounter unforeseen conditions, it is impossible to precisely define responsibility for each and every activity, so a shared understanding—which requires character—of the appropriate reaction to these conditions is required for successful project execution.

5. Information may be communicated visually, verbally, in numbers, or in symbols, and the project manager and all major project participants must be expected to master and use all these forms of communication.

6. Project management personnel need a time horizon of at least 2 weeks.

7. Most, but not all, project participants have a natural tendency to be motivated, but this tendency must be encouraged and developed.

8. Experienced and well-trained project management personnel will be unbiased but must manage the biases of others.

9. Compensation in money is the most effective and efficient motivator for employees in all project positions.

10. The limited capacity to alter the character, capacity, and tendencies of people and companies within the time frame of the project must be recognized and included in project planning.

11. The percentage of the construction trade workforce that is union varies significantly by area of the country and is usually accompanied by strongly held beliefs and biases.

12. Some federally funded projects are covered by the Davis–Bacon act and can mandate "prevailing wage," which in practice usually means union construction.

Test Your Understanding

1. A talented and ambitious carpenter foreman who has worked with your firm for 7 years seeks to transition into an assistant superintendent position, and you have been asked to grant or deny his promotion. Discuss how you will evaluate his character, capacity, ways of thinking, time horizons, and bias to make your decision.

2. Your project requires use of a proprietary sole source product for which there is no acceptable equal. You must use a subcontractor who has no motivation or desire to be a team player and perform how and when required. Discuss what portions of the company's nature and tendency are troublesome for the project and which might be managed to improve their performance.

3. Rank the following project participants in descending order from longest time frame and broadest view to shortest and narrowest. Not all can be equal, but ties are possible.
    Project manager
    Project engineer
    Office manager
    Project accountant
    Estimator
    Cost engineer
    General superintendent
    Assistant superintendent
    Mechanical superintendent
    Electrical superintendent
    Safety director
    Carpenter foreman

CHAPTER
3.2

Human Resource Organization and Management

Steeple erection   *photo 2 of 15*

Human Resource Organization and Management

Knowledge and decision must be distributed to the project site

All companies require structures to organize personnel. A chart of a company's formal organization, which resembles a chart of the team pairings for a basketball tournament, is often drawn—and most recognize that this chart neither represents the real lines of communication nor has much to do with how things are accomplished.

Where facts are found and stored—and judgments and decisions are made—defines the real organizational structure. A top-down command and control structure restricts judgment and decisions to the upper levels of the organization, which provides specific instructions to the lower levels. A distributed knowledge system requires facts to be known, and judgments and decisions made at all levels.

The top-down command and control, and distributed knowledge organizational structures are compared below. Two unworkable structures to avoid—the bureaucratic and matrix structures—are also discussed.

Mechanization reduces required manpower—sophisticated products require increased knowledge

The days when construction was a place for strong backs and weak minds—and construction sites looked like anthills—are gone. The number of workers required for a task has been reduced by mechanization. For example, a large piece of earth moving equipment can do the work of 50 men with wheel barrows and shovels. Trade worker knowledge requirements have increased because of more proprietary and sophisticated products that require knowledge and experience to install. For example, in 1940, paint and varnish products were mixed on the job with recipes—just like baking a cake. These coatings required no special knowledge to mix or apply—and achieved only adequate performance. Paints and other coatings are now sophisticated in formulation, application, and performance. These are factory mixed and require specific knowledge and training, and sometimes certification, about surface preparation and application techniques.

Another requirement for knowledge is caused because computers are built into many construction components. For example, heating and air-conditioning units will contain a microprocessor. Knowledge of this computer system is required to make the unit run at all. If the entire building is controlled by a building automation system, integration of the unit into this system can require significant additional knowledge and experience.

Although there are still unskilled positions in construction, there is no trade or class of work that is unskilled—all require some knowledge and judgment.

Construction organizations must have flat hierarchies—few layers

Construction companies are almost all family-owned enterprises that are less than three generations old. Construction has unsteady work volumes—peaks and valleys—so management must stay lean. Deep benches and top heavy organizational structures can seldom survive very long. One management level—such as project managers and superintendents—above those executing the work is a common limit. Very large companies may have one additional vice president (project executive) level. Additional levels will soon produce loss of control—with disastrous outcomes.

An illustration of the workability of flat organizational structures is the development of special projects divisions. Special project divisions are developed at some construction firms that typically perform very large projects, but wish to also perform small projects. To achieve the speed and responsiveness required for these smaller projects, layers of management are slashed to one, and rules reduced or eliminated. That this reduction is necessary and does work is a negative comment on the larger multilayered structure. This is reinforced when the larger project personnel are temporarily without a project assignment and attempt to move to the special project division. Cost over-runs of up to several times the project value frequently result, and firings follow.

Organizational structures are flat also because project management is highly focused, with few external considerations. For example, a common trade union rule for termination requires 15-minute notice and delivery of a paycheck—thus eliminating many of the functions of the human resource department. A finance department—since the project is financed by the owner—also has reduced work.

Projects are in many locations—and so are judgments and decisions

Construction projects are in locations remote from the construction manager's office, so travel times make the management and control that could exist in a factory unfeasible. Judgment and decision must be made at the job site level. As the knowledge required to execute tasks increases, the amount of job site decision and judgment increases further. Shorter decision times caused by accelerated schedules further add to the need for job site decision and judgment.

Centralized and Distributed Systems Compared

The centralized and distributed systems for organizations have similar principles to the rules and incentives for people as discussed below. The centralized system works by rules—the upper level makes them and the lower level follows them. The knowledge of the subordinate ranks is lost and wasted. The centralized system cannot possibly be better than the instructions of the top levels and, because of variation in human performance, will always be worse.

The distributed system realizes that the people closest to the work know it best. Facts must be found and analyzed, and judgments and decisions must be made at all levels. Establishment of a workable purpose and approach is essential and must precede the execution of the work. This requires the involvement of many, but cannot succeed without the commitment and leadership by the highest levels. Clear communication of this workable purpose and approach gives context, so all can understand how their part fits into the whole. It also gives a concrete way for each person to check that they are doing their job right as they are doing it—and self-correct when required.

A comparison: Ford's centralized system—Toyota's distributed system

A comparison to illustrate the two systems can be found with the early years of the Ford Motor and the Toyota companies. Ford Motor began manufacturing cars—the Model A in 1903 and the Model T in 1908—when America had a large geographical area and population that could afford to purchase and benefit from an automobile. The available work force was typically lower income people used to working for wages and doing what they were told. Ford Motor's response was to set up a system of detailed instructions on an assembly line producing a basic model in any color you want—as long as it is black. Large quantities of this uniform product were sold.

In contrast, Toyota began making automobiles in 1937. After the manufacturing interruption of World War II, Toyota made only 1,008 passenger cars in 1950 (Ford was making 7,000 cars per day at this time). High volumes were not immediately possible, and more variation in the product was required.

Further, the Toyota workers were typically farmers who tended their own small farms and were therefore used to seeing the whole picture, and making all the parts work together. They were not accustomed to simply taking directions. The Toyota approach became a flexible operation with a higher degree of worker decisions expected and included in the process. Mass customization of rapidly changing and improving products was the goal and result.

Construction by nature is done in small batches, usually batches of one. So, the Toyota mass customization model with distributed decision making is vastly more suitable to construction than the Ford model mass production of central command and control. Yet, the command and control model is frequently used in construction—with the expected inferior results.

Management Structures That Do Not Work in Construction

Bureaucratic management structures guarantee no results will be achieved

Bureaucratic structures have rigid job titles and responsibilities, have rigid rules, and perform processes and procedures rigidly. Protection of the organization and the employees in the organization is the goal. Achieving results is of little or no importance.

A bureaucratic model is used by government agencies. Unfortunately, this type of thinking frequently creeps into private firms. There are some "program managers," "construction managers," or "owner's representatives" who are full-fledged construction bureaucrats watching and finding fault with others, but accomplishing nothing themselves. A natural human tendency to feel "there ought to be a law against that" produces this kind of thinking. Yet, that there are still criminals indicates that laws do not guarantee success.

The bureaucrat believes:

The process matters—results do not.
Although bureaucrats say they are trying to achieve results, their actions say the opposite. They are only concerned with processes and procedures. This is particularly difficult for people in construction to believe since everything in construction is judged by results.

Rules rule.
Bureaucrats who have never accomplished anything believe they can tell everyone else how to do everything. For this, they write rules—many and complicated.

Rules apply only to others.
Bureaucrats believe rules apply to others never to them. Even those who are quite decent in their personal lives never see this position as inconsistent and unfair.

No bureaucrat is personally responsible for anything ever.
Everything is depersonalized. Things are done by the organization, agency, specialists, or analysts, not by real people with real names. Real people do not act this way.

Punish them all.
Rules are enforced by coercion—physical threats (jail), penalties (taxes, fines, firing, demotions). Incentives are rarely used.

Slow them down—stop them if you can.
Waiting, slowing all activities, fabricating delays, waiting them out, or stopping all accomplishments are the standard operating procedures. And this again is not done for any reason, or to accomplish some alternate result, but only because this is what bureaucrats do.

Speak a foreign language.
Use of jargon and pointless complexity when mangling the English language is used to hide that they have little to say, or that what they have to say would be unacceptable if plainly spoken.

We want more.

More money, more time, more staff, more authority. Whatever the reason, or even without a reason, the bureaucrat's answer is always "We want more."

Since the bureaucratic structure does nothing to achieve results, and since everything in construction is organized to achieve results, all parts of the bureaucratic model should always be completely avoided. Even a few bureaucratic procedures can compete with those trying to get results, and use up all the oxygen in the room.

Matrix structures complicate communication and add cost and time

You cannot serve two masters—A house divided against itself cannot stand

A matrix structure requires parties to report to more than one boss. An example is a company that has four regions. The functions of the company are divided into three departments, each with its own head: project management, field operations, and accounting and finance. If a person trying to execute a project reports both to the head of the northern region and to the head of each of the other three departments, immense time would be taken up in communication, resolution of power struggles, and personality conflicts. A similar conflict is common between heads of field and office operations in companies with only one region.

The matrix structure can appear to function in the short run if there is vast profit to allow for these inefficiencies. But a lean and well-run organization cannot function under a matrix structure. One master alone must be selected.

The number and location of project staff vary by project size and type

"Office" management staff consists of project managers, estimators, project engineers, and accountants. "Field" management staff consists of superintendents, foremen, and support staff such as safety officers. Larger projects can develop hierarchies for each position. For example, a general superintendent and assistant superintendents for each of the areas of structural, mechanical, and electrical—and each of these may have assistants as well. If a project includes multiple buildings, a superintendent(s) may be assigned to each of these buildings.

The division of office staff will vary by project size and type. The small and medium-size projects will typically have a project manager mainly stationed in the office responsible for multiple projects—but the project manager will be probably stationed on site for larger projects. On fast-track projects, which require continual estimate updates, the estimator may be stationed on the project site—but on a hard bid lump sum contract that has few changes, the estimator will remain in the office. And for most projects, the accountant will also remain in the office, but if extensive time and material work or detailed subdivision among accounts for the owner's requirements is needed, full-time accountants may be stationed at the project site.

The decision about the location and the commitments of staff must be planned in the early stages of the project so that availability of the needed personnel can be ensured, and appropriate costs included in the general conditions for these personnel commitments. The resource calendar associated with the project schedule can materially help manage the scheduling of the needed manpower resources.

Virtual teams (where in person meetings are rare, and communication is electronic or by phone) is a fashionable subject that has gained wide acceptance in some areas such as information technology. Virtual teams exist to a very limited extent in construction project management where off-site fabrication requires significant coordination. But virtual teams for management of the project itself are not effective or attempted. Much project information is best viewed graphically and involves the human element—that can be viewed best and fastest in person.

Managing People with Rules and Incentives

Rules enforce minimum standards, incentives execute all possibilities

The activities of a group, such as a company, the staff of a project, or a crew require communicated goals, expectations of behavior, boundaries, and rewards and consequences. Rules and incentives are two different ways to encourage people to achieve these tasks and objectives. Rules enforce minimum standards and are always needed. Incentives can encourage all possibilities and are required to achieve excellence and continuous improvement.

For example, when driving a car, there are lane-marking lines, directional arrows, and stop signs. These are necessary rules and must be followed, but following them will not make you a good driver or get you where you want to go when you want to get there. Signs such as "20 mph when school children present" or "bridge slippery when wet" try to guide judgment, but help only a little. Good, safe driving does not come from rules alone, but also judgment produced by experience, and influenced by the situation. If your goal is safe and defensive driving, you many slow down or move over when you sense a dangerous driver near you. But you may exceed the speed limit on the way to the hospital if you have a passenger requiring urgent medical attention. Rules are a necessary starting point, incentives finish the job.

Rules—Recognized Customs, Boundaries, and Instructions for Task Execution

Recognized customs

First are the types of rules that are not intended to achieve tasks, but are really customs where many ways will do equally well. You just need to pick one and change it as infrequently as possible. Examples—red light means stop and green means go, drive our cars on the right side of the street, pay periods end on Sunday, and payday is on Tuesday.

Boundaries

Second are rules that define a playing field, boundaries of behavior, and the minimum standards of behavior. These consist primarily of "thou shalt nots." They intend to keep us from doing bad things, but do not tell you how to execute a specific task. Examples—no company tools or vehicles can be taken for personal use, no drugs or alcohol at the job site, report injuries immediately. The Ten Commandments are examples of this second type of rule—relying heavily on "thou shalt nots." After we received these commandments 3,500 years ago, most people can follow most of them, most of the time. But excellence has not yet been achieved.

Instructions for task execution

The third type of rules are detailed directions on how to execute a specific task. Use of this type of rule requires the belief that some higher authority can specify all the exact steps to do the task. These rules are enforced by catching people doing something wrong and punishing them. This will work only if the task is repetitive without variation and requires no judgment. The results can never be better than the original intent. And because of human imperfection, the results will always be somewhat less than expected.

Incentives—goals and rewards

Incentives, by contrast, use a stated goal and feedback to accomplish a task. This requires that

1. A goal is stated
2. Everyone understands the goal
3. Everyone has the ability to decide how to reach it

4. Everyone knows when they have accomplished it
5. Everyone gets a reward at completion

This is a process of assisting and encouraging people to do something right and then giving them rewards. Because there is individual latitude in execution of the task, the final result can be superior to the original expectation.

For example, a stated goal might be to "finish on time and on budget," but in the real world, goals are seldom this simple. A more realistic example is a restoration and reconstruction of an enclosed pedestrian bridge between two buildings. The technical concerns are maintaining existing electrical power and communication during construction, installing a trouble-free new roof while keeping the existing adjacent roofs watertight, and providing the highest level of cosmetic finishes both interior and exterior. There are two owner representatives to keep happy—one cares about mechanical systems and one cares about finish material appearances and fast execution. This owner has six other similar bridges needing restoration, and you want to perform this project in such a way that you also negotiate and perform the additional work. Coming close to budget is important, but getting the next six jobs is more important.

These are the goals. You know when you have achieved the goals when you complete the first project well and close to budget, and get the next six projects.

Communication of Rules and Incentives—Gravity Flow of Information

Communication flows by "gravity" downward from superiors to subordinates, but must be moved upwards with effort. For example—in a downtown hi-rise building, superiors can have the parking attendant park their cars in the lower level garage, pass the security guard on the way to the elevators, and pass the receptionist on the way to their offices. It is not uncommon for the car parking personnel to call the security guard, to call the secretary, and communicate who was in the party, what they were discussing, and their mood at the time. The superior may not know this is happening, or even these peoples' names.

This one way flow of information restricts the knowledge of the subordinates from reaching the superiors. For example, if the parking lot attendants knew that a fence around the parking lot had been broken and criminals were entering and vandalizing cars, they may want to let management know, but the effort might be too great—or they might fear being blamed.

Information flows downward by gravity, because the subordinates rely on the superiors for continued employment, raises, and satisfactory employment conditions. Also, most people are not used to being asked about what they want. For example—with a house purchase, mortgage, car purchase, school for their children, taxes, and medical care choices, you can chose from preset options, but not specify exactly what you want. Variations exist and everyone has to pick and choose and craft an acceptable solution from the options available.

But simple picking from existing options is not enough—you must work with and around the rules, and consider options not covered by rules at all. Most of what employees learn is learned by example—from those around them including equals, subordinates, and superiors. They respond to incentives to achieve their goal. They need to be able to check their results against the stated intended purpose. They will watch and mimic what you do, more than listen to what you say.

A Workable Approach Defines the Rules—and Emphasizes Incentives

Stating the workable purpose means that everyone can know what is supposed to happen, and will have a standard against which to check if they are achieving it. The definition of workable purpose communicates the goal in a way everyone can understand. Counting everything and finding a workable plan (described in the previous chapters) both define the rules and provide the means for everyone to know when they have accomplished it. When these conditions exist, self-control also exists.

Definition of the workable purpose and approach requires continuous management involvement—working with others—or it will not happen at all. Management's effort setting goals, determining methods to achieve these goals, and counting everything communicate by example and gravity that this is real and important.

Finally, with a purpose that can be achieved, and the information to determine it is achieved, everyone can verify that their part fits in the whole. Providing incentives that match their success with your success will enforce creditability throughout the entire process. When employee incentives match the goals of the project, employees can work in their own self-interest and achieve the project goals as a result.

Public and individual awards and incentives can produce big returns at low cost

Public recognition, such as news release articles and news media events such as ribbon-cutting or topping out ceremonies, can produce big benefits in morale and productivity at a very low cost. Project personnel feel proud to be part of something big and important. Individual awards—shirts, work jackets, and other company spirit wear—for performance such as number of safe workdays, similarly can produce great satisfaction at a low cost. Although year-end bonuses for management employees are common and welcome, money is not the most effective project performance incentive.

Each company has a culture that can only be changed a little, slowly, and with great effort

Companies have cultures and personalities with shared systems of beliefs, capacities, procedures, and comfortable habits. This culture is an asset that produces effective performance for a range of project types and owners, but will be totally ineffective and inappropriate for others. An aggressive high-production road contractor will probably be unsuitable for a negotiated renovation project within an existing operating facility. A company culture cannot be changed in time for one new project, so present company culture must be evaluated when selecting project participants.

Summary

Construction companies have few layers of management—usually one, sometimes two. All construction operations require knowledge at all levels and for all trades. Sophisticated products require knowledge to install, and the project's remote locations and fast pace require increased decision making at the job site. A distributed organizational structure with facts, judgments, and decisions made at all levels is, therefore, required. This must be accompanied by clear communication of the workable approach and purpose. Bureaucratic and matrix structures cannot succeed, and must be avoided.

Rules that are conventions and boundaries are needed to define the playing field and enforce minimum standards for behavior. Set them early, and leave them alone. Incentives can produce results that exceed expectations. Whenever possible, incentives should, therefore, be emphasized over rules that are detailed direction on how to execute a specific task.

Management's work with others to define the workable purpose and approach provides the information for others to work by incentives. Since management has the same goals and incentives, it also communicates by example and gravity what management says is real, and believable.

Planning the layout and slopes of temporary haul roads is an important task for larger earthwork operations.

Review Questions (True or False)

1. The construction management firm's organizational chart represents the real lines of communication for a project.

2. A top-down command and control structure restricts judgment and decision to the upper level of the organization, whereas a distributed knowledge system requires facts to be known and judgments and decision made at all levels.

3. Mechanization and the increase in proprietary and sophisticated products decrease the number of trade workers required, and increase their required knowledge.

4. Most construction companies are publicly traded enterprises with multiple levels of management.

5. When large construction firms also seek to perform small projects, a special projects division is sometimes developed to achieve the flatter more efficient organizational structure required.

6. Both because projects are highly focused and have fewer external considerations, and are in locations remote from the construction management firm's main office, more decisions must be made at the project site.

7. A centralized system that works by rules developed by upper management and executed by project personnel is the most effective way to enforce rigorous standards.

8. A distributed system realizes that people closest to the work know it best, and facts obtained and analyzed, and judgments and decisions must be made at all management levels. This distributed knowledge system can only be effective with leadership and support from the highest levels of the construction management firm.

9. Bureaucratic structures have rigid job titles, rules, and processes, and value the process over the result of the process.

10. A matrix structure that requires parties to report to more than one boss is an effective structure for more complex projects.

11. The staffing of a project office, and therefore general conditions costs, is influenced by the project size type, organizational structure, and project approach and must be included in project planning and costing.

12. Virtual teams (with the participants in remote locations communicating electronically and by phone) are the dominant and growing organizational structure for construction project management.

13. Rules enforce minimum standards and are always needed, but cannot guide complicated processes. Incentives can encourage all possibilities and achieve excellence and continuous improvement.

14. Rules define recognized customs and boundaries and should be definitively stated and changed as infrequently as possible.

15. Complete definitive instructions for task execution that require no judgment by the installing personnel should always be developed.

16. Communication readily moves down from management to line workers, but upward flow of information requires more effort.
17. Effective motivation aligns worker incentives with project goals.
18. Money is the most effective and frequently used incentive.

Test Your Understanding

1. Which of the following can be defined by rules, and which must be managed by distributed knowledge and judgment:
   Hours of work
   Designated parking location for employees
   Employee entrance gates, permitted access roads, and paths of travel
   Designated smoking, break/lunch areas
   Subcontractor material storage locations
   Subcontractor job site office locations
   Requirements for weekly toolbox safety meetings
   Procedures for incident reports
   Emergency phone numbers and emergency response procedures
   Coordination of HVAC ductwork location and fire protection sprinkler piping
   Change order request procedures
   Dispute resolution and claims management
   Responsibility for provision of starters and disconnects for HVAC equipment

2. You are building a 100,000-square-foot outpatient surgery center shell and core (no tenant work) in your town. The HVAC system includes multiple systems to provide the required outside air, purity of filtration, and humidity control supported by a sophisticated building automation system. Laboratory hoods and process gas systems are also included. Both critical and emergency power are provided by connection to two power grids, fully supplemented by on-site generators. Data and communication systems require dedicated data rooms with appropriate fire protection systems.

   You complete and close out the shell and core contract, and are then awarded a second contract for the first 10,000-square-foot build out.

   Discuss the difference in organizational structure required for the two projects, including which portions of the required staff would be stationed in the home office, and which would work full time at the project.

3. Your construction management firm has a flat organizational structure with most personnel dedicated to working full time at a project location. You can secure a full-service multiyear construction management contract, but the project owner with whom you will have significant interaction works under a bureaucratic matrix structure. Discuss your possible organization, staffing, and contractual arrangements, particularly in reference to general condition costs, that would be needed to effectively respond to the owner's different management structure.

CHAPTER
3.3

Communication Starts with Correct Observation

Tight urban sites have extremely limited space for staging and storing of materials awaiting installation. Organization of the delivery times and sequences becomes critical.

Communication Starts with Correct Observation

Quantitative and qualitative observation are both necessary

Consistent units, measurement, and terms are essential

The designed and engineered project must be executed to organize and manage people. So careful and the consistent observation and measurement essential to science and engineering must carry through for project communications. But communication customs and natural biases must be managed as well for effective communication. This chapter discusses the integration of rigorous observation and measurement and the human perception of these measurements.

Observation is for a purpose

Observation is noticing and describing things and characteristics of things—for a purpose. The purpose determines what can, should, and will be observed.

The parties who build parts of a building see different things in the completed structure—and can and do observe different things:

> The earthwork contractor sees volumes and grades of earth, possible placement of equipment, and haul roads.

> The foundation contractor sees the foundation, methods of forming, shoring, and temporary drainage. Most of these are concealed from view or even removed from the site after completion of the foundation.

> The bricklayer sees types, numbers, and configurations of bricks, blocks, reinforcing, mortar, and possible methods of scaffolding.

> The window contractor sees the type and quantity of windows, and probable method of anchorage and sealing windows.

> The interior designer sees colors, textures, lights, and shadows.

Each party's observation is correct for its own purpose. But if each party made and used only their own observations, there would be a Tower of Babel—each speaking their own language, unable to communicate with others. The purpose is not just to perform earthwork, or install foundations, brick, and windows, and decorate them, but to build a complete building.

For this purpose, observations are required that can be made, organized, and used many different ways—by many people. These observations must be able to be organized in many ways to convert data (facts) to information (knowledge), which is necessary for the purpose of successful project completion.

Quantitative Observation Involves Measurement

Quantitative observation is possible of:
> Length, width, height, thickness, and volume
> Weight
> Force, power, energy, and light
> Indivisible units such as people
> Money
> Time

Each party can measure these quantities, understand them, and use them. The use of standard quantities makes communication possible—establishing facts that all agree are facts. These quantitative observations (facts) are the necessary starting point for all knowledge and decision making—and must be maintained throughout the decision-making process. But facts alone will not produce knowledge. Qualitative observation is also necessary.

Qualitative Observation Involves Impressions, with Support

Qualitative observations are impressions, which are supported by information that is less complete and precise than one would want. This is so because some of what would be useful information is not available, or the subject is too complex and subjective to permit quantitative measurement.

Everyone needs and uses impressions, feelings, intuitions, and instincts in daily life. Use in the business world is also required. But because business is people working together to take measurable inputs to produce measurable outputs in a mutually agreeable way, convincing support—though incomplete—is required to communicate and gain agreement with others. "It is so because I feel it is so," lacks any supporting information that others could check and has no useful purpose in the business world. On the other hand, recognizing only observations that can be quantitatively measured misses many of the observations people use everyday in the real world.

For example, the impression that there are difficult and corrupt cities that discourage legitimate business activity is widely accepted. Some documentation is possible—length of time and cost to obtain permits—but others such as bribes paid are concealed as much as the perpetrators can manage. The mix of hard data (time and cost of permits) and the occasional conviction for bribery constitutes the less-than-complete, but generally accepted, support for this impression.

Similarly, the impression that some workforces are motivated and some are not is also widely accepted. Productivity, and changes in productivity, rate of defects, absenteeism, higher-than-normal use of sick and personal days, and quantity of employee suggestions are not measures of motivation itself but are considered supporting indications of motivation.

The qualitative observations and the supporting data must be both true and generally believed to be true if they are to be accepted and used by others.

Which pickup truck is "best" can be described by the manufacturer's detailed description of size, weight, engine, transmission, load capacity, and other information on features. Although this information is available to all, it is not generally accepted as support for the selection of the "best" truck. Many buyers are blindly loyal to one brand of truck for life. Because the support for "best" truck is not generally accepted, it cannot be used when communicating with others.

Both Quantitative and Qualitative Observations Are Needed

Both quantitative and qualitative observations are necessary to make the most informed decisions. When building a construction project, the most obvious, basic, quickly, and cheaply obtainable quantitative facts are obtained, and then a qualitative reaction to these facts is made. This two-step process is repeated with increasing detail—for both the quantitative and the qualitative observations—until the qualitative and quantitative reasonably agreed. These ideas are illustrated in the following example.

Starting a four-story office building in Chesterton, PA

1. Basic quantitative observations:

    A four-story office building is proposed for a 3.6-acre site at the southwest corner of Main St and First Avenue in Chesterton, PA. The project budget has been established, financing obtained, and a desired completion date established.

2. Qualitative observation:

    Chesterton and the surrounding county both claim jurisdiction for permits and inspections, so these activities will need more time and effort. The site is in a congested built-up area with slow access roads, so access, staging, hoisting, and storage of materials will take more time and money to properly manage.

3. Additional quantitative observation:

    The structure is to be a conventional structural steel building, but the owner of the building is an affiliate of a foreign company engaged in manufacture and erection of aluminum and glass atriums and skylights. Their product is to be used on this building, but it has never been installed in this country.

4. Additional qualitative observation:

    The unfamiliar atrium and skylight product will require all parties to learn the system and the implications for their work. The construction personnel may want changes to the structure or the mechanical system for unanticipated structural, heating and cooling loads, and unusual hoisting. The financing personnel may have insurance impacts and financing restrictions. The government permitting agencies may have code evaluation difficulties. This requires time and effort, and the conclusion could be that the system is unfeasible at this location at this time with the budget available.

Effective Communication of Observations and Measurements

Reduce the clutter, write or draw facts, talk about judgments

Define terms consistent with both industry standards and common usage

Definition of all terms is required for understanding and communication: "If you don't know what you mean, no one else will either." Single items by one trade usually are understood by common trade names, and only the grade and quality need to be stated. 4-inch cast-iron hub pipe of a specific grade needs no further definition. However, assemblies and systems need definition in every case.

The terms *general conditions, supplementary conditions, rough carpentry, finishes, equipment, special systems*, just to name a few, have no commonly accepted definitions. Further, for any work item, waste, sales tax, shipping, payroll taxes, tools and equipment, vehicle expense, supervision, and home office overhead may or may not be included. There are contradictory attempts at industry standard definitions, but even these are unknown to many and used by few.

The importance of definition applies also to the previous discussions about observation, organization of observations, and determining the workable approach but is discussed here because the importance becomes more noticeable when organizing and communicating the previously obtained information.

Definitions are required and must be confirmed for each project. But no one alone can change everyone much or soon. So the practical rules that help are (1) use standard industry terms that communicate to all when possible, (2) use a consistent method to allocate burdens (as described above: waste, sales tax, shipping...) to every line item and have this allocation visually evident in all presentation material, (3) use an organizational structure recognized by many such as the CSI (Construction Specification Institute) system, and (4) define only the remaining terms not defined by steps 1–3. But define them in as many places as they first occur. Even with these steps, frequent and repeated communication will be necessary.

Every person in a management or supervisory position handles 15,000–20,000 tasks in a year. Every task is required and therefore important. But no single person can remember this volume of tasks. And no group possessing individual collections of 15,000–20,000 tasks can possibly communicate—or even function.

Selection of tower cranes and man and material hoists are critical management decisions that affect productivity and schedule.

People can only think of one thing at a time and, usually in western culture, only for 7 seconds—then they have to think about it in a different light or from a different angle. People can think of at most a group of seven related things at a time, but many people can only think of about three. After that they must bundle things into groups. There are two distinct approaches required to manage the inevitably large volume of facts.

Facts—write or draw, then talk

For information that is objective (facts)—write or draw the fact and put it in an organizational structure—available to all. Following up the written or drawn facts with additional verbal explanation is required for most people, but the writing or drawing must come first.

All facts are entered individually and put into racks for information storage. Get them stored and out of the way, but not lost. This has the advantage that everything urgent and nonurgent can be addressed in the chosen order. Also, the facts will be stored and available for all, so people who process information at different paces can come back in their own time. People who prefer written communication, verbal, numbers, or touching and feeling physical things can all make the same facts real and understandable in their own way. In this way, all the facts can be available to all in a way that is usable by different processing styles.

Judgments—talk, then write

Judgments, intuitions, impressions, and people judgments must be first discussed—not written. Except that the conclusion of the judgment that will be used in action can be written. Reading detailed written descriptions of subtle information is a limited skill not shared by the full range of people with different information processing styles. So, it should be avoided. Writing well about judgments is a yet rarer skill. But a project requires the judgment of many, so alternate methods of communication useable by all are required. Subtle communication is possible by all with in-person verbal communication. And this is the appropriate and effective manner to discuss and analyze judgments and impressions.

By writing the facts and talking about the judgments, clutter can be reduced and one can choose to focus on the important, not merely the urgent. Further, when the facts are fully identified, organized, and available, all will be equally informed. Ignorant statements, wild baseless conjecture, and analysis of impossible options will be substantially eliminated. The discussion about judgments will focus on the few crucial areas required for determination of the workable approach. Since the participants are informed, the discussions are shorter and conclusive. The conclusion of these discussions, but little of the discussions themselves, can and must be documented in writing.

A successful example

Effective use of these principles occurs with the following project estimating process:
1. The plans and specifications (facts) are provided to all estimating personnel.
2. Estimators perform quantity surveys (obtaining facts) and request vendor pricing or sub proposals where required (soliciting facts).
3. A preliminary scope and nature of the project emerges (facts and preliminary judgments).
4. A job site walk-through with owner and architect is conducted, and the owner's, architect's, and estimator's impressions and feelings are verbally communicated (some facts and some judgment).
5. The estimator completes estimate (judgment and some facts).

Here, the facts come first and occupy over 95% of the time. All can gather facts and form independent preliminary judgments in their own way and time—followed by discussion of these judgments with others.

An unsuccessful example

The alternate unsuccessful but frequently used approach is:
1. The owner sends request for proposal describing the project in the most favorable light (judgment).
2. The plans and specifications are distributed at the job site walk-through—differing in part from the request for proposal description. Without time to even unroll the plans, ignorant questions are asked (an attempt at judgment in the absence of facts).
3. The estimators return to their offices and complete steps 2 and 3 described in the successful example above.
4. The estimator questions the architect and owners by phone and in writing (request for facts).
5. The estimator completes the estimate in the absence of any substantial meeting of the minds with the architect and owner (unresolved attempt at judgment).

Judgments are made without facts—and initial judgments can be altered only partially and with difficulty. Ignorant judgments will later produce errors and arguments.

Careful observation and effective communication must remain integrated

Many in construction management are familiar and comfortable with a careful and consistent observations and measurements needed in science and engineering—yet struggle to maintain this rigor when managing people. This chapter offers deceptively simple but effective methods to maintain the integration of engineering and management, which is the starting point for effective communication. Next chapter will build on these principles to discuss the practical application of project communication.

Summary

Qualitative and quantitative observations together are necessary for informed decisions. First, quantitative observations (facts) are obtained that are agreed to be facts and therefore permit communication. Then, qualitative impressions are obtained that are partially supportable and are believed to be true. Quantitative facts permit and encourage qualitative observation. Qualitative facts give meaning and insight and suggest further areas where quantitative facts can be obtained.

Managing people and information involves facts and judgment. The facts are many, and each is important. Facts must be organized and made available to all—with sufficient time for all to analyze them in their own way and at their own pace. Facts, therefore, must be presented in writing, not verbally. Judgments have to be discussed, not written because all can understand subtle and complicated nuances in person, but few can process the same information well in writing, and fewer still can write this information. Facts and judgments are both required. Obtaining and processing facts comes first and occupies over 95% of the time and is done in writing. Judgments follow the facts and are discussed verbally, with conclusions documented in writing.

Review Questions (True or False)

1. Communication requires integration of rigorous observation and measurement and human perception of these measurements.
2. Each party will make observations that are correct for their purpose, and all project participants should be expected to learn to understand these observations.
3. The use of standard measurement units for quantitative observation is essential for good communication.
4. Qualitative observations (that are subjective and less complete and precise than one wants) are essential but must be supported by at least some information that others can check.
5. A progressive cycle of quantitative and qualitative observations continues until reasonable agreement between these observations is reached.
6. Rigorous standard definitions are required to maintain consistency for multiple projects.
7. A manager may handle tens of thousands of tasks per year but can only mentally grasp three to seven tasks at a time, so organizational structure is critical for information management.
8. Facts are most effectively communicated by drawing and writing, and then placing these facts in an organizational structure.
9. Judgments, intuitions, impressions, and people judgments must be first discussed, and then a conclusion reached. Documentation of the discussion and the conclusions must be included in the project records.
10. For very small fast-paced projects, judgments can effectively precede quantitative analysis.

Test Your Understanding

You are preparing a bid for a project that consists of three additions to an existing operating high school.

1. The bid documents consist of general conditions, supplementary conditions, instructions to bidders, plans, specifications, soil engineering report, and a site survey. Using the cycle of quantitative and qualitative analysis, in which order would you review these documents?

2. The following factors can affect productivity and therefore time and cost, but are imperfectly defined by the bid documents:

Hours of work

Definition of barricades required for school security

Security clearance of trade employees

Method of handling school-mandated work stoppages due to noise complaints

Schedule of breakthrough from the additions into the existing school buildings

Definition of method to handle concealed conditions that may be encountered at the intersection of the addition and existing building

Permitted location of access roads

Designated areas for job site trailers, temporary facilities, and materials storage

Which of these factors can be definitively defined quantitatively and which require qualitative judgments?

3. At what point during the review of the documents, itemize in 1 above, can the job site walk-through be most effectively scheduled? And when in this review process, can requests for information and clarifications be most effectively presented by the bidder to the architect and engineer?

CHAPTER
3.4

Organization of Observations Requires Organizational Structure

On congested sites, hoisting usually must be performed for 60–80 hours per week. The resulting overtime costs, which must be included in the general conditions, are more than offset by the huge increases in productivity and schedule reduction. Planning this trade-off will be new to those accustomed to light commercial on less congested sites where overtime is usually minimized.

Organization of Observations Requires Organizational Structure

A reusable organizational framework helps change facts into information, information into knowledge

Once useable observations produce single objective facts, organization helps a reasonable person change the observations (facts) into information (knowledge)—to make informed decisions.

The Number of Observations Can Get Unmanageable

The number of observations needed and made for all purposes on a project vastly exceeds the capacity of any person's memory. For example, ordering wall framing lumber requires the following steps:

1. Estimate the required quantity.
2. Obtain a price from the supply house.
3. Make a notation of quoted price.
4. Determine precise quantity of each size of material to be ordered.
5. Determine the portion of the entire order that can be stored and used at the job site without double handling.
6. Place the order.
7. Make notation of order placed and balance of order to be placed.
8. Place balance of the order.
9. Receive order and place it in required location.
10. Determine that received count matches ordered count.
11. Determine if any material is defective.
12. Notify supply house of defects.
13. Notate defective materials on shipping ticket.
14. Receive replacements for defective material.
15. Determine count is correct.
16. Determine if any material is defective.
17. Receive invoice for material.
18. Match invoice with delivery ticket for the first shipment and for the second shipment of replacement materials.
19. Pay invoice.
20. Record invoice in accounting system.

20 steps are required to obtain the wall-framing material. If any step is missed, performance will suffer—for example, payment for material never received, installation of defective material, avoidable double handling of material, late payment to the supply house, and loss of job cost control. And ordering wall framing material is just part of framing the walls. And walls are just one part of all framing, and framing is just one part of the building. The number of required observations on a small building project completed in 3 months might be 5,000. Larger projects can easily have hundreds of thousands of observations.

If 100,000 or even 5,000 material orders, delivery tickets, and invoices are dumped on a person's desk with the instructions "make sense of this and get it right, it is very important," the average person will give up. The unusually hardworking would struggle and achieve, at best, second rate results. With organizational structure, such failures can be avoided.

A Framework for Facts Stores and Organizes Information

An information organizational structure must be set at the very start of the project.

It will:

1. Identify all required work items.

2. Organize a place for all facts.

3. Avoid personal point of views and itemize all work items and facts with equal consideration, weight, and detail.

Such a framework will be used (with some modifications) for all projects, regardless of the size, scope, or nature. At the start of the project, the framework will be empty. The framework structure will stay the same for the entire project and get fleshed out with additional information.

Without such an organizational structure at the start of the project, important facts and observations will be temporarily or permanently misplaced. Constant rework and reorganization of facts that are not properly stored exceed the attention span of almost all project participants. People will give up and shoot from the hip.

One such system that fulfills these requirements is the CSI (Construction Specifications Institute) system. This system uses an organizational structure that is in the approximate normal order of project construction. This helps building the project mentally and on paper. It is the most common organizational system now in use. Other systems, such as the Army Corps of Engineers system, also work.

A new organizational system should not be designed for each project. It is a far more difficult task than it appears and will require the participation of many people, with many different points of view. Also, a new organization system will tend to use one viewpoint, emphasizing the familiar and customary, and this is usually very different from the requirements of a whole project.

One example of this bias occurs when a carpentry contractor attempts to grow into a general contractor. Their usual organizational system for approaching a project is very heavy on the carpentry items and may miss entire portions of the other 85% of the project. Many such contractors have gone out of business because of these missed costs.

Having an organizational system in place that counts everything at the beginning of the project is critical to all following steps. Even the smallest item must be identified so that its implications are not overlooked. For example, window blinds can increase or decrease the solar heat gain or heat loss out of a building. These heat gains and losses affect the heating, ventilation, and air-conditioning system sizes, which can, in turn, affect the size of the electrical service. Although blinds may be only a fraction of a percent of the project value and seem trivial, "leave it to the decorator later," they cannot be overlooked without consequence. All projects have many similar examples.

Establishing the Purposes for an Organizational Structure

An organizational structure filters, sorts, and sets in order observations for a purpose.

So, establishing the purpose must come first.

Possible purposes for your organizational structure

Build an excellent product—common to all projects.

Make a profit—almost always a stated purpose but frequently not accompanied by the necessary action.

Get paid and pay your bills on time—common to all successful projects.

Manage a vast number of tasks with many participants—a need common to all projects but found on few.

Owner accounting—accounting for construction cost by owner requirements, such as by department, by financial year, or by different depreciation periods, for shell, core, and tenant development.

Financing documentation. If the project is financed by a construction loan, accounting and documentation will have to meet the lender's requirements.

Satisfy government regulation well enough to avoid government interference—a purpose by default.

Process improvement—documentation of ongoing activities so quality can be improved or costs reduced for future projects—exists, but it is rare.

Selecting your purposes—many sound nice, but only a few are achievable

Clear, complete, and realistic purposes of the project are required before a good organizational system can be selected. If the purpose is not selected before the start of the project, catch up later is not possible. Many of the required observations will not have been made. And the time to make them has passed. If purposes are too ambitious—demands exceeding the capabilities or time available for execution—the system will be too cumbersome for effective use, and multiple failures will occur.

Organizational System Characteristics That Work

Organizational systems that will work (and be used) have these characteristics:

The system structure is immediately apparent without explanation.

Observations can be entered successfully by data entry personnel with little training.

Observations recorded in the system can be verified.

The system purpose will tend to be realized due to the structure of the system, even if the purpose is not immediately apparent.

An observation can be used by many people for many different purposes.

Observations can be reordered for multiple purposes, without re-entry of data.

Filter out "useless" characteristics

Useful observations must have the following characteristics:

They have a purpose for more than one party.

They are in standard units of measurement.

All observations that do not have these characteristics are useless and must be discarded before sorting and setting in order.

"Sort and set in order" characteristics

Three sortings of observation are usually the limit of the patience of most people. It is also the limit of what is necessary to get the result. (For example, it is usually true that one can locate a person anywhere in the country with three phone calls.)

Two Levels of Organization are Useful for Construction Projects

Sort by the objective facts of the observation

Alphabetically by name, number such as street address or age, or time order of occurrence—phone books, dictionaries, employee listings, and job site activity logs are examples. The purpose is only to record information for easy recall. No assistance in transforming this information into knowledge is provided by this organizational structure.

An employee list, for example, with name, trade, job assignment, and dates of employment could be sorted by name and date to answer the question, "Did this guy work for us two years ago?" or could be sorted by date, job assignment, and trade to answer the question, " How many electricians did we have on that job last July?" This is useful information that is obtained only by sorting, without further data entry. It cannot answer the questions "Was this a good employee?" "Was the staffing of that job about right?" But it does answer some of the questions that must be answered.

A system that is structured for and assists a defined purpose

The structure of these "good" systems resembles the purpose they serve—making use obvious and achievement of the intended result probable.

An example in the construction industry is the CSI system for organizing projects. This system (through the 1995 edition) uses a numeric system (1–16) to organize the project by trade and by the usual sequence of installation. The purpose is to build a project—make a detailed checklist of all required tasks, order these tasks, and define their relation to other tasks.

The CSI MasterFormat® system headings are listed below. (There are hundreds of more detailed subheadings.)

Division 1 General Requirements (e.g., administration, contracts, insurance)

Division 2 Site Construction (e.g., earthwork, drainage)

Division 3 Concrete

Division 4 Masonry

Division 5 Metals (e.g., structural steel, ornamental railings)

Division 6 Wood and Plastics (e.g., wood framing of the structure, wood cabinets)

Division 7 Thermal and Moisture Protection (e.g., roofing, waterproofing)

Division 8 Doors and Windows

Division 9 Finishes (e.g., walls, ceilings, flooring, painting)

Division 10 Specialties (e.g., lockers, mailboxes, flagpoles)

Division 11 Equipment (e.g., kitchen, church, prison, appliances, fixtures)

Division 12 Furnishings (e.g., furniture, artwork, theatre seating)

Division 13 Special Construction (e.g., swimming pools, ice rinks, dog kennels)

Division 14 Conveying Systems (e.g., elevators, escalators)

Division 15 Mechanical (e.g., heating, plumbing, fire sprinklers)

Division 16 Electrical

With the exception of the mechanical and electrical trades, who work continuously throughout the project, this is a listing in the usual order of installation. The order of the organizational system is the same as the order of construction. This makes "building it in your head before actually building it" or "building it on paper" easier and therefore more likely to succeed. In other words, the organizational structure encourages and helps good planning.

This 16-section format has existed in very close to the same form for over 40 years and achieved widespread acceptance not only in the construction field but also in related fields such as finance and even tax law. A substantial revision of this organizational system was adopted in 2004, but many in these allied fields have not yet recognized or are even aware of this revision—so use of the pre-2004 systems is still widespread.

The 2004 CSI MasterFormat® system reflects new technologies and construction responsibilities

The division numbers and titles for the 2004 MasterFormat system are listed below.

Division Numbers and Titles
Procurement and Contracting Requirement Group

Division 00 Procurement and Contracting Requirements

Specifications Group

General Requirements Subgroup

Division 01 General Requirements

Facility Construction Subgroup

Division 02 Existing Conditions
Division 03 Concrete
Division 04 Masonry
Division 05 Metals
Division 06 Wood, Plastics, and Composites
Division 07 Thermal and Moisture Protection
Division 08 Openings
Division 09 Finishes
Division 10 Specialties
Division 11 Equipment
Division 12 Furnishings
Division 13 Special Construction
Division 14 Conveying Equipment
Division 15 Reserved
Division 16 Reserved
Division 17 Reserved
Division 18 Reserved
Division 19 Reserved

Facility Services Subgroup

Division 20 Reserved
Division 21 Fire Suppression
Division 22 Plumbing
Division 23 Heating, Ventilation, and Air Conditioning
Division 24 Reserved
Division 25 Integrated Automation
Division 26 Electrical
Division 27 Communications
Division 28 Electronic Safety and Security
Division 29 Reserved

Site and Infrastructure Subgroup

Division 30 Reserved

Division 31 Earthwork

Division 32 Exterior Improvements

Division 33 Utilities

Division 34 Transportation

Division 35 Waterway and Marine Construction

Division 36 Reserved

Division 37 Reserved

Division 38 Reserved

Division 39 Reserved

Process Equipment Subgroup

Division 40 Process Integration

Division 41 Material Processing and Handling Equipment

Division 42 Process Heating, Cooling, and Drying Equipment

Division 43 Process Gas and Liquid Handling, Purification, and Storage Equipment

Division 44 Pollution Control Equipment

Division 45 Industry-Specific Manufacturing Equipment

Division 46 Reserved

Division 47 Reserved

Division 48 Electrical Power Generation

Division 49 Reserved

Some of the changes recognize new project work areas, such as telecommunication, which was formerly installed only by the phone company monopoly. And electronic controls in buildings (security, building automation) were a pioneering technology in 1970, and pollution control systems were much less common and developed. So an organizational system had to be revised to accommodate these new realities.

Much of the useful structure was retained, but some was lost. For example, earthwork was moved from Division 2 to 31—thus moving it out of the order of installation, making the format less helpful for "building it mentally and on paper." Also, 49 sections is too large a number for most people to grasp and remember.

Some Common Practical Organization Conventions for Administrative Documentation

The organizational systems described above address much of the critical technical project documentation, but other administrative documentation must be ordered as well. The categories listed below are frequently used.

Contracts and change orders—includes the original contract and all approved, pending, or rejected change orders.

Permissions—includes notices to proceed, stop orders, building permits, certificate of substantial completion, and occupancy permits. This category at one time contain few items and required limited effort—but now continues to grow and can become a significant effort spanning years of preconstruction activities.

Insurance—includes project specific insurance policies such as builder's risk and certificates of insurance from all required subcontractors.

| Steeple erection | *photo 3 of 15* |

Pay requests—applications for payment with the accompanying documentation followed by lien waivers can be a time consuming meticulous process. Since even one missing or improperly prepared document can slow or stop payment, organization is key.

Transmittals of technical documents or physical samples are numerous and usually routine but occasionally key, so nothing can be missed.

Chronological files listing each and every document are still frequently used as a backup for misfiled or lost documents.

Many documents such as contract change orders, permissions, insurance, pay request, and lien waivers usually still require hard original paper copies—this old tradition dies hard. Some larger owners are transitioning to electronic systems, but government and insurance companies are more reluctant to make the transition from paper to digital files. Increasingly, routine transmittals are recorded and organized in electronic information systems. Construction management firms increasingly transition to digital files wherever possible, and a well constructed, accepted, comfortable digital filing system is a significant company asset.

Organizational Structures That Are Not Useful to the Project

Organization by arbitrarily defined structure may be imposed by the owner of the project or by the construction company itself. Organization by geographic region, department, or customer account, for example, lacks clarity. The Midwest region in the United States has been variously defined as a half dozen states surrounding the Great Lakes, all states between the Appalachian and Rocky Mountains, and all states west of the Appalachian Mountains plus Japan. Department definition is not standard across companies, nor is the responsibility and authority. Customer account can mean anything from a certain product or project type for the customer to anything that can evolve out of the customer relationship.

These organizational structures are unrelated or even contrary to the purpose of the project, but they can be imposed very forcefully. If employee compensation or continued employment depends on achieving profitability goals for region, department, or customers, quality and timely completion of an individual project will be secondary and poor results may follow.

Summary

These organizational principles can be applied on all project sizes. They work for back of the envelope, limited checklists, and sophisticated computer systems. The principles for all systems remain the same:

Define the purpose of the project

Observe and establish objective facts

Filter the facts

Sort and set the facts in order in an organizational system that serves the project purpose

The purpose of this organizational structure is to change data (facts) into information (knowledge) so that communication and informed decision making is possible.

Review Questions (True or False)

1. There can be 5,000 observations on a small project and hundreds of thousands of observations on a larger project, both of which are unmanageable without an organizational system.

2. At the start of a project, a framework for facts and an organizational system will begin with (1) identifying all required work items, (2) organizing a place for all facts, and (3) itemizing all work items with equal weight, detail, and minimal bias.

3. All possible purposes for organizational structure can and must be included in an organizational system.

4. Workable organizational systems have the following characteristics: (1) the system structure is immediately apparent, (2) data entry personnel with little training can successfully enter observations, (3) observations can be verified, and (4) observations can be used for many purposes without re-entry of the data.

5. Observations that are for the purpose of one party only may be in the units of measurement most customary for that party.

6. The organizational structure must both sort by objective facts and assist a defined purpose.

7. The CSI MasterFormat system is the most common organizational system for building construction. The 1995 edition contained 16 divisions ordered in the approximate order of installation, and the 2004 revision had 49 divisions with similar, but altered, ordering.

8. Common practical organizational conventions for administrative documents address the categories of contracts and change orders, permission, insurance, and pay requests.

9. Altering the project organizational system for company-wide requirements such as geographical region, project type, or customer account can be readily achieved with little impact.

10. The principles for all organizational systems are (1) define the purpose of the project, (2) observe and establish objective facts, (3) filter the facts, and (4) sort and set the facts in order in an organizational system that serves the project purpose.

Test Your Understanding

1. You will build a two-car detached garage for a single-family home. The garage will have a concrete floor, wood-framed structure, wood-sided walls (requiring field painting), one window, one man door, one overhead door with an automatic operator, two lights, and one switch. Fence revisions and landscape restoration will be required. A building permit and the required licenses, bonds, and insurance will be obtained. The contract payment terms are 25% down, balance at completion. List the division numbers and names in the 1995 and 2004 CSI formats that will apply to this project.

2. For the same garage project, what common practical organizational conventions for administrative documentation will be needed?

3. Obtain a specification manual for a commercial project. In the table of contents of this manual, count the divisions used and the subcategories for each division.

CHAPTER
3.5

Managing Information, Documentation, and Communication

Most of the Wheaton Bible Church foundations were spread footings, but the long span trusses for the sanctuary required caissons.

Managing Information, Documentation, and Communication

Planning a communication structure and process is essential for effective management

Communication is a key management task—and time is a critical dimension

Communication and documentation help define and refine the scope, build relationships, manage expectations, and minimize claims. Communication does not process any and all data and information but only the portion that has meaning for multiple parties. The Project Management Institute defines communication as "timely and appropriate generation, collection, distribution, storage, retrieval and ultimately disposition of project information."

Large fixed overheads and the high cost of waiting time and rework make timely availability of data and information particularly critical in construction project management. So, the goal is to provide all needed information (but no more) exactly when needed.

Project communication must be planned, structured, and organized. Formats may be reused from past similar projects to reduce planning effort, but a fresh look is required for each new project. This five-step approach is described below. The earlier steps in the process receive heavier treatment not because of importance but because if well executed, the later steps become increasingly easy.

The volume of information and the channels of communication must be managed

Even the smallest construction project has many small steps, each important, that can total thousands or tens of thousands of steps for the project—larger projects can total hundreds of thousands or millions of steps. And the potential communication channels are vast as well.

The number of potential channels can be calculated by:

Number of parties × (number of parties − 1)/2

This produces 45 channels of communication for 10 parties, and 4,950 channels for 100 parties—too many for effective management. Management structure is needed to reduce these channels so the project manager can control all essential information—including the results of informal communication between other parties. But these focused channels must be tempered with communication of the overall project progress that shapes participants' perceptions—to make them feel valued and included—and help avoid claims.

Some studies say that 90% of a project manager's time is communication, but this is somewhat misleading. Information seeking, collaboration, negotiation, and building personal relationships may occur at the same time as transmission of information—and then the updated information and agreements must be formally communicated. This balance between managing the quantity of "need to know" information and "need to be involved" is discussed below.

Step 1. Identify Project Participants' Communication Needs and Preferences

The participants who must or should receive information must be identified and segregated into broad categories of rights and responsibilities and frequency of involvement.

Common useful categories of participants are as follows:

Participants involved with the project every day

(These parties have a contract related to the project and resulting ongoing authority and responsibility.)

       Project owner

       Project owner's sponsor

       Construction manager firm's personnel

       Designers and engineers

       Subcontractors

       Material suppliers

Participants with intermittent oversight or control

(These parties have a regulatory or contractual relationship with the project, but only intermittent authority and responsibility.)

       City building departments

       City police and fire departments

       Government regulatory agencies such as storm water and environmental management

       Labor unions (where applicable)

       Financing companies

       Bonding and insurance companies

Parties indirectly affected and involved

(These parties have no regulatory or contractual relationship with the project but may exert pressure that must be managed, or may provide promotion and recognition that can assist project approvals or the construction manager's and owner's business purposes.)

       General public

       Industry organizations and associations

       Professional associations

       Advocacy groups, for example, environmental concerns or minority participation

       News media

The participants continuously involved with the project will exist on all projects, but the specific parties and their responsibilities must be identified for each new project.

Participants with intermittent oversight will vary by project and must be specifically checked. For example, the relations with the city police and fire department may be as simple as correctly posting emergency response telephone numbers at the job site. Or, for addition and remodeling of existing facilities (containing sensitive data or operations) that maintain their own police or security forces, the relationship can be more complex and demanding.

The regulatory agencies affecting the project will vary by type of facility, construction means and methods, size of the facility, and applicable regulations at the job site. Labor union relations can involve area jurisdictions, trade jurisdictions, and the terms and conditions of work—and can become quite involved and demanding (with negotiations lasting months) and impact cost and schedule. But in non-union areas, these discussions do not take place. Similarly, finance, bonding, and insurance companies may require frequent inspections and notification of achievements and problems, or only a few milestones—depending on the project type and size.

Once a listing of project participants with their relationship and desired impact on the project is developed, filtering what they need to know and when they need to know it becomes more focused and achievable.

Step 2. Plan Communication to Reduce Information Volume and Manage Timing

Formal communication channels include the project manager, informal channels may not

The project manager must establish lines of communication that maintain control while avoiding participation in nonessential transactions. (Project managers who insist that all communication must cross their desk are not really managing at all and will soon be overwhelmed by data.) Identification and maintenance of information on milestones that define scope, time, and cost or affect the quality of relations between participants should be sought.

For example, development, review, and approval of the fire protection sprinkler shop drawings might have the key points of shop drawings requested, shop drawings received, coordination with affected trades, drawings approved by the engineer, drawings submitted to the fire department for approval, and fire department approval recorded. But the multiple discussions and negotiations related to each of the steps may be omitted from documentation.

Filter What Must Be Communicated and to Whom

Requirements by contract or regulation

The key information that must be communicated to direct project participants will usually be specified in the agreements with these participants. And general and supplementary conditions of the contract will specify the types and timing of many types of communication. Relationships with participants having intermittent oversight, such as building departments, finance companies, and bonding insurance companies, will be specified in their agreements or regulations as well.

Requirements by "need to know"

Subcontractors and vendors prepare shop drawings and submittals that are then transmitted through the construction manager to the affected subcontractors for coordination review, and then to the engineer or designer of record for approval. The construction manager's decision about who is affected is an important decision requiring technical knowledge and management judgment. Restricting circulation of submittals to those most directly involved and accustomed to interacting with other subcontractors in this manner is best—overloading other vendors or subcontractors with submittals that might only remotely affect their work will not receive the desired attention and will ultimately be counterproductive. Common examples of normal coordination are provision of major mechanical equipment submittals to the electrical contractor for coordination of the power and control wiring, and coordination of drawings of large-dimension electrical duct banks, steam, chilled water, and HVAC distribution systems.

Information gathering to define and refine the scope

The drawings and specifications received at the start of the project, even if extremely well crafted, will not be fully complete or perfect. Further, these documents may show the design intent only—and not much of the detailed fabrication information necessary for construction. Supplemental design and detailing work remains to be performed. Requesting, developing, and approving this needed information are a significant construction management tasks and must be meticulously controlled and documented.

Shop drawings and supplemental design refine the work, scope, and time

Shop drawings were originally detailed drawings needed to assist shop personnel fabricating the work. Types and grades of materials, highly detailed dimensions, and methods of attachment were shown.

These drawings were typically developed by the fabricating subcontractor, and reviewed and approved by the architect or engineer. Manufacturers' product data supplement these documents.

As the complexity of the shop-fabricated materials increased, the complexity of the design component of the shop drawings escalated. In some cases, the shop drawings now constitute a significant part of the design process, including calculations and certifications by professional engineers. These more complex documents are still usually reviewed and approved by the project architects and engineers of record—even though they did not perform the design work depicted by the shop drawings. This can produce approval with qualifying hedges such as "reviewed but not approved," "reviewed for concept only," or "reviewed for intent"—that increase uncertainly.

Shop drawing logs are maintained on a spreadsheet for small projects and on a database program for larger projects. Major milestones are documented in the project schedule. Shop drawings may involve multiple reviews and revisions, so turnaround time becomes contentious—"Was the shop drawing submittal late or was it deficient?" or "Was the architect's review slow and unresponsive?" These can be support or defense for claims of schedule extension.

Choose Appropriate, Well-Accepted Forms of Documentation

Documentation starts before installation, as described above, continues during execution and monitoring, and ends in project closeout documentation. Written, visual, and verbal exchanges (confirmed by written documentation) are all needed but do not carry equal weight. Stronger preferred types of documentation are listed below. In all cases, the records are best developed contemporaneously by those directly involved with the activity. And "normal course of business" documents by a disinterested party that confirm the transaction are best.

Formal documents are always strong
Recognized documents in a standardized form are generally considered reliable. Examples include contracts, formal written factory warranty, building permit, certificate of occupancy, executed change orders, notice to proceed, or stop orders.

Third-party written records of transactions are also strong
Customary business records generated in the normal course of business are also considered reliable. Examples include signed receipt delivery tickets, meeting minutes with sign in sheets, and payroll records. A superintendent's daily log, if focused on facts not opinions and consistently maintained, is also accepted.

Test reports and expert certifications are also considered good
Examples include independent laboratory testing reports, notifications by disinterested parties uninvolved in the project (such as government entities), and photographs (some projects require photographs be taken by a professional photographer, not project personnel).

Accounting records are standardized and may be communicated selectively
Financial job cost accounting records are standardized by regulation and company policy and will change little for each project. Communication of accounting data can be quite extensive for time and material construction management type contracts—but on a hard bid contract, virtually absent. Discussions of accounting data between construction manager and project owner will usually focus on the contract values adjusted by the change order reduced by previous payments—more extensive accounting data is not shared.

"Normal course of business" records

Normal course of business records document occurrences in a consistent factual manner that does not attempt to assign meaning or purpose to the records.

Examples of "normal course of business records" are:

Daily logs (narrative of work activities, deliveries, and key events and observations)

Inspection logs (of inspections by outside parties, such as building inspectors)

Telephone logs

OSHA (Occupational Safety and Health Administration) safety logs

Incident reports (accidents, fires, spills, labor, and weather disruptions)

Submittal logs

RFI (request for information) logs

ASI (Architect's Supplemental Instructions)

Change order logs

These records assign no meaning to the data and are not communicated to others unless an event arises that makes this data relevant. The most common event is a claim that must be managed.

Opinion letters and one-sided historical narratives have little value

Self-serving letters stating one point of view, particularly of an accusatory nature, are largely discounted. And historical recaps by one party of a chain of events, if unaccompanied by convincing documentation, are substantially discounted or ignored.

Filing Systems Must Be Established During Project Initiation

Each construction management firm will typically have an established filing system that must be adjusted slightly for each new project.

Common filing system categories are:

Contract between owner and construction manager including all changes to the contract. (Originals of the contract are typically maintained at the construction manager's home office and a copy at the site office.)

Contract between construction manager and subcontractors containing the original contract and all approved changes. A single file for all subcontractors may be maintained in the smallest projects, but a single file for each subcontractor may be required for larger projects.

Pay requests to the owner with associated lien waivers. Pay request documentation is regulated by law, regulation, and custom and must be precise and meticulous. Pay request processing, if handled properly, can be routine—but otherwise can become a major administrative burden and an impediment to the schedule.

Permissions consist of application and receipt of permits from building departments and other regulatory authorities. (Retention of document originals at the project site is frequently required by government regulation.)

Shop drawings and submittals files are maintained, at a minimum, for each subcontractor on the smallest projects, with additional subfolders for each subcontractor submittal for larger projects. Since it is common to write technical questions and notes on submittal transmittals, transmittals are usually filed with the submittal.

Correspondence not specifically needed for other purposes will be filed in general correspondence. When the purposes are not clear or there are multiple purposes, filing of multiple copies in multiple locations may be needed.

Chronological files of correspondence and transmittals are typically maintained to compensate for any filing errors and for claim analysis—"What happened on or about this date?" This redundant and seemingly unnecessary step can compensate for much human error.

Document registers list the current documents (drawings and specifications) with revision dates included in the scope of work. Revisions may be frequent, and all parties must know the exact scope to be executed at all times, so maintenance of the register is a key project management task. Attention to detail and precision is key—listing drawing author, number, title, and revision date is needed. The all too common "current set" or "most recent drawings" is inadequate for execution of the work or claim defense.

Record documents. The record documents are the latest or final approved version of designer's and engineer's drawings and all relevant submittals and permissions. Maintenance and updating of record documents continue throughout the project, and the final drawing of each document is archived at conclusion of the project. Similar to the document register, precision and accuracy are essential.

Obtaining Needed Information and Managing Scope Changes

Scope definition and changes must be communicated selectively
Submittal of documents that can or do affect the scope, time, and cost should also only be communicated to marginally affected subcontractors on a "need to know" basis. It is true that changes in scope and timing may have subtle consequential effects on the progress of the project and therefore productivity of many parties—so it could be argued that all changes affect everyone. But these effects are better handled by communication of the progress of the job in job meetings and progress updates, not as a specific analysis for each and every clarification or scope change. Management of this distinction has a large impact on claim management.

The RFI process
When a construction manager observes problems or conflicts with the contract documents or changed conditions, direction and resolution are sought from the architect or engineer with an RFI. The architect and engineer will provide a response that may or may not affect the project cost or schedule.

Changes in the cost and schedule initiated by the owner or architect
Bulletins (notifications of changes in the work), also called CCD (construction change directive) or ASI, frequently accompanied by revised drawings or sketches may be issued by the architect or engineer. The architects or engineers may issue the notice with a direction to proceed if they believe that the bulletin does not affect cost or schedule. If the construction managers believe there is a cost or schedule impact, they may present a proposal and request for change order. If the architects know the change will produce a cost or schedule impact, they will issue an RFP (request for proposal) with the notice, thus shortening the resolution of the change, as described below.

The architects and/or engineers may themselves notice conditions in the documents requiring alteration or correction with cost or schedule impact, or the owner may request changes in the work. Work descriptions and specifications and drawings documenting of these alterations will be provided to the construction manager, usually with an RFP, who will in turn identify the impact on cost and schedule.

Changes to cost and schedule initiated by the construction manager
Cost and schedule are usually initiated through the RFI or bulletin process, but can also come directly from the construction manager as a change request. Examples include resolution of allowances or change in cost due to quantity verification within an agreed unit cost structure. In these cases, the construction manager will initiate the change request with the format specified by the general conditions of the contract.

Documenting the agreed scope, cost, and time changes

In the AIA (American Institute of Architects) document format, once agreement on the change request is reached, the architect will prepare a formal change order for the owner's and the construction manager's execution. Under the AGC (Association of General Contractors) construction management system, the construction manager may prepare this document for the owner's execution.

The time required to review and process this documentation is usually a critical project management problem. Response from even the most efficient organization will not be instant. Action and needed changes may be best performed immediately to maintain the needed work progress, but immediate action will not be immediately accompanied by an agreement to pay for the work. Prompt attention to what is frequently viewed as a low-level clerical task is needed, as well as some level of trust. If both these do not exist, project schedules can be extended for even the most minor change, or subcontractors will not perform needed tasks at the required time — requiring costly rework.

Document flow for changes is specified by contract

The document flow for changes is:

> RFI or change order request
> Proposal
> Proposal negotiation, revision, and resolution

If the owner agrees that the change alters the project cost and time, the following documents will be executed:

> Change order between owner and construction manager
> Change order between construction manager and subcontractor (when appropriate)
> Change in project cost and, when appropriate, schedule
> Accounting changes to ensure accurate billings to the owner and payments to subcontractors
> Document register update

If the owner does not agree that the change alters project cost and time:

The change order between owner and construction manager is deleted, and the cost of the additional work is deducted from the construction manager's profit in the accounting change step. (Or, the change is not performed.)

Documentation of scope changes is usually by both project management and accounting programs

Similar to the shop and certification logs described above, the RFI bulletin and change order logs are managed with project management database programs for all but the smallest projects (that use spreadsheets or manual lists). However, since the volume of scope of changes and missing information is unknown at the start of the project, these changes are not included in the initial project schedule. If changes are significant, this schedule must be periodically revised.

Step 3. Distribution of Information—Types and Methods of Communication

Formal communication is required by contract, regulation, or custom—and is still mostly on paper

Contracts, change orders, and certificate of substantial completion are formal documents prepared on industry accepted forms. Formal notifications, such as notice to it to proceed or terminate, are usually prepared on letterhead. Permits and licenses are prepared on forms established by the issuing agencies. Although there is no compelling reason not to transition to electronic communication at this time, most formal communication is still on paper.

Normal course of business communications uses mixed methods

Normal course of business communications consists of submittals, correspondence, delivery tickets, and purchase orders. These communications increasingly are transitioning to electronic where the construction manager has a choice—but are usually limited by the paper documents received from outside sources. Formal meetings include a written agenda and approved minutes and a sign in sheet. The agenda and minutes can be either electronic or paper, but the sign sheet, which is proof of attendance for claim defense, limits full transition to electronic communication.

Informal communication is verbal or by e-mail

Informal discussions of ongoing activity or coordination of minor technical or scheduling details is verbal or by e-mail. No attempt is usually made to meticulously document each of these transactions—but care is needed so that these remain routine to avoid inappropriately use as a proof when others press a questionable claim. So, the general rule is paper for formal, and electronic or verbal for informal communications—but milestones and decisions reached by informal means must be documented in writing.

Verbal, written, and visual communication are all required

"Get it in writing" is a bedrock documentation principle and should be consistently sought and obtained. Memories get fuzzy, and the volume of data on even the smallest project overwhelms the reliable memory of most.

Much of construction is documented visually—either the drawings and diagrams or the physical constructed work. This visual documentation becomes central to construction management communication but must be supplemented with written and numerical descriptions.

Although verbal communication alone is frowned upon as a rigorous form of documentation, it is essential to the construction management communication process. Shared values and agreements on common goals and methods must be established for each project, and this can be done best with in-person communication. This is particularly true in construction, which is a people business dealing with things.

Project status meetings for day-to-day project participants

Sound project management theory, as well as the requirements of model construction management contracts, requires meetings at specific intervals and milestones. The number and timing of meetings are frequently specified by contract—and for the construction management delivery systems, these can be quite numerous—up to multiple mandatory meetings each week. Sound procedures require meetings at start-up and closeout, and usually at each milestone. Weekly job site meetings are required for mid or large-size projects. (These are in addition to mandated meetings such as weekly tool box safety meetings.) Additional submeetings of affected participants on focused tasks will be needed. (A brick-layer does not need or want to know about control wiring on mechanical equipment.)

The agenda for a meeting should be published at least 2 days prior to the meeting, a sign in sheet signed by all attendees, and minutes distributed promptly and at least 2 days prior to the next meeting. Any exceptions to these meeting minutes are noted in this next meeting, and then the corrected minutes become the accepted documentation. (These meeting minute procedures are also found in *Robert's Rules of Order*—used in government meetings and in mandated corporate governance procedures.)

Meetings effectively communicate the combined transmittal of written and graphic information along with face-to-face communication that reveals subtleties of attitudes. These multiple methods of

| Steeple erection | *photo 4 of 15* |

| Steeple erection | *photo 5 of 15* |

communication effectively relate to those who prefer verbal, written, and thinking communication styles—so all are reached.

Data documentation integration—still a work in progress

Project management, accounting, and scheduling software programs are fundamentally different. Data entry and maintenance of each of these programs by specialized less-skilled personnel are possible, but entry into all three programs at the same time is a rarer higher level skill. The common practice is to maintain separate logs, and then enter initiation and completion of tasks into the other programs. For example, the initial submittal and final approval of the shop drawing may be entered in the scheduling program, but all intervening approval steps will be omitted. Or, the agreed change order values for the construction manager and subcontractors may be entered in the accounting program but all preceding steps omitted.

So, separate documentation systems for change orders, accounting implications of change orders, shop drawings, overall project documentation, and schedule are maintained. A comprehensive integrated project information processing software program is possible and would initially seem desirable but is not commonly used. Entirely paperless document management systems exist; however, to be effective, all project participants must have and be competent and comfortable with the applicable software. This can only occur on multiyear projects or for project groups who perform multiple repeat projects. If one of the project participants is not fully up to speed, someone else must act as their secretary and correctly enter all the data—a tedious task with some additional liability.

News media and public relations may be a demanding task—or nearly absent

Public communication must be planned to interact with participants such as the media. The public relations must be managed because of the sensitive nature of the project, or the owner wishes to promote the business to be served. There is usually interaction with the project owners planning these communications, and frequently, they will hire a media relations firm. The construction manager may, on projects with significant public exposure, designate a project spokesperson. Relations with the media may be absent on small and midsize project of a more routine nature—or may be handled by a few interviews with media reporters.

Step 4. Manage Project Participants' Expectations

Managing communication involves filtering the information and providing only the information that is needed when it is needed. Yet, the pace of the project materially affects all. So, all project participants' anticipation of performance must be managed to match the actual performance. This is done through the normal course of business meetings at start-up and each key milestone, and supplemented by coordination meetings on specific topics between affected subcontractors.

But there will always be a slight disconnect between expectation and the actual. To resolve this discrepancy, specific scheduling of the overall project approach will be included in contracts, and adjustments discussed in meetings. Subdiscussions will be held on scheduling and coordination issues such as hoisting, haul roads, temporary power, and sequencing of the work. Subcontractors will then feel their voice was heard and concerns or needs accommodated—which hugely minimizes potential claims. And the construction manager's actions must match the promises.

Step 5. Report Performance—Tailored to the Owner's Capabilities and Preferences

Reports of performance of the scope, time, and cost, as well as risk management, must be provided to the owners with the level of detail and at the time they require. Lump sum bids in the public sector may only require notification of potential failure to meet to agreed schedule dates. The construction management forms of project delivery may demand far more detailed reporting.

In all cases, management needs to know:

> Scope status, including RFIs and change orders
> Achievement of schedule milestones
> Cost performance
> Risk management threats and opportunities

Project owners in a cooperative relationship may be able to provide material assistance from outside sources to overcome needed obstacles such as permission and community relations. Communication of the project status both qualitatively and quantitatively helps early owner participation for maximum benefits.

Some project owners who are not technically oriented may only want milestone and verbal descriptions of progress. Others, particularly in the engineering, manufacturing, and technical sectors, may demand more sophisticated performance reports such as earned value and control charts. The level of detail the owner requires must be provided but carefully—too much information will be confusing and counterproductive.

A common format for such reports suggested by the Project Management Institute is:

> Analysis of past performance
> Current status of risks and issues
> Work completed during the period
> Work to be completed next
> Summary of changes approved in the period
> Other relevant information that must be reviewed and discussed

Summary

Communication must be planned to reduce the volume of information and number of communication channels.

Getting the information that must be known to those who need to know when they need to know it requires planning and organization, starting at project initiation and continuing through planning, execution, control, and closeout.

This involves a five-step process:

> Identify participants
> Plan communications
> Distribute information
> Manage expectations
> Report performance

Appropriate well-accepted methods of communication including written, electronic, verbal, and graphic must be selected and guided by contract, regulation, tradition, and normal human tendencies.

Review Questions (True or False)

1. Communication and documentation help define and refine the scope, build relationships, manage expectation, and minimize claims.

2. There are eight possible channels of communication between four parties.

3. Project participants' communication needs and preferences will be influenced by their daily project involvement, intermittent oversight or control, and their contractual relation to the project.

4. The diligent project manager will review all project communications.

5. Not all parties on the project should receive all communication. Information must be filtered by requirements specified by contract or regulation, relevance, and "need to know."

6. Information gathering to define and refine the scope and shop drawing and supplemental design to refine the work, scope, and time must be performed both for the needed purpose and to avoid and manage potential claims.

7. Formal documents, third-party written records, and test reports and expert certifications are all strong forms of documentation.

8. It is an essential and the normal business practice to retain originals of all formal documents at the project site office.

9. Changes in scope that produce a change in cost and schedule are most commonly initiated by the owner or architect but may also be initiated by the construction manager.

10. In the AIA document format, the architect prepares change orders, but in the AGC format, the construction manager may prepare the same document. In both cases, prompt execution of the change order that may affect the project schedule is a critical management task.

11. For most projects, formal communication is still mostly on paper, and normal course of business communication uses mixed electronic and paper forms.

12. A fully paperless office is fast becoming a reality for all project types and sizes.

13. Communication to the media and the public about the progress of the project is an essential task for all project types.

14. Formal communication to the project owner of the status of the scope, schedule, cost and management of threats, and opportunities to the progress of the project is required at frequent intervals for construction management projects but much less frequently for lump sum hard bid projects.

Test Your Understanding

1. Lump sum hard bid and construction management project delivery methods have different communication requirements. Discuss the differences in type and frequency of formal, informal, verbal communication, and meetings for the two delivery methods. Then, discuss the differences in staffing needs and organizational structures that would be influenced by these differing communication needs.

2. Your project has an approved scope change that affects cost and time. Discuss which of the parties will receive notification of this change and the form of communication:
Owner
Architect
Subcontractors directly affected
Subcontractors not directly affected
Material suppliers
Accounting department

3. A college class will use both formal and informal communication. Discuss how informal and formal communication will be used for the following:

Midterm and final tests

Quizzes

Term papers or projects

Lectures

Labs

Class discussions

Then, estimate the percentage of these communication transactions that are verbal and a percentage that are written.

CHAPTER
3.6

Cost Control Is Crucial for Cost Management and Productivity Improvement

Placing the rebar for the Wheaton Bible Church was assisted by excavations that provided both a safe slope and adequate work area.

Cost Control Is Crucial for Cost Management and Productivity Improvement

Achieves short-term correction and long-term improvement

Feedback obtains information about the present execution of a task, and control uses this feedback information to make necessary adjustments. In the short run, feedback and control are used to check the work as it is being performed—to ensure the workable approach is achieving the purpose—and to make required adjustments in real time. In the longer run, it is used to make approach improvements for future similar projects.

Checking and Adjusting the Execution of the Workable Approach

Feedback and control—the top-down approach

The company's organizational structure governs the type of feedback and control system that can be used. A top-down command and control organizational system restrict information, knowledge, and judgment to the upper levels of the organization. Those doing the work will have imperfect knowledge of what they are supposed to do, so mistakes will be made, sometimes frequently and persistently. Feedback consists of finding defective work and tearing it out and doing it over—or discovering cost overruns have occurred. This feedback may be in the form of a very elaborate job cost accounting system requiring and producing many reports, but no control is achieved. One is just documenting and fixing past failures. With knowledge only that a mistake was made, but not how it was made, improvement for future projects is not possible. Excellence and continuous improvement are, therefore, not possible with this approach.

Feedback and control—the distributed knowledge approach

With a distributed knowledge organizational system, excellence and improvement are possible. When fact gathering, decisions, and judgments are made by those doing the work—and a workable approach has been established and communicated—self-control is possible.

Self-Control

Self-control requires:

1. Knowing what is supposed to be done
2. Knowing what is being done now
3. Having the ability to change 2 into 1

This can only be done in a distributed knowledge system—where facts, judgments, and decisions are made by those doing the work. Self-control is greatly enhanced when those doing the work help develop the workable approach. They understand how it was developed, feel ownership, and believe it will work. With the expertise of all built into the approach, it is frequently completed with only minor corrections. Required minor corrections noticed early can be corrected early and therefore stay minor.

Feedback for Process Improvement

Continuous process improvement is necessary to maintain the long-term health of a construction management company. Construction is, however, a short-term discontinuous process, with many tasks going on at once. So, getting continuous process improvement is challenging.

Traditionally, record keeping in construction has been poor. This is partially because the personnel attracted to construction do not tend to be interested in record keeping. Also, the discontinuous nature of the process—with no identical, and few quite similar projects—makes standard record keeping (alone) of limited value when seeking detailed information on specific tasks.

Many process improvement techniques that work in manufacturing—where the processes are more continuous and long term—cannot work in construction. But what can work for construction is as follows:

1. *Check what is possible when it is possible*

   The project has many tasks starting and stopping at different times, so checking the project as a whole produces no information on specific tasks. If one task is right, and another task of equal size is wrong, these activities may cancel and give the impression that both tasks are being performed "average." More specific detail is needed. One activity that a crew is performing exclusively for days or weeks can be selected and analyzed as a productivity benchmark. Noting the factors that change productivity—travel time to the work area, congestion at the work area, scaffold, ladders or hoists required—this benchmark can be used for future projects. And once the productivity of one task is known, others can be found. For example, if 500 man-hours was spent on two tasks in the last week, and the benchmark task is known to have taken 300 man-hours, the other task must have taken 200 man-hours.

2. *Break the project into short time periods to find periods of good and bad performance*

   Another approach is to break the schedule into sections to find the portions of good and bad performance. Two-week periods are most useful. This will lead to suspicions about the performance of some tasks that merit further investigation. Determining if the suspicions are correct will require further investigation. This approach requires detailed information on the manpower, materials, and equipment estimated and allocated for each task—so estimated can be compared with actual. This can be done manually, but this clerical effort is usually found too burdensome. Scheduling computer programs can provide this same information automatically.

3. *Study three tasks and make improvements*

   Select the three tasks with the greatest possibilities for improvement and review the tasks in detail. Are the right trades and crew sizes assigned? Is the right equipment used and positioned correctly? Ask the personnel (including subcontractors and material vendors) doing the task and the preceding and following tasks about delays, breakdowns, and possibilities for improvement. Based on this information, make the required changes to the work approach to achieve the needed improvements.

4. *The cycle of continuous improvement*

   Check the results of these changes, evaluate again, and pick three more tasks for improvement. This is a circular process of continuous improvement—check performance during real time, get the facts, make a judgment about what these facts mean, get more facts to see if the judgment is correct, and make an improvement. Once this is part of normal operations and has been repeated hundreds or thousands of times, repeating patterns emerge. Rates of productivity can be determined within seconds of entering a job site. This is not intuition but "experience" produced from facts and judgments.

These are simple techniques that do not use fancy statistics, charts and graphs, and computer programs—but they work. This simplicity is required first because knowledge is always in short supply. Limited knowledge limits the analysis of this knowledge. It is also required because real-time improvement by the people doing the work is required for the best results—and this requires speed. Having others take the information and later make a report provides stale information too late for use.

A benefit of these simple techniques is that everyone can understand them. Applied knowledge, real-world judgment, and common sense stay in the mix. But simplicity is not a reason not to document efforts—the facts obtained, judgments made, improvements attempted, and the results. Without written documentation, productive communication with others is not possible, and how improvements were realized will be soon forgotten.

Productivity

The largest opportunity for cost and schedule reduction

"Watch your labor" is a priority for all experienced project managers. Labor productivity is the greatest source of profit increase or decrease for most projects. It can also provide the earliest warning of other problems, such as poor selection of construction equipment.

One third of the work day is actually productive work

Productivity is measured as the percentage of the work time spent moving material *once* (from the point of entrance at the job site to point of installation) and installing it *correctly* so no rework is required. It does not matter whose fault it is—any work that does not fit this description does not count. For example, double handling of material does not count. Incorrect installation of material, which must be removed or reworked, does not count. One may go home very tired at the end of a day having worked very hard and having accomplished nothing. Competent, hard-working, well-meaning workers can still have low productivity.

Construction trades average about 32% productive time. That is, 32% of their workweek is transportation and correct installation of their work, and 68% is nonproductive "waste." The cause of which is listed below:

- Waiting 29%

- Traveling 13%

- Instruction 8%

- Tools and materials transportation 7%

- Late starts/early quits 6%

- Personal breaks 5%

Reducing this unproductive time is the largest opportunity for increased project speed and profit. Further, it should be noted that the nonproductive parts—waiting, traveling, and instructions—are only partially within the control of the trade whose productivity is being measured. Improvement also requires design of a workable approach by management. The trades people can improve productivity somewhat themselves, but not greatly without management's commitment and effort.

Studies of productivity typically are done by management studying the productivity of trade employees, but management productivity must be considered as well. Field supervisors, field office personnel, home office personnel, designers, and owners all spend time that has costs. Obtaining information, processing changes, meetings, and documentations should be substantially minimized, and in most cases entirely avoided. Small and mid-sized projects can and should be done with virtually no changes. Large projects can have few changes. Therefore, the time spent obtaining information, processing, and documenting changes is considered unproductive time. Nonproductive management time of up to 90% is not uncommon. Further, management's failure to do their job correctly or on time further reduces trade labor productivity.

| Steeple erection | *photo 6 of 15* |

Measuring and Analyzing Productivity

Quantitative analysis with much judgment

Dr. James J. Adrian, PE, CPA, of Bradley University developed techniques to measure productivity and quantify causes of productivity reduction. Adrian's engineering knowledge brings careful measurement and statistical sampling, and his accounting knowledge brings job cost dimensions to the evaluation.

Only three types of quantities need to be identified or measured:

1. Production unit

2. Production cycle

3. Production cycle time

Measurements are made in the field by visual inspection and a stopwatch—so the quantities to be measured are structured within these limits. The production unit must be visually identifiable, and the cycle time with no productivity deficiencies should center around 1–5 minutes. Good examples of units include: a ½-cy concrete bucket, and a 20-cy yard dump truck. Bad examples include installation of individual bricks (multiple individuals working on the wall at once, so precise quantities are difficult to assess visually from a distance) and installation of the concrete floor for 1/4 of the building (cycle time is too long, and the unit is not repeatable).

And five causes of productivity reduction are identified as

1. Environment, such as soil conditions
2. Equipment missing or operating poorly
3. Labor poorly trained, confused, tired, or lazy
4. Material defective or unavailable
5. Management—congested job site with conflicting operations

A worker then observes an operation and enters observations in a matrix shown below.

Production Cycle Delay Sampling

Unit: Second

Method: Crane Bucket Concrete Pour   Production Unit: Concrete Drip

| Production: | | Delays: | | | | | | |
Cycle	Cycle Time (sec.)	Environment	Equipment	Labor	Material	Management	Notes	Minus Mean Non-delay Time
1	120			√				27
2	126		√					33
3	98						√	5
4	112		√					19
5	108						√	15
6	1122					√	crane move	1029
7	116		√					23
8	214		√					121
9	92						√	1
10	88						√	5

Then, average delay times by cause and variation from the averages can be calculated to identify areas that could provide the largest productivity improvements. The largest few causes are identified for needed correction.

The approach has the following desirable features: the worker observing the operations does not need to be highly skilled, the technique uses sampling so may be performed intermittently only, not continuously throughout the project to be effective, and the data analysis and manipulation use only four-function arithmetic so is accessible and understandable by all. This is a more quantitatively demanding application of "measure what you can measure when you can measure it".

Increasing Productivity

Having information available when needed is crucial

Having a workable approach and counting all the building blocks will produce significant immediate improvements in productivity. When what is to be built and the sequence of operations and time of completion are known, and the needed components and building blocks are available when needed, most instruction and much of waiting can be eliminated. Information produces the single largest increase in productivity. When talented, hard-working, motivated personnel know what to do, they can and usually will do their best.

Reducing travel time can pay big productivity dividends

The next largest source of productivity improvement is managing travel time from the site entrance to the work area. For materials, this trip should be made only once in the job. For personnel, it should only be made once per shift. This requires a clear path of travel—unencumbered by obstructions—and storage space for the materials in the immediate work area. To achieve this, all materials must be ordered for short installation durations. A few days would be ideal for productivity, but 2 weeks is more achievable—the limit of the delivering vendor's tolerance. Note: The tendency to stock the entire job to save a few hundred or a few thousand dollars in delivery charges can produce tens or hundreds of thousands of dollars in increased labor cost caused by lower productivity.

The means of transport must also be appropriately selected. Travel on foot, manpowered carts, machine-powered transportation devices (carts, trucks, forklifts), or hoisting devices (lifts, cranes, and temporary elevators) must be selected carefully. Especially, designed or modified transportation devices for the particular task or job site can greatly increase productivity and ensure a single trip from the job site entrance to the work area.

| Steeple erection | *photo 7 of 15* |

Finally, there must be the necessary support services, such as electrical power, heat, water, communications, toilets, break areas, and rubbish bins in the immediate work area. Trade personnel will then have no reason to leave the area.

Reducing mobility restriction in the work area helps as well

A clean unobstructed work area is necessary to achieve maximum productivity. Any moving of material (double handling) is a reduction in productivity. This requires short ordering durations for materials—as described above. Where possible, leaving some material on carts for minor relocation will help further. The number of workers assigned to a work area must be below the density limits.

Next, the work area must be properly manned so that all men and machines have unobstructed circulation space. Hoisting devices for high work must be properly selected. Fully stocked gang boxes for tools and equipment storage in the immediate work are also essential.

If the work is in an occupied space, or extremely congested space, such as a mechanical room, careful scheduling must be considered—including the use of multiple shifts. A 50% time premium may seem high, but if it can produce a 300% increase in productivity, the cost can be justified.

Scheduling can manage the effect of weather on productivity

The effect of weather on productivity can be huge. Snow removal, pumping water, and work stoppages due to extreme heat or heavy rain can reduce productivity to zero. Although the weather cannot be controlled, it can be very broadly predicted—rainy seasons, heat in summer, and snow in winter. And these effects can be managed by project planning and scheduling that minimizes sensitive operations at the times weather impacts are likely to be greatest. And to a lesser extent, field supervision can alter planned operations in response to 2-week weather forecast.

Lead by example and momentum—pick "pushing trades"

Additional productivity improvement is gained by example and momentum—by selecting a "pushing trade." Choose a trade that is a significant portion of the project work, and preferably one that has work that has large installed dimensions. Examples include the concrete structure, HVAC ductwork or, on civil projects, large underground piping. Choose an aggressive subcontractor, or self-perform this trade. Give this trade the opportunity to move fast, and then push them.

The other trades on the project will see the example, and will first react as, "If he can do it, I can do it too." And second, since the pushing trade's work is large, everyone knows they must keep up with or get ahead of them, or their productivity will suffer greatly when later working around the large installed work.

Quantitative analysis and feedback control

This chapter highlighted a primarily qualitative approach to feedback and control, which is an essential first step and necessary framework. If this attitude and approach is not in place, quantitative analysis will produce no useful information.

Quantitative analysis is heavily used, essential, and occupies a significant portion of the project manager's analytical time. Job costing described in the earlier cost accounting chapter and some of the analysis described in the following chapter on quality will be analyzed each week for each project.

Summary

Feedback and control are used to obtain information about the work as it is being performed—to evaluate progress toward the goal and to make necessary corrections. This same information can also be used to improve the approach to future projects. Feedback must be both facts (man-hours, units of work) and judgments on crew size, equipment selection, and positioning of equipment. Feedback and control are a continuous cycle of facts, judgments, and more facts to check the judgments, then improvement. Control and improvement together can only be realized in a distributed knowledge system, not in a top-down management system.

Since field productivity averages 32%, some large portion of a 300% increase in productivity is reasonably achievable. Information, reduced travel time, and an unobstructed work area can produce much of this improvement. Management must be involved and committed to productivity improvement from planning through execution and control to achieve maximum benefits.

Review Questions (True or False)

1. Feedback obtains information about the present execution of a task, and control uses this information to make necessary adjustments. Real-time adjustments are best, and long-term improvements for future projects are also sought.

2. A command-and-control organization can best tightly control execution of the work and therefore costs.

3. In a distributed knowledge organizational system, facts are gathered and decisions and judgments are made by those doing the work, and self-control is possible.

4. Self-control requires (1) knowing what is supposed to be done, (2) knowing what is being done right now, and (3) having the ability to change 2 into 1.

5. Feedback and control focus exclusively on correction of the work as it is being performed. Once the work is completed, feedback and control produce no additional benefits.

6. Construction is a discontinuous process with many activities performed at the same time, which can make productivity evaluation troublesome. Some practical techniques that work are (1) check what is possible when it is possible, (2) break the project into shorter time periods, usually about 2 weeks, and find periods of good and bad performance, (3) study three tasks, make improvements, and note the results.

7. The process improvement cycle of obtaining facts, making judgments, making improvements, and noting results involves judgment and simple mathematical techniques but still must be rigorously documented in writing.

8. In construction, approximately one-third of trade labor work hours are productive. This low productivity is caused mainly by poor work habits of lazy workers.

9. Management productivity must be considered for its cost implications, but also because unproductive management may not provide the information to trade labor when needed, which further reduces trade labor productivity.

10. Adrian's production management approach uses the production unit, production cycle, and production cycle times to identify causes of reduced productivity.

11. Material handling devices and temporary facilities and services are determined when estimating the project's general conditions can seldom be changed by field personnel.

12. Feedback and control for short-term correction must be integrated with more rigorous quantitative control, job costing, and quality improvement.

Test Your Understanding

1. Most detached single-family homes are constructed using only ladders and fixed scaffolding. Discuss types of mechanized material-handling equipment or man hoists that might be considered to increase productivity.

2. Visit and view, even from afar, a medium-sized commercial or industrial project and note the factors for productivity enhancement discussed in this chapter. Specifically, temporary facilities consisting of electrical power, water, and toilets (to minimize travel time), and storage methods and amount of stored material (that affect mobility), and mechanized material-handling or man hoists. Note productivity-reducing conditions and possibilities for productivity improvement.

3. This chapter discusses evaluating cycle times for construction operations, but your access to construction operations may be difficult, so productivity for a fast-food restaurant will be evaluated instead. Evaluate the cycle time for order placement and fulfillment during a busy mealtime for a one half-hour period. Time the cycle time from customer approach to the order counter to delivery of the order. Note the causes of the order fulfillment delay in the following categories:
Customer unfamiliar with menu or undecided
Customer socializing with order taker
Order taker unfamiliar with order entry equipment
Order taker performing other tasks
Ingredients not available when needed
Food preparers slow or understaffed
Food preparation equipment not working properly
Record data in the type of matrix developed by Adrain and list the three top causes of delay.

CHAPTER
3.7

Cost Accounting Seeks Real-Time Information and Improvement

The well-organized worksite and good housekeeping aided productivity of the foundation wall installation for the Wheaton Bible Church.

Cost Accounting Seeks Real-Time Information and Improvement

Project management seeks record keeping that is achievable with available personnel

The term *managerial accounting* is used in general business, *cost accounting* more frequently in manufacturing, and *job costing*, *job cost accounting*, or *cost engineering* in construction. The objective is the same, but the emphasis and details differ by industry. All seek to answer the following questions:

What is the intended project outcome?

What have we done to date?

What are we doing right now?

What is the impact of our performance on the intended outcome if nothing is changed?

What can we change to better achieve the project outcome?

Cost Accounting Detail and Importance Varies by Industry

Cost accounting is more precise and complicated in manufacturing than in construction

Manufacturing cost accounting seeks to determine the cost of a single manufactured part in a continuous production run. Variable operating costs of equipment types and labor groups, and different acquisition costs for batches of inventory all must be considered. And the selection of inventory group costs can also help manage taxable income. Cost accountant can be a full-time career job in these industries.

Although construction does not have this complexity, it can be useful to know this difference when constructing a building for a manufacturing owner. If construction cost data is shared, construction data, without explanation, could appear weak and lacking detail.

Many industries do not use cost accounting at all

Many industries, such as banking, insurance, telecommunication, and government, rarely attempt to use job costing. The project management concept of "earned value"—which requires job costing data—is completely foreign and incomprehensible to those who do not keep records in this manner. A lighter presentation of job cost data may be more appropriate when communicating job cost information in these industries.

Construction job costing is more focused, but timing is crucial

Construction projects have no inventory—material is delivered to the job site for a specific intended use—so costing of inventory batches is not needed or done. Also, unlike manufacturing, which is a continuous process, a construction project has a defined start and end date. This makes both timing of observations and correction of deficiencies more important for the project.

Financial accounting records historical data but uses time frames that are too long for job costing. For example, financial accounting payroll costs may not be accurately known for a year, and financial accounting of equipment costs including lease, or purchase and financing costs, and tax implications have a multi-year view. Job costing requires weekly payroll and equipment costs, so estimated hourly costs must be used. Presentation of these estimated costs to the project owner can be troublesome and requires management attention as discussed below.

Job costing involves accounting but also requires engineering judgment. Determination of the portion of work correctly and finally completed requires a theoretical understanding of construction plans, specifications, and engineering principles—coupled with a practical field understanding of construction means and methods. This determination can be done by a skilled project manager or, on larger projects, by a cost engineer.

Combining accounting data and engineering judgment in a project management system assists understanding, management, and control of outputs. The level of detail, report form, and the method and timing of inputs varies hugely by project size, type, and availability of skilled personnel as discussed below.

Consistent accurate observations are key—and must match the capabilities of assigned personnel

Accurate observations recorded in the same way for the entire project are needed to produce reliable information. So, any job costing system must work within the capabilities and tendencies of the personnel continuously assigned to the project. Small projects staffed with a few or only one capable manager may require simple infrequent data entry into cleverly structured and organized job costing systems. Larger projects that can justify full-time cost engineers may use more robust systems with greater detail. One system does not fit every project—the selected system must match the capabilities of the available personnel or the results will be unreliable and unusable.

Organization Consistent with Both Accounting and Project Management is Needed

Reuse the WBS (work breakdown structure) from the cost estimate and alter slightly to accommodate data entry needs

Standard cost code systems

Building construction estimating overwhelmingly uses the CSI's (Construction Specification Institute) MasterFormat system. Power plants, heavy engineering such as dams, process plants such as oil refineries, and road construction find the CSI system provides insufficient detail for their most important and costly work items. These industries may borrow from the CSI system and add their own categories, or may develop a completely new system. But none of these systems have achieved the rigorous structure and wide acceptance of the CSI system.

One of these cost systems will be used for the organizational structure of the estimate—including the level of sub-detail necessary and appropriate for the project. This cost structure should be used in the job cost accounting system as well. This ensures that the planned task values are the executed and evaluated values and saves time and effort—while minimizing error.

A small extract from a quantity survey and cost estimate for gypsum framing and drywall shows the form of the labor and material cost data in the estimate.

QUANTITY SURVEY AND PRICING FOR:				GYPSUM FRAMING, DRYWALL								
PROJECT NAME:	Sample Project			DIFFICULTY OF PROJECT		1			PREPARED ON:	Sample Date		
PROJECT OWNER:	Sample Owner			DIFFICULTY OF WORK ITEM		1			REVISED ON:	No Revision		
PROJECT ARCHITECT:	Sample Architect			MH TO DOCK ONE WAY:		0.08			WASTE:	5%		
SALES TAX:	9.00%											
COST PER SF:	$3.64							TOTAL COST FOR GYPSUM FRAMING, DRYWALL:				$39,488.31
% OF TOTAL:	1.50%									SF IN PROJECT:		3877
	TOTAL LF OF PARTITION			796								
	LF OF PARTITION PER 100 SF:			21								
	GYPSUM TOTAL			15374	SF							
						LABOR	LABOR	LABOR	LABOR	MAT	MAT	TRASH	ITEM
DESCRIPTION	L	W	H	QUAN.	UNIT	UNIT $	UNIT MH	COST	MH	UNIT $	COST $	COST $	TOTAL
WALL 3-5/8", 25 GA, 5/8" GYPSUM X FULL HEIGHT INSULATED													
				48	LF								
	48		14	672	SF								
	0		0	0	SF								
	0		0	0	SF								
	0		0	0	SF								
	0		0	0	SF								
TRACK (RUNNER)				96	LF	$3.17	0.0455	$304.32	4	$0.45	$43.20		
METAL STUD				672	LF	$0.87	0.0125	$584.64	8	$0.57	$383.04		
INSULATION				672	SF	$0.87	0.0125	$584.64	8	$0.26	$174.72		
GYPSUM DRYWALL				1344	SF	$1.09	0.0157	$1,464.96	21	$0.30	$403.20		
ANCHORAGE											$58.77		
SUBTOTAL								$2,938.56	42		$1,062.93	$0.00	$4,001.49

Project and company specific codes

Companies may seek to classify expenditures both for job costing and for nonproject management purposes, such as evaluation of profitability of all company projects by project type or geographical area. Additional cost codes may be added for this purpose. A few examples are listed below.

Project number. The numerical project identification.

Project initiation date. The year the project was started.

Area facility code. Subdivision of a larger project into identifiable, useful subcomponents. For example, on a project consisting of eight buildings, each building could be assigned an area facility code. Codes for each floor of a high-rise are also common.

Project type. Identifies unique project types such as building, highway, or power.

Work description. A numerical code, usually in the CSI format, that identifies each task's work type such as concrete, masonry, or structural metals.

Financial classification. A numerical identification of the categories of labor, material, equipment, and subcontract costs.

There is no standard format for these codes, but a sample for a larger project is shown below.

|XXXX| |XXXXX| |XX XXX| |XXXXXX||X|

Project Initiation Year

Project Number

Area-Facility Code

Work Description
(WBS, usually in CSI MasterFormat numbering)

Financial Classification
(e.g., labor, material, equipment, subcontractor)

A smaller project might abbreviate this cost coding system as shown below.

|XXXXX| |XXXXXX| |X|

Project Number
(includes year)

Work Description
(Each subcontractor may have only one WBS (e.g., 51200 structural steel framing), so coding of each payment would be redundant. In this case, this cost code may be omitted.)

Financial Classification
(also frequently obvious and therefore omitted.)

For small companies and projects, job cost codes entered by field personnel may be reduced to just a job number. This reduces effort of the field personnel but does not eliminate the coding. The office accounting personnel still code each payment.

Two weeks is a magic number

80 work hours is the suggested maximum task duration by the Project Management Institute, a respected project management authority. The 1-week midpoint is consistent with the usual maximum time horizon of a working foreman. And trade payroll and most material expenditures are paid and recorded weekly.

So, when these expenditures are recorded in 1 week, a week still remains to correct productivity deficiencies. The limits of accounting and management capabilities make a week the smallest achievable "real-time" interval. Comparing estimated and planned expenditures at these short durations makes variations crystal clear.

Documenting the Inputs

Much accounting, with some management judgment

Material financial accounting data can be used in job costing with limited adjustment

Invoices for basic materials such as lumber, concrete, and gravel are billed at the time of shipment. Payment is regularly due in 30 days, but prompt payment discounts, such as a 2% discount for payment in 10 days, are frequently offered. These expenditures can be accurately used in both financial accounting and job costing. However, if materials that will not be installed within a month are delivered, a temporary manual adjustment in material completed will be needed, as described below.

Labor costs are recorded weekly using estimated hourly unit costs

Trade labor is paid weekly, but the total costs of labor burdens are paid at irregular longer intervals, so weekly accounting costs are an unsatisfactory representation of actual labor cost. Estimated burdened labor hourly unit costs are required to approximate total short and long-term costs. For labor cost, the financial accounting and job cost entries differ.

Equipment costs should use an estimated hourly cost as well

Equipment may be purchased for cash, purchased and financed, or leased, and each of these acquisition methods has a different tax and accounting consequence. And the timing of each of these transactions is far different than the progress of the project. It is best to establish and use a calculated hourly equipment cost that fully reflects total ownership and maintenance costs. Again, the financial accounting and labor cost entries differ. (The tax benefits of ownership are too complex to be included in the calculated hourly rate. These tax savings then become a source of hidden profit for the firm (but not for the project).

Subcontractor costs should be documented with change order management

Subcontractors agree to perform a specific scope of work for a specific cost. If the owner alters the agreed scope, the agreed cost will be altered as well, and there will be no budget over-run. If the subcontractors are managed well and no unjustified cost changes (that will not be reimbursed by the owner) are requested, the initial cost, plus approved changes, becomes the final cost and the anticipated profit remains unchanged.

Subcontractors usually bill monthly less 10% retention and expect payment within 30 days. The billed amount may imperfectly correspond to the work completed, and the retention and the payment time delay make actual expenditures a poor representation of work completed to date. Careful monitoring of change orders and documenting any subcontractor change orders that are approved but that are reimbursed by the owner will show subcontractor cost variation. Once again financial accounting and job cost accounting entries differ.

Job costing indirect costs use estimates also—discussion and agreement are required
The complexity of payment terms and differing time frames exceeds the patience of most

Indirect costs—cost for necessary efforts that do not become part of the permanent building—such as management and supervisory time, over-the-road vehicle expense, and general company insurance—can and should be job costed. All expenses related to the execution of the job should be job costed to identify the real total cost of the effort. This is definitely necessary under construction management or time and material contracts to capture all expended costs. The statement of home office overhead can help clarify the office-project cost distinction. If it is not on the office overhead schedule, it should be job costed.

The costs for full-time on-site activities are rarely controversial. But off-site activities, such as a project manager located in the home office but working on project matters or on-road vehicles that leave the site, can raise owner objections. Home office supervisory and clerical support, as well as general company insurance, are usually controversial. Clear definition in the original contract negotiations is the only solution.

Finally, small tools and equipment are commonly assigned to a tool crib on the job or to a specific crew. Costing of these tools as a percentage of labor is most common, but, with great effort, each individual tool can be identified and job costed. This is more common on time and material projects where all costs are reimbursed. This reimbursement can be a source of hidden profit. (The hourly tool cost is calculated with an assumed tool life. If careful use and maintenance extends the tool life, reimbursement then becomes profit.)

These indirect costs consist of material, labor, and equipment, so have the same job costing complexities described above. The estimated unit costs must be established at the project start and communicated to the project owner (for CM but usually not lump sum hard bid projects).

Good Job Cost Reports Require "Real World" Data Entry

Labor distributions attempt to measure expended labor for each task in the estimate
Labor expenditures are key to productivity and cost management. One approach is to export the very detailed WBS line by line from the cost estimate to form the labor data entry framework. Trade labor is then required to distribute their work hours into these categories on their time cards each day or week. An abbreviated sample appears below.

DAILY LABOR DISTRIBUTION REPORT

Sample CM Company

Date of Work: Sample Date	Job No. Sample Number
Prepared by: Sample Signature (Signature)	Job Name Sample Name
	Job Address Sample Address
Approved by: Sample Signature (Signature)	Job City, State Sample City, State
	Area - Facility Warehouse

Work Hours by Cost Code

Employee No.	Employee Name	Time Code	Craft Or	31100 Concrete Forming Hours	32100 Concrete Reinforcing Hours	33100 Concrete Placing Hours	33500 Concrete Finishing Hours	38100 Concrete Cutting Hours	Hours	Total Hours ST	1-1/2x	2x
1	Name 1	ST	15	4	4					8	0	0
		1-1/2x										
		2x										
2	Name 2	ST	10			8				8	0	0
		1-1/2x										
		2x										
3	Name 3	ST	10		2	6				8	0	0
		1-1/2x										
		2x										
4	Name 4	ST	10			8				8	0	0
		1-1/2x										
		2x										
5	Name 5	ST	14			8				8	2	1
		1-1/2x				2						
		2x				1						
		ST								0	0	0
		1-1/2x										
		2x										
		ST								0	0	0
		1-1/2x										
		2x										
	Totals			4	6	22	11	0	0	40	2	1

One problem with this approach is definition of terms. The terms from the estimate that now appear on the labor distribution are not defined and are frequently unclear. (The sample daily labor distribution report describes cost codes in words and number. In the real world, only numbers are commonly used.) Tradesmen will seldom exhaustively study all the plans when installing the work as the estimators did when preparing the estimate.

Another problem is that data entry is not contemporaneous. Tradesmen do not carry their time cards at all times, so data entry occurs daily or weekly. Multiple labor distribution work items may be performed at the same time (e.g., embeds may be attached to the forms as the forms are installed), so segregation of man-hours is unreasonable. When precise labor hours expended for undefined terms such as *edge form*, *set anchor bolts*, and *set embeds misc.* are to be recorded on time cards on Friday afternoon, the tradesmen frequently just guess and write down approximations, so they can go home. Unreliable data placed in a precise format produce unreliable information of little value.

The level of detail sought by a labor distribution can only be consistently achieved if cost engineers, not tradesmen, monitor the work and record results.

Accurate records of completed work in 2-week maximum task duration produce better results

Less precise but more accurate observations are key

Costs are recorded with this approach for all tasks for the entire project—no segregation by WBS task is attempted. Material costs are entered as invoiced. (If significant material is preordered, temporary manual adjustment may be needed.) The percent completed should be determined by the project management staff who will have access and knowledge of estimating terms and costs—so additional detail is available when needed. A very accurate percentage complete for the period and to date for each work item can be calculated using these short durations—weekly final completion of tasks minimizes the need for estimates that can produce bias and error. Confidence in this early accuracy aids timely corrective action.

The project manager should have an expected outcome in mind before inspections. Then, this expected value is compared with the observed and an explanation sought for the variance. After a project manager has repeated this exercise a few thousand times (only a few years' experience is required to reach this number), a feel for the amount of variance can be estimated in about 15 seconds. This is experience, not intuition. And tradesmen will recognize this capability and begin to offer explanations and answer questions that were not asked to defend their work—providing valuable insights about field conditions and attitudes.

Those performing the trade work should record the hours expended for the week—time cards that seek precise segregation of man-hours by task are not attempted. This segregation of duties helps manage the bias of both parties who might tend to show desired, not actual, results. Both can record their entries once a week—which is more realistic than in ½-hour increments expected by a labor distribution—and the results will still be adequate. Weekly observations that are inaccurate by plus or minus 10-25% will tend to cancel and produce overall project accuracy in excess of 95% for a 52-week project. Controlling bias and seeking accuracy over precision is key.

The schedule's task identification should use the WBS from the estimate and from the original project planning. These tasks must be subdivided, if necessary, into 2-week maximum durations so the problems are noticed as early as possible—when corrective action is feasible. An abbreviated job cost report appears below.

Job Cost Report

Division Number	Description	Contract with CO	% Complete	Labor Cost	Labor Overage	Material	Material Overage	Equipment Cost	Equipment Overage	Sub Cost	Sub Overage	Total Overage
1	General Requirements	$19,791	25%	$11,181	-$1,813	$6,310	-$451	$2,300	-$623			-$2,887
2	Earthwork	$41,860	100%							$41,860	$3,620	$3,620
	Demolition	$18,500	100%							$18,500		
	Landscaping	$23,769								$23,769		
3	Concrete	$52,683	83%							$52,683	$1,530	$1,530
4	Masonry	$86,500	90%							$86,500	$890	$890
5	Metals	$5,360	100%							$5,360		
6	Rough Carpentry	$79,215	91%	$42,737	-$7,200	$36,478	-$3,620					-$10,820
	Millwork	$23,339		$21,162		$2,177						
7	Roofing	$36,419	95%							$36,419		
	Fire Stopping	$1,850								$1,850		
	Caulk	$2,960								$2,960		
8	Hollow Metal	$4,390	18%			$4,390						
	Wood Doors	$5,272				$5,272						
	Finish Hardware	$4,688				$4,688						
	Door Hardware	$7,260	14%	$6,991	$182	$269						$182
	Double Acting Doors	$2,556								$2,556		
	Aluminum Framing, Glass & Glazing	$28,900								$28,900		
	Skylights	$2,400	100%							$2,400		
	Metal Cladding	$27,857		$10,640		$17,217						
9	Gypsum Drywall	$39,488	23%	$29,195	-$1,826	$10,294	-$630					-$2,456
	Painting	$34,700								$34,700		
	Fiberglass Reinforced Plastic	$3,913		$1,422		$2,491						
	Acoustic Ceiling Tiles	$14,109		$8,965		$5,144						
	Floor Preparation	$4,300								$4,300		
	VCT	$7,659								$7,659		
	Sheet Flooring	$11,109								$11,109		
10	Specialties	$5,819		$1,582		$4,237						
11	Equipment	$850				$850						
15	Sewer and Water	$12,550								$12,550		
	Plumbing and Process Gas	$58,760	38%							$58,760	$860	$860
	Natural Gas	$5,410								$5,410		
	HVAC	$78,200								$78,200		
	House VAC	$2,500								$2,500		
	Pipe Insulation	$2,860								$2,860		
16	Electrical	$56,839	18%							$56,839	$1,420	$1,420
	Subtotal	$814,635		$133,874		$99,818		$2,300		$578,643		-$7,661
	Overhead	$63,967										
	Total	$878,602										

This approach is the optimal approach that can realistically be achieved for all small and medium, and some large projects.

"Earned Value" Plans and Measures Cost and Schedule Performance Together

Earned value is a planning and measurement tool that integrates scope, schedule, and cost for the life of the project. This requires cost and schedule measurements integrated into a rigorous WBS. The schedule tasks must be resource weighted and driven—the task is assigned resources (that also have a currency cost), and these assigned resources determine the task duration.

Since each task has a currency value, currency values can also be used to monitor schedule progress. It is the integration of schedule and cost planning and management that makes earned value different from the other job costing methods described above.

Earned value was developed by the U.S. military—then slowly moved to the private sector

PERT (originally program evaluation research task, now performance evaluation and review techniques) scheduling was developed after World War II for complex weapon development projects. Since the schedule tasks also represented resources, the schedule and costs (cost is a resource) could be monitored at the same time with similar tools. The U.S. Department of Defense developed C/SCSC (cost/schedule control system criteria) in 1967 for this purpose.

The transfer of earned value methods to the private sector started with the Project Management Institute's inclusion of a mention of earned value in the 1987 edition of the *Project Management Body of Knowledge*—which was developed further in later editions. The American National Standard Institute codified and the Japanese Project Management Association adopted the methodology in 1998.

Because this system is structured, rigorous, labor intensive, and not immediately obvious, the reaction has been lukewarm or hostile. Only a small portion of the construction management community has adopted earned value.

How Earned Value Works—Analyzing Cost and Schedule Together

Part of project planning and execution, not just a control tool

Earned value is a powerful planning and analytical tool that integrates cost and time—two elements of the triple constraint of cost, time, and scope. The use of simple formulas to produce simple variance numbers or indices to express the cost–time relationship eases use and aids understanding.

The WBS schedule and cost from project planning must be used as the basis for earned value analysis. A late add-on of "now that we planned it, let's get a tool to control it" cannot work. Although frequently considered only a control tool, earned value can only work by integrating planning and control for the life of the project.

Inputs, Except "Earned value," Are Similar to Job Costing

The terms for earned value are similar to those for job costing except the term *earned value* itself. The earned value terms and explanation are listed below.

BAC (budget at completion). The budget for the project.

AC (actual cost). The costs expended at a point in time as documented by job cost records.

EV (earned value). The budgeted (currency) value of one or more completed tasks.

BAC × % actually complete

PV (planned value). The planned (budgeted and scheduled) cost for one or more scheduled tasks at a point in time.

$$BAC \times \% \text{ planned to be complete}$$

CV (cost variance). The difference between actual and expected spending at a point in time.

$$EV-AC$$

SV (schedule variance). The difference between actual and expected schedule performance at a point in time.

$$EV-PV$$

CPI (cost performance index). How well project performance is meeting cost expectations.

$$EV/AC$$

SPI (schedule performance index). How well project performance is meeting schedule expectations

$$EV/PV$$

EAC (estimate at completion). The estimate at completion if present performance continues unchanged.

$$BAC/CPI$$

ETC (estimate to complete). The projected cost to complete.

$$EAC-AC$$

Earning rules must suit the nature of the project

Consistent determination of completion of tasks in progress requires rules. For the early Department of Defense projects, which involved significant risky innovation, a task would only be considered complete when finally complete—no partial credit was given for work in progress (a 0/100 rule). Although this rule recognized the possibility that an innovation might fail, when earned value also determined the amounts to be paid, the rule proved unworkable. A 25/75 rule (25% recognized at task start and 75% at completion) was used as a compromise. Many simple, complex, or fine-tuned earning rules can be developed to suit project requirements—there are no universally accepted standards. But the agreed rules must always be established at start and used for the life of the project.

Since most private construction projects usually have few or no truly innovative components, the tasks are usually recognized as earned when installed—partial payment is allowed for partial completion. Further, mechanic's lien law requires that the amount of payments corresponds to the amount of work installed (improvements to the real estate), so prepayment for work not yet installed is troublesome.

Analysis and Output—Simple Results Produce Useful Clarity

First, numerical measurement, then graphs

These simple measures (all built on job cost records and EV and PV) produce clear and consistent meaning: positive variances and indices greater than 1 are good—indicating the project is under budget and ahead of schedule. Cost variances produce a currency value that is useful for cost projections for a specific project but cannot compare different projects. Indices can compare performance of very different projects.

These are the basic building blocks of analysis needed to generate useful output and may be altered to produce more refined outputs such as:

$$EAC = AC + (BAC - EV)/CPI$$

This states: "Actual costs expended to date are facts that cannot be changed. If performance to date continues for the rest of the project, this will be the cost outcome." Segregation of actual cost to date permits identification of different CPIs needed to achieve desired goals. In this way, earned value can be both a reporting system that aids understanding of present conditions and a management tool that aids correction.

Graphical Representation of Earned Value

Earned value is frequently illustrated graphically as shown below.

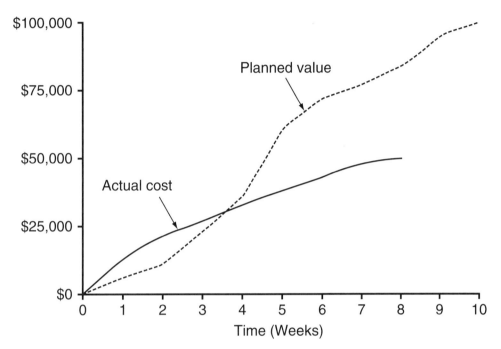

Project tracking without earned value does not conclusively define cost and schedule performance together.

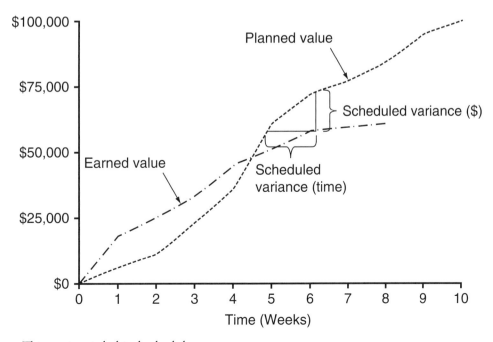

This project is behind schedule.

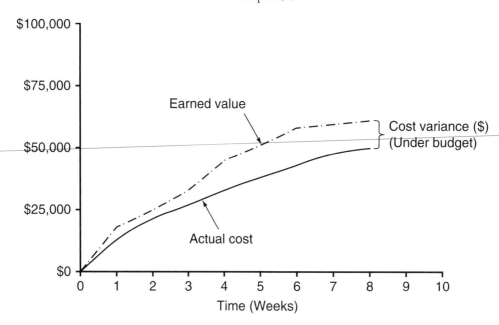

This project is under budget.

Time is usually shown on the x-axis and cost on the y-axis. The planned values are plotted using the estimated scheduled values and usually resemble an S curve. (Projects are slow to start, move faster in the middle, and are difficult and slow to finish.) Budget and schedule variations are also frequently noted graphically.

This graphic representation quickly alerts the construction manager to developing problems and opportunities. But the needed quantitative detail showing the size of the problem cannot be determined precisely enough from the graph—which limits the value of the graphing effort.

How Earned Value Is Used in Construction

Two numbers—the CPI and the SPI—can be used from afar by those unfamiliar with the project details to decide to kill a troubled project that cannot be saved. For complex military projects, the project output might be production of a prototype—with production of usable inventory delegated to a future project. If the prototype is troubled, the production will also be troubled, so immediate termination may be a wise decision.

And not only are military projects technically challenging but are also buffeted by the whims of changing elected officials—which compromises planning and correction possibilities. A U.S. Air Force study in the early 1990s found that a CPI at 20% completion does not change more than 10% for the remainder of the project.

However, in private sector construction, there are no prototypes. The cost to demolish or temporarily secure an abandoned project is high, and a completed project will usually have some value—so the voluntary decision to terminate a building project is rare. Private construction also has greater capacity for mid-project correction.

Earned value can also be used to calculate the value of progress payments due—if all parties are on board. Because of the differing accounting systems of subcontractors and project participants who change by project, earned value for payment calculation is not used in private sector construction.

Earned value can be used as a job costing and project management tool for construction projects. However, effective use requires commitment and competence by the owner, construction manager, and principal subcontractors and vendors, which are usually only found on larger multi-year projects. The powerful integration of cost and schedule can provide great benefits, but only if all project participants are capable and willing.

| Steeple erection | *photo 8 of 15* |

| Steeple erection | *photo 9 of 15* |

Smaller or midsize firms may have never used, or even heard of, earned value. But the understanding of the tools and process can aid the decision to begin to use earned value—or avoid it entirely.

Home office management commitment is needed for success

Segregating financial accounting from job costing is essential for real-time management, and this requires home office upper management support. Financial and tax accounting are important, but upper management must tell the comptroller that job cost accounting is important as well.

Field project managers and superintendents must be evaluated by their achievement of job cost targets. Project performance is the goal, and job cost accounting is the report card used to manage and monitor achievement of this goal. Evaluation by other financial accounting standards unknown to and beyond the control of field personnel will damage morale and degrade performance.

Summary

Cost accounting structures records to assist project planning and control. Data collection and organization must be consistent for the life of the project to be credible and useful. This requires selection of a cost system that can be executed by the personnel (who have certain capabilities and tendencies) who will be continuously assigned to the project. Accurate but not extremely precise results produce usable information. Seeking extreme but unachievable accuracy produces nothing.

The cost accounting system and information presented must be tailored to the sophistication of the project owner to maximize communication and understanding. Finally, the CM's firm must understand that financial and cost accounting must be segregated to maximize project performance and control.

Continuing use of the WBS started in the project cost and schedule planning is key. Use of maximum 2-week durations, and weekly accounting data minimize field record keeping and maximize the importance of the project manager's evaluation of the percentage of task completion. Once this structure is established, weekly monitoring can be done with minimal effort. And this is the closest to real-time evaluation possible for small, medium, and most large projects.

Review Questions (True or False)

1. Cost accounting, which has a different focus and purpose than financial accounting, seeks to answer the questions:
   a. What is the intended project outcome?
   b. What have we done to date?
   c. What are we doing right now?
   d. What is the impact of our performance on the intended outcome if nothing is changed?
   e. What can we change to better achieve the project outcome?
2. Hourly unit cost for labor and equipment represent exact financial accounting costs not estimates.
3. Cost codes include a minimum of the project number and WBS work description (usually in CSI format) for small projects, but may also include area or facility code and financial classifications for larger projects.
4. Two-week maximum job cost period for analysis is consistent both with sound management practices and with weekly trade labor payment procedures.
5. Payments for both materials and subcontractors accurately represent work completed and may be used in cost accounting without alteration.
6. Job costing of indirect costs such as management and supervisory time, over-the-road vehicle expense, and small tools and equipment is essential on both hard bid lump sum and construction management or time and material contracts. For construction management or time and material contracts, these indirect costs, if carefully defined during contract negotiations, can be a source of profit.
7. Data for labor distributions (which attempt to segregate payroll hours by detailed cost codes) can be accurately entered by the tradesmen or foreman performing the work.
8. Accurate job cost records can be obtained if those performing the trade work record hours expended for the period and experienced project managers or engineers record work completed for each work item for the same period.
9. Earned value measures cost and schedule performance together.
10. If both the CPI and the SPI are greater than 1, the project is under budget and ahead of schedule.

Test Your Understanding

1. Identify the cost expenditures from the list below that would be included in financial accounting but not cost accounting.
   Material costs
   Income taxes
   Depreciation
   Payment to subcontractors
   Payment and performance bond premiums
   Additional insurance premiums due to year-end audit
2. Using the quantity survey and pricing for gypsum framing and drywall shown earlier in this chapter, calculate the cost for 1 labor-hour. Then, calculate the total labor cost for a work item completed in 40 straight time hours, 2 hours of time and a half, and 1 hour of double time.
3. For a project with the costs and percent completion listed below, determine if the project is under or over budget and ahead or behind schedule by calculating the CPI and SPI.
   BAC (budget at completion) $100,000
   Percent actually complete 60%
   AC (actual cost) $55,000
   Planned percent complete 65%

CHAPTER

3.8

Schedule Implementation and Management Are Integrated with Cost Management

Use of gang forms can reduce the number of ties through the foundation wall as can be seen by the foundation wall at the right where forms have been removed.

Schedule Implementation and Management Are Integrated with Cost Management

Adjusting the workable approach so success is probable, and revisions unusual

Making a schedule that could be made to work was discussed in the last chapter. Here we discuss making the schedule work well so that success, even with normal error and variation, is the normal outcome.

The beginning of scheduling systems

Fredrick Taylor and Henry Gantt developed industrial production time and motion studies in the early 1900s in America. They believed that the source for specifying and reducing activity duration was scientific management (upper management—not the production worker). Their graphic tool, the bar chart (also called the Gantt chart), assembled bars representing activities, with lengths representing durations, organized in their proposed order of installation. Bar charts represented their opinion of how things should be done. But they could not be used as a tool for management and control of these activities because they presented the conclusion, but did not show how the conclusion was reached. This was management's conclusion and used no input from production workers.

Scheduling systems that permit management and control

Scheduling systems began after World War II in the United States—about the same time as project management. In 1956, the DuPont companies began developing CPM (Critical Path Method) scheduling for construction projects. In 1957, the U.S. Navy, working on the Polaris submarine project, began developing PERT (Performance Evaluation and Review Technique) scheduling. Unlike the bar chart described above, these scheduling techniques showed the relationship between activities and assigned resources to the activities. This produced an overall project schedule duration based on how facts influence activities, rather than the opinions of upper management. Management and control of the schedule, and therefore of the project, was then possible.

These techniques were originally applied to very large projects—with 1,000s or 10,000s of activities. Computers were, therefore, required to process and reprocess these data sufficiently fast to be of any use—and this required engineers. The engineers processed massive amounts of data on mainframe computers to produce workable, supportable solutions—solutions where the logic and information that produced the schedule was still clearly visible in the schedule itself. This engineering mentality and personality is still required and in use for most scheduling efforts. Shoot from the hip, seat of the pants managers lack the discipline, and willingness to do the hard work it takes, to make, use, or evaluate a schedule. They are top-down managers (who start with a conclusion and then get the facts), while scheduling is a bottom-up process (get the facts then build a solution).

Why is this history important? Scheduling is a unique and powerful tool now available to many that can adjust the approach to help make project success normal. Even with these historical improvements, it is still in a form understandable by few. While scheduling was developing, project management knowledge and decisions also became more dispersed to more participants. Scheduling using the knowledge and decisions of many, done by the few, with the benefits then used by many is the result—and is discussed below.

Few work well with scheduling charts, graphs, and symbols

The schedule is a management tool only for those ready, willing, and able to work with it as a management tool—a very small group. Only management personnel who have over a 2-week time horizon can possibly work with the benefits that can be gained by scheduling. Many people do not like to plan—they prefer to operate and react, and many people cannot understand interrelations between activities. Also, few people will do the required tedious detail work.

Further, most people are incapable of using the graphs, mathematical symbols, and tables that are part of scheduling. They just do not think this way naturally—and education helps only a little. Presentation of a schedule to people who do not possess the ability to read it will produce unhelpful reactions such as (if their activities appear too long) "We've got plenty of time, we can take it easy on this one," or (if their activities appear too short) the reaction is "The office is wrong, they have no idea how things are really done out here." Many owners with no review or thought will say, "How can we take 10% off of this?". Less than 5% of project participants can positively and effectively use a schedule.

Schedules Presentations Must Communicate to All Project Participants

Few can or will make a schedule, yet input and reaction are required from many

This is a paradox—scheduling is a bottom-up activity requiring the participation of many, but most cannot read or work with a schedule. Yet, there is no other tool that can so rapidly analyze, adjust, and confirm a workable approach that makes success probable. The solution is to obtain the input in words and numbers from many project participants. Valuable information that could not be obtained any other way will be gained. Also, since most people greatly exaggerate the size of their contribution, many will feel ownership—or think they single-handedly created the schedule themselves. Someone in the 5% that can then makes the schedule using this input. Later adjustments and revisions are best done not with the schedule, but with verbal, written instructions, and with technical information the 95% are accustomed to.

Scheduling information is understood by few, job cost reports by many. For example, "Completion of schedule items 135 with related coordination is required between work days 65 and 72" would probably be understood only by the scheduler. But "Pour floor 1 northwest quarter from next Monday until the following Tuesday with a crew of 8 laborers and 6 finishers. Plumbing embeds must be installed, electrical penetration will be cored later" will be understood by those installing the work. The confidence that these instructions are correct was produced by the schedule, but the directions are communicated by other means—words and numbers. The process is: get the input in words and numbers, make the schedule with symbols and graphs, and show the results in words and numbers.

Make a CPM schedule, show the bar chart or milestones, then add words and numbers

The CPM scheduling, as described above, takes real activities, assigns resources, and specifies their relationship to predict a real result that can be managed. This can be presented as a graphic showing the relationships between all preceding and succeeding activities—as well as their duration and resources. This permits ready visualization and management of problems and opportunities. It, however, is difficult for most people to grasp. Some say, "It looks like a wiring diagram."

All information contained in the critical path schedule can be condensed into a bar chart that shows only the bars representing the durations of the activities, sometimes accompanied by mathematical notations of predecessors and successors and assigned resources. The activities and durations of the critical path schedule can be contained on the bar chart, but none of the relationships are visually apparent and therefore management of the schedule using a bar chart is unfeasible. The critical path schedule can be condensed into a bar chart, but a bar chart cannot be expanded into a critical path schedule. Further, an attempt to begin the scheduling process directly with the bar chart cannot work. Durations and relationships between activities are only a statement of wishful thinking based on no facts and expressed as graphic images. This has no use in a successful project. A CPM diagram is needed for management and control.

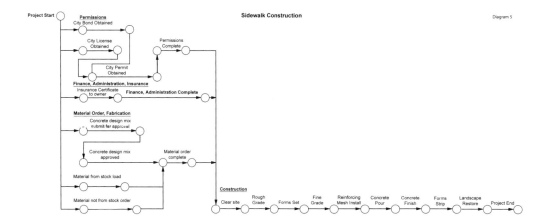

This is an extremely simple and short schedule. The on-site construction work has end-to-end activities that might all be completed in 2 days (one day to prepare the site, set the forms, and place the concrete, and one day to strip the forms and restore the landscaping)—so their sequence is a line of activities. The permissions and material order parts of the schedule have more interaction and look more like a usual schedule.

When the schedule preparer must give the schedule to someone in the other 95%—the bar chart and accompany the schedule with supplemental information presented in other forms—usually words and numbers, not the critical path version, work best. Their reaction will be "OK, they did their homework, now what are we going to do?" and the words and numbers will give the instructions. An extract from the bar chart, the milestone chart (which shows only the milestones but no supporting activities), may work well for management not directly involved with the project or external parties such as banks or bonding companies—especially for very short presentations.

Scheduling Helps Refine and Improve the Approach

The project priorities should have been set in planning well before the scheduling tools are used, but the confirmation and refinement of priorities and the visualization of their impact can more readily be seen at this point, and then adjustments made. The project will be scheduled to optimize a particular priority, always at some expense of other priorities. The schedule can be developed to complete the project in the absolute minimum time possible, it can be developed to optimize productivity and therefore minimize cost, or it can recognize limited resources to work with their limits, or the priority can be the steady use of one resource. For example, if a contractor has a core crew of excellent high-production personnel and wants to keep them operating at optimal capacity to achieve optimal production and profit, the schedule can be adjusted to achieve this result (such an approach must usually be disguised from the owner who usually has different priorities).

The most common approach to scheduling is to find the project duration expectation that is normal and customary in the project area and try to work to this time. The cost will go up slightly, and the grade of material may vary somewhat to achieve the expected project duration. Skillful adjustment of resources and relationships can improve productivity and profit, and improve manageability somewhat—but any improvement must be within the requirements of the owner's workable approach and purpose.

The minor revisions—techniques to achieve the intended results—discussed in the previous chapter are the following: resource allocation changes, predecessor and successor changes, lead and lag adjustments, and working calendar revisions. If these minor changes still cannot achieve the intended result, or larger improvements are needed, such as huge increases in productivity or profit, more radical scheduling revisions can be explored as discussed below.

Radical Scheduling Changes Can Produce Big Improvements—and Risks

Method and location of production can be changed

Substituting machine production for hand labor can overcome production limited by scarce skilled labor. Fabrication of components off site can overcome job site density limits. Purchasing site prefabricated components from an outside vendor could also solve this problem. These decisions will usually have an effect on cost, grade, and time—so the costs and benefits need to be weighed. Also, they may be executed by different companies (the subcontractors used for hand labor may not have the machines for a mechanized solution), so these decisions must be made before awarding contracts.

Big approach changes can be considered

A radical change in planned execution will increase some costs in exchange for the possibility of decreasing other costs or time. For example, a sewage treatment plant with many separate concrete structures and much connecting piping is usually constructed by individually excavating and backfilling each structure for each trade—with much duplicated effort. A radical alternate approach could be to excavate the entire multi-acre site to the bottom of all the concrete structures and build them all at once. Large increases in earthwork costs might be overcome by a 300% increase in labor productivity for the concrete structures. This is a big and risky bet with possible big payoffs.

Changing systems and components can provide big benefits—but big consequential effects as well

A change in building system type will affect grade, cost, and time. One common example is the selection of a concrete or steel-framed building. Selection of prepackaged roof-top mechanical units or a multi-component site assembled system in an enclosed mechanical room is another example. The merits of these will vary with the prevailing construction customs, availability of labor, material price, and market forces of each project at each location and time. These decisions affect design of the component and probably related systems such as structural and electrical. So, these decisions should or must be made early in the project development process.

| Steeple erection | *photo 10 of 15* |

Change start, finish, and delivery time

Changing a project start date when one phase of the project is affected by weather can reduce general condition costs, increase productivity (decreasing cost or increasing profit), and in some cases reduce overall project time. For a project in an occupied building, changing the owner's proposed phasing that maintains ongoing operations can change both the delivery time and cost. For example, the cost of constructing temporary facilities for owner operations may be offset by the savings of vastly improved field productivity, with the additional benefit of reduced project delivery time.

Schedules can be Fine-Tuned to Make Success Probable

Build on opportunities and build in problem avoidance

Any pinch points or resource over allocation must be identified and corrected. This is done after the schedule appears to work. Any activity that is scheduled beyond the available resources, or the production limit of the job site, must be adjusted to conform to these limits. Scheduling programs automatically produce multiple reports that show the over allocations and make this effort easy and fast. Once these adjustments are made, the schedule can be made to work. Then, it can be made to work well, as described below.

The largest opportunity to ensure success is to make the critical path consist solely of the activities that can be best controlled. Placing tasks to be self-performed by tradesmen who predictably perform on time, or tasks to be performed by strong subcontractors on the critical path helps maintain the schedule. Similarly, any activities that are less controllable, such as weak and less-than-competent subcontractors, or activities that still require approval from outside agencies or the government should be made uncritical.

Next, choose activities that can lead by example and momentum and make them critical. Then, schedule related tasks by the less aggressive trades slightly earlier than usual—get them involved early. Many people need to physically see work before they feel urgency. Identifying a series of baby steps for the weaker contractors will build in an early ramp-up of production, and drag them along.

Further, it is best to make the activities surrounding a critical activity supportive of it and with a more tolerant fit. If a critical activity begins to appear incapable of maintaining the required duration, some of the supporting activities around it can be accelerated or slowed to assist the speed of the critical activity. For example, if other activities in the work area can be finished earlier or later, the work area will be less congested—permitting more resources and greater productivity for the critical activity.

The tolerance of the fit surrounding critical activities can be seen by the activity's float. Float is the number of days that actual duration can miss the planned duration without changing the overall schedule. For example, if an activity has a float of 5 days, it can be up to 5 days late without changing the project's critical path. (Activities on the critical path by definition have no float.) The critical path was altered—by altering resources, successors and predecessors, and lead and lag times. The activities surrounding the critical path can be altered in the same manner. Increasing the float of the weaker activities surrounding the critical path will increase the tolerant fit. By managing the weaker activities in this manner, their poor performance and schedule slippage will not increase the overall project duration.

Precision of the estimated quantities and resources for activities is readily achievable, and should have been done in the estimate. This precision is good—get it done right once and leave it alone. Precision of the fit between the activities, in contrast, is not desirable and will not produce a schedule with the give and go to absorb the variation in results that always occurs. (We are dealing with people here, so there will always be variation.) A tolerant fit between activities, with well-placed shock absorbers, is the goal.

Adjustments to the critical path made in the planning stage by changing resource allocation, changing responsibility for a task (self-perform, or sub out to one or more parties), or changing relationships between activities to start earlier can be done at some cost, no cost, or sometimes less cost. The cost of getting it right early is always less than fixing a problem later.

| Steeple erection | *photo 11 of 15* |

Getting out of first gear and overcoming the goal line defense

As all experienced managers know, getting started and up to full production, and getting finally completed (every last detail including documentation), requires focused management attention. The schedule can be organized to assist this management effort. First, more milestones can be added early and late in the project so a sense of urgency and opportunity for management are created—not, "Oh we have lots of time, no need to rush now." All activities—administrative, engineering, fabrication, and shipping—are work tasks. Once people start working, it is easier to get them to work more and in the way required.

Next, build in completion as part of doing the work. Ideally, all closeout documents, adjustments, repairs, and certification should be done before the trades performing the work leave the job site completely. If they are totally gone, return trips and getting familiar with the job again will drag out completion unnecessarily. Also, in the schedule there should be certain certifications and demonstrations to make completion a debugging and verification process, not just end-of-project paperwork. All closeout activities—testing, certifying, and documenting—are work tasks.

Schedule updates during the project should be rarely needed

The properly constructed schedule described above will almost never have to be updated unless the scope changes. All activities, their relationships, and resulting durations are based on actual estimating data. Schedule slippage usually means cost slippage. Pinch points or over allocations of resources have already been identified and corrected to achieve a tolerant fit. Over 95% of the schedules constructed in this way achieve the original completion date with competent, but not extraordinary, management of the project.

The schedule will identify where management needs to focus attention. The critical path, strong and weak and activities, driving and weak players, probable problems, and opportunities are learned and managed when making the schedule. So, even project personnel who have no knowledge of the schedule can know the right priorities. Working on the right problems, the reasonably competent and hard working will probably succeed.

A schedule should only be updated during the course of the project if an extraordinary event occurs that alters the critical dates by more than a week. (Extraordinary events are by definition rare and may not occur in a person's entire career. Normal seasonal weather variation, late decisions by government officials, labor disruptions at time of labor contract renewal, seasonal delivery difficulties for some materials, and troublesome weak subcontractors are normal and should be included in project planning.) A major change in scope will, of course, require a corresponding schedule change.

A practice used by some of a 2-week schedule revision means that there was no schedule established at all. Every 2 weeks new descriptions of what fires are being put out at the moment are itemized. The status of the failing project is described, and guesses of firefighting for the next 2-weeks are presented.

Schedule monitoring and control use both the schedule and cost analysis

Scheduling programs permit comparison of planned and actual performance—which can be a useful qualitative diagnostic tool. The cost and time are directly related, and the cost diagnostic tools are more highly developed, particularly for quantitative analysis. Job costing, with the oversight of the accounting department, will highlight performance variations early. And the cost analysis technique of earned value quantitatively analyzes the effects of cost and schedule together.

Control charts used as part of the quality process can also highlight schedule variations both quantitatively and qualitatively. This integration of scheduling, cost, and quality tools is used to monitor and control the schedule.

Scheduling Used for Other Purposes

Scheduling for job costing and management communicates poorly

Scheduling to monitor the productivity of the job can be done with the scheduling tool. Those familiar with and competent in scheduling techniques will see this powerful tool as obvious and natural. However, as described above, these people are few. Everyone else did not understand the original schedule, so they also will not understand the updates. (This failure to understand will also include those in accounting responsible for job cost accounting.) Attempts by the few to manage with the schedule that others cannot understand will sound like, "It is so because I say it is so. Now just do it." This attitude will neither convince nor help cooperation.

Litigation—lawyers wearing hard hats

When a project has failed so badly that the rubble and ashes are being sifted in court, scheduling tools can be used to show the location, cause, and size of the failures. All the decisions above and in the previous chapter are directed toward increasing possibilities for improvement to make success probable. If these improvements were not made, or no planning took place at all, the same tools can be used to measure the resulting failure. The methods are the same, but the numbers for failure are usually much larger.

Summary

Scheduling takes the knowledge of many in word and numbers, makes a schedule by a few with charts and symbols, and then provides the results for many in words and numbers. Scheduling shows the time that results from decisions on approach, grade of materials, and cost—then adjusts these components to get closer to the project purpose. A tolerant fit between activities provides the shock absorbers that make success normal and revisions unusual—even with the unavoidable performance variation and error.

Review Questions (True or False)

1. Fredrick Taylor and Henry Gantt developed the bar chart that showed management's conclusion and used no input from production workers.
2. The PERT chart showed the relationship between activities and assigned resources using worker input to produce a project schedule based on how facts influence activities. But these schedules were developed and managed by engineers, and the output was sometimes difficult to communicate to other project participants.
3. 95% of project participants can understand and evaluate a schedule.
4. Gaining the input in words and numbers from many project participants, developing the project schedule using mathematical and graphical techniques, and then communicating the output with verbal and written technical documentation help develop the project participants' feeling of schedule ownership.
5. The critical path schedule can be condensed into a bar chart, and a bar chart can be expanded into a critical path schedule.
6. A schedule showing only milestones can be useful for brief presentations to management.
7. The schedule can be adjusted to keep a core crew of excellent high-production workers operating at optimal productivity.
8. A well-developed project schedule shows the result of all previous decisions and therefore should not be influenced by the normal and customary schedule expectations in the project area.
9. Substituting machine production for hand fabrication of components, and off-site fabrication can improve the schedule and may be implemented anytime during the project.
10. Changes in building systems and components can produce big schedule benefits, but only if decisions are made early in project development.
11. If the critical path consists solely of activities that can be best controlled (strong subcontractors and reliable predictable vendors), fewer mid-project schedule corrections will probably be required.
12. If the critical path is strong enough, the activities surrounding the critical path cannot benefit from further management attention and refinement.
13. Effectively starting and closing the project can be assisted by placing meaningful milestones, that define completion of activities or subprojects, into the project schedule.
14. The 2-week schedule revision is a normal and useful project management tool.
15. Integration of scheduling and job costing is a powerful tool that communicates well to the project owners.

Test Your Understanding

1. Scheduling decisions are best made early in project planning. Discuss the schedule improvement techniques that can only be implemented in early project planning but never for mid-project correction
2. Discuss how to obtain input from nontechnical project owners to develop the schedule and how to effectively communicate (PERT charts, Gantt charts, milestones, verbal or numerical reports) the output of the schedule.
3. Discuss what techniques can be used to develop a tolerant fit—maximizing the impact of strong subcontractors and vendors and managing the deficiencies of the weak.

CHAPTER
3.9

Precision Takes Time and Money, and Can Impact Scope

Use of gang forms can decrease the time of installation and labor required, but needed hoisting equipment must be planned.

Precision Takes Time and Money, and Can Impact Scope

Choosing the best achievable level of detail

Needed precision adds value, but excessive precision is wasted

Precision refers to the acceptable variation from a stated (perfect) value or point. For example, "this 10-foot-long board is straight plus or minus 1 inch." Exact precision (perfection) never exists in the real world. One can, with effort, move closer to perfection, but because variation exists in all things and people, exact precision is never reached. A measurement may at first appear precise, but a new, finer measuring tool will show the object's variation.

Precision is discussed briefly in cost accounting and in more detail in discussions about quality. Normal statistical distributions describe, and control charts monitor and control, this variation. It is also discussed here in relation to scope so that the needed and achievable level of precision is planned and can carry through, with little alteration, to execution and control.

Variation Is Everywhere, Precision Nowhere. Manage Variation to Be "Precise Enough"

The purpose determines the level of precision required. So, the purpose must first be clearly defined. Without a clear purpose, the range of precision possible is too vast to permit selection of the right level of precision for the project. Setting an arbitrarily high standard—"let's just get the best"—is not achievable and will fail.

Once the purpose is clearly defined, common sense, industry standards, and a determination of what is available at an acceptable price will guide selection of an appropriate level of precision—as shown by the following examples.

> When traveling from a house on the east side of the country to a factory on the west side of the country, arrival is achieved at the parking lot. A spot on the east side of the lot, or 400 feet away on the west side, is close enough.

> When regrading earth on a square site measuring 1,000 feet on each side that requires raising some parts 6 feet and lowering some parts 4 feet, final achieved grades within feet or inches of the specified grades are precise enough.

> Wood and steel rough framing is sometimes considered exact at within 2 inches, and sometimes within 1/4 of an inch—while cabinet and millwork construction gaps of 1/4 inch in finished work are unacceptable.

> Pump and pump motor alignment requires 1/1,000 inch shims to make the pump and motor run without excessive vibration and wear.

These hugely different levels of precision seem appropriate and obvious because the purpose was defined. Location in the factory parking lot would not be measured to the same 1/1,000 of an inch that would be appropriate for the pump alignment. All these examples may be viewed as precise enough for the intended purpose. But if finer measuring tools—a better ruler, a magnifying glass, or a microscope—were used, the variations would be apparent—and the variation might be unacceptable, depending on how much precision is needed.

| Steeple erection | *photo 12 of 15* |

Variation exists in all things and people—industry standards must be known

Manufacturing methods are usually similar in an industry, and there are accepted industry tolerance standards.

Steel mills are factories stretching for miles producing around the clock, every day for years. The steel companies have agreed how much variation will be allowed. For a 30-foot-wide flange beam, sometimes referred to as an I beam, the industry has agreed that 3″ out of line is "straight enough."

Rough lumber such as 2 × 4s is produced by giant timber companies and small mills with a few employees. The wood products industry has agreed on allowable variation. For a 2 × 12, 16 feet long, the industry has agreed that 1–1/2″ out of line is "straight enough."

Some tolerances have improved and may continue to improve over the years. But specifications will *not* change in time for the project. This may sound obvious, but expectations and specifications that assume these tolerances do not exist, or will be changed by writing specifications on a piece of paper, are common.

Human variation exists in all activities. A professional baseball pitcher, for example, may be talented, skilled, and trained, but can rarely pitch a no-hitter. Similarly, human variation and achievable levels of precision must be recognized and managed in the construction process.

Realizing the optimal level of precision for the project

Precision is frequently thought to mean "better" and is found in the name of many construction firms—such as Precision Drywall, Precision Mechanical. But because precision has a cost and more precision than necessary is wasted. Precision does not necessarily mean better.

Seeking more precision takes effort and usually costs money. If a more precise product costs more, some think it is "better." But this is not necessarily so. Precision that is greater than what the user can see, measure, or needs is not harmful to the installed work, but it is wasted—such as measuring a car's location in a factory parking lot to 1/1,000 of an inch.

A common approach is to seek a level of precision in components that is far in excess of what is required, or maybe possible, in the hope that this greater precision of one component will somehow

| Steeple erection | *photo 13 of 15* |

overcome the lesser precision of other components—producing a completed project achieving the desired level of precision. But good intentions and "just hoping" will not make it so. The requested precision will not always be available at an acceptable cost.

And one precise component can never increase the precision of another component. The lowest level of precision in all components that achieves the purpose is the optimal level. More precision (at the same cost) will neither hurt nor help. But there usually is a cost—higher purchase cost for unnecessarily precise materials, schedule delay costs to wait for these less common materials, or elimination of otherwise desirable vendors from consideration.

How Much Precision Can the Project Afford?

Increased precision usually takes effort, time, and money—which are all limited. An illustrative description of the effort required for various levels of precision is as follows:

100 man-hours to achieve 67% precision, being wrong 33% of the time, is considered unacceptable.

200 man-hours to achieve 90% precision, being wrong 10% of the time, is considered acceptable for only some purposes.

300 man-hours to achieve 95% precision, being wrong 5% of the time, might initially seem that "we could do better" until the cost and feasibility is evaluated. Then, this level of precision may look "ok."

400 man-hours to achieve 97% precision, better, but at a great cost for the improvement.

500 man-hours to achieve 98% precision, cost becomes excessive for almost all purposes.

600 man-hours to achieve 99% precision, seldom used because of the excessive cost.

Note: If an entire industry increases precision over time, the costs will decline—maybe hugely. But the purpose is to build a project here and now with the workers and materials available—so future possibilities cannot be considered.

Getting the Best from the Level of Precision That Fits Your Purpose

Determining how good is "good enough"

Some logical steps should be followed:

1. Define the purpose the project will serve.
2. Determine the precision of the components and capability of labor now available in the market at an acceptable cost.
3. Rule out the levels of high precision and the levels of low precision that are inappropriate for the purpose. Start the selection of the remaining levels by working bottom up, not top down. Define the lowest available precision of components that will achieve the purpose as the minimum standard. Then, define the highest standard achievable for this project possible, but not necessary the upper limit.

The level of 95% is now the most frequently selected level of "good enough" for projects. Lower levels of precision are offered by many. Higher levels require effort, time, and cost that are only used for "whatever it takes, cost is no object" projects such as manned space travel. In this case, there is usually a third party, such as the taxpayer, paying the bill.

Making the building appear more precise with "tolerant fit". Improving fit while decreasing cost

Once the desired level of precision for the project is determined, then the completed project can be made to appear more precise than the components—usually for lower cost. This is done with "tolerant fit" that designs more "give and go" in the assembly of the components. This approach takes the components that are available and assembles them in such a way that their lack of precision is less apparent—as illustrated by the following examples.

> A door frame that butts to a finished wall can appear incorrectly installed with an 1/8-inch gap. If a gripping frame that overlaps the same wall is used, wall misalignment of up to 3/8″ can be completely hidden.

> A door-release electric strike designed to operate at 24 volts can be damaged or fail to operate if the supplied voltage varies. If the same strike is designed to operate from 8 to 32 volts, supplied voltage can vary and the strike will still function perfectly.

The completed building appears more precise and functions more precisely than the actual precision of the individual components. Tolerant fit results from clever selection of components (usually with lower material costs) and assemblies of components (usually with lower labor costs) that look "like we meant it that way."

Communicating the Precision Used

Formats consistently communicate the precision achieved

When a level of precision for a purpose is selected, this selection is communicated by writing all measurements with that level of precision, and no more. Everyone is entitled to believe and will believe that the written "12–1/8″" was intend to be and was measured with 1/8″ accuracy—not 1/4″ or 1/16″. (This idea is called significant figures in science.) All measurements are for a purpose, and since the parts must fit together, all should have the same level of precision.

Also, it is clearer if all measurements for a purpose are written in exactly the same format. For clear communication, the measurements in the form 12-1/8″ (inches only) should not be arbitrarily changed to 1′–0 1/8″ (feet and inches), even though the measurements are equal.

Summary

Perfection does not exist in the real world, and precision is not itself a virtue. The optimal level of precision is the lowest level that fits the purpose. This level is protected and made to appear more precise with a tolerant fit. This achieves excellence, and the appearance of high precision—which helps make project success normal. Building the appropriate level of precision into the initial scope specification aids execution and control.

Review Questions (True or False)

1. Precision refers to the acceptable variation from a stated value or point. Because variation exists in all things and people, exact precision is never reached.
2. The project purpose determines the level of precision required. Without a clear purpose, the range of precision possible is too vast to permit selection of the right level of precision for the project.
3. Tolerances have improved and may continue to improve, so specifying a high level of precision will achieve higher quality for the project.
4. Precision takes time and effort and usually costs money.
5. It is best to seek a level of precision that is far in excess of what is required so that even with variation, acceptable results will be achieved.
6. The lowest level of precision in all components that achieves the purpose is the optimal level.
7. Getting the best from the level of precision that fits your purpose involves (1) defining the purpose the project will serve, (2) determining the precision of components and capability of labor available at the time of the project, (3) work bottom up not top down to define the available precision that achieves the purpose as the minimum standard.
8. A level of 95% precision is now the most frequently selected level of "good enough" for construction projects.
9. Tolerant fit designs more "give and go" in the assembly of components and usually has higher material and labor costs.
10. The level of precision in measurement numbers communicates the intended and measured level of precision.
11. Numerical measurements in different formats communicate the same values and so may be used effectively interchangeably.

Test Your Understanding

1. Using the reference standards of organizations listed in the appendix (ACI, AISC, AWI, PCA), the book *Architectural Graphics Standards*, or other engineering reference manuals, find a specified tolerance for one of the following: concrete floor flatness, dimensional lumber width and thickness or straightness, structural steel shape chamber. Calculate the percent variation of the allowed tolerances.
2. For one of your recently completed classes, list your grades for all graded work (quizzes, paper, labs, midterm, and final exams). Give each grade an equal weight and use the scale A = 90, B = 80 C = 70 D = 60, F = 50, to calculate the mean and percent variation from the mean for each grade.
3. A common tolerance for concrete slab flatness is 1/8″ in 10 feet. Using a tight string (dry line or chalk line) and ruler, measure variation from this specified flatness for an interior concrete floor and for a sidewalk. Then calculate the percent variation for each measurement.

3.10

Quality Management Achieves Targeted Performance

Planning the installation sequence and scheduling of masonry construction can permit use of jack-up scaffolding shown here, which can increase both productivity and safety.

Quality Management Achieves Targeted Performance

Reliable achievement of planned results lowers mid and long-term costs

Quality Management Definitions and Common Misconceptions

The most satisfactory results may require a lower grade

Quality management is a process and cultural attitude led by management

In everyday language, quality means high grade and usually high cost. But in general management and construction project management, quality means reliable achievement of planned results—regardless of the grade planned. These results are achieved by managing the statistical variation that normally occurs in all materials and processes. Quality management affects the entire approach to project management—a cultural shift—lead by management.

Quality and grade are not the same

The ISO (International Standards Organization) defines quality as "the degree to which a set of inherent characteristics fulfills the requirements," and defines the grade as "a category assigned to products or services having the same functional use but different technical characteristics." So, an unnecessarily precise, feature-rich (high grade) but higher priced product or service that does not fulfill the cost requirements of the triple constraint would be of a lower quality than a lesser and more economical, but still satisfactory, grade. The lowest grade with the most tolerant fit that fulfills the purpose is usually the most economical, achievable, and desirable solution—and therefore the highest quality.

Precision and accuracy are not the same—precision can be more easily managed than accuracy

Precision means that the values of repeated measurements are tightly clustered with little scatter. Accuracy means that the measured values are very close to the intended values. Although precision and accuracy together would be best, precise but not accurate is easier to manage than accurate but not precise. For example, when target shooting, precise shots high and to the left can be corrected by adjustment of one variable—the gun sight—to adjust the location of the precision for consistent accurate bull's eyes. But if the shots are randomly scattered in all directions surrounding the bull's eye, no single variable can be adjusted to improve accuracy to consistently hit more bull's eyes.

Quality Manages the Entire Delivery Process—Catching Defects Is Not Enough

Prevention is more efficient and effective than detection alone

The cost of quality compares the cost of conformance and the cost of nonconformance

The cost of quality refers to the total cost of all efforts needed to achieve and maintain the desired result throughout the life of the project. This includes planning, construction, and activities that occur after substantial completion such as callbacks, warrantee work, and reputation enhancement that help win future projects. The cost of quality must compare the cost of conformance to the cost of nonconformance. Components of these costs are listed below.

Costs of conformance—to avoid failures

Prevention costs

Planning quality in management processes, procedures, and activities

Planning a robust design with tolerant fit

Value engineering, so the initial scope and cost achieves the intended purpose

Training of personnel

Equipment—of the needed types and serviceability

Communication of needed information when needed

Appraisal costs

Personnel costs to monitor and control processes

Testing costs—internal and independent testing laboratories

Destructive testing material costs (usually a trivial cost for most construction projects)

Cost of nonconformance—costs and impacts of failures

Internal failure costs—directly related to project performance

Higher cost due to lower productivity and rework

Higher material cost due to waste and scrap

Schedule extension caused by low productivity, correction, and rework

Higher costs due to use of unnecessarily high (and expensive) grades of material

External failure costs—consequences after project completion

Legal liability for failed work

Additional cost for callbacks and warranty claims

Reputation damage that reduces future business

Although a sloppy hurried job is usually initially cheaper and faster, the total life cycle cost is usually higher. Note that conformance activities focus heavily on management functions—which, although not cost free, can be performed by few people, quickly and cheaply. In contrast, the cost of nonconformance requires some management time and involves construction labor, material, and equipment, which add large costs and time. This economy—achieving the desired result at lower cost—is a strong reason to adopt the quality process.

Continuous monitoring and adjustment for improvement are more effective than defect detection

Production processes that do not use the quality process instead use a large filter at the end of the process—the inspection or "quality control" department. The product is produced (with few or no controls), and then the final result is evaluated for conformance to planned standards. Nonconforming products are either scrapped or sent back to production for rework. With this approach, the cause of defects may remain unknown, and defective work will continue to be produced.

Quality processes monitor each step of production both for conformance with planned standards and to assess the causes of deviations. Catching and correcting potential defects at or before occurrence (prevention not detection) more precisely and accurately achieves the needed results and minimizes rework or scrap of the finished product.

Statistical sampling is needed for prompt analysis and correction, and for efficiency

To achieve continuous improvement, analysis of present performance and prediction of the impact on future performance requires statistical sampling. Since analysis is performed throughout the project, the observations by nature will be a fraction of the entire process—a sample. Sampling is also needed for the practical reason that measurement and analysis has personnel costs that must be efficiently managed. So careful observations at discrete intervals, and organization and analysis of these observations, are used both to manage present performance and to predict and correct future performance.

Since obtaining consistent reliable data sets at the pace of the project is challenging, data sets in construction are not large. So simple statistical analysis and elementary charts, as described below, are used for analysis. The simplicity of this analysis and charting permit communication to all, even those with limited technical capabilities—which is a huge communication management advantage. (In manufacturing, the data sets of long production runs can be much larger than construction—up to millions of observations. Although these production runs permit greater precision, the statistical analysis and presentation tools are similar to construction—again permitting communication to many.)

The Quality Process in Construction Learns from Manufacturing
The attitude and approach can provide great benefits, but techniques are borrowed selectively

Historical origins of the quality process
The quality process began in the early part of the 20th century in manufacturing. Scientific methods, such as time and motion studies, were applied seeking efficiency improvements, and cost reductions followed. Careful and consistent measurement and analysis by control charts developed. Walter Shewhart (1891–1967) developed a control chart in 1924, which is still in use.

Two early proponents of this movement that popularized quality were Edward Deming (1900–1993) and Joseph Juran (1904–2008). Shewhart, Deming, and Juran all worked for parts of their career at the Western Electric manufacturing complex on South Cicero Avenue in Chicago, IL—although it is believed Juran and Deming never met at that time. Deming emphasized an engineering approach of statistical process control—with a heavy emphasis on the needed cultural change and management support required for this process. This meticulous and repetitive approach was not always enthusiastically embraced at that time. Juran developed a more qualitatively analytical approach that could be applied to many industries, including service activities such as sales.

Deming found a more receptive audience in Japan, and moved to Japan and worked on quality improvement processes. (Juran also consulted with Japanese companies during this period.) The Japanese management style embraced these concepts and integrated them fanatically to achieve world-leading quality for many manufactured products. Denning later moved to Ford Motor Co. in Detroit and instituted similar improvements with similar results. Juran continued to develop his processes during the same period.

Widespread adoption of quality processes by manufacturing firms worldwide in the second half of the 20th century then followed. Systems such as Six Sigma, Total Quality Management, FMEA (Failure Mode and Effect Analysis), and ISO certification developed and became mainstream.

Quality in construction uses smaller data sets but can still produce big gains
Construction projects by their nature are short production runs of unique products. So some of the quality processes developed for longer production runs, such a Six Sigma, are not employed in the construction industry. But construction is strong in scope management, including value engineering, that more precisely defines the intended result initially. And quantitative analysis and control of cost and schedule is highly developed in the construction industry.

Further, the construction project management approach described in this text is very similar to the quality process itself: determining the reason and purpose for the project, planning the method of execution, and monitoring and controlling to achieve the intended result.

Quality processes by Deming consist of plan, do, check, act. *Quality processes by Juran* (the trilogy) consist of quality planning, quality control, and quality improvement. *Project management processes* consist of initiate, plan, execute, monitor and control, and close. All these processes are very similar in approach and execution.

| Steeple erection | *photo 14 of 15* |

Planning Quality Involves Grade and Precision, Cost, and Time

Management must lead to manage the triple constraint

Planning quality starts with defining the purpose and level of precision of the scope (including grade), time, and cost—the interactive elements of the triple constraint. Truthful definition of precision of grade is essential for monitoring and controlling to produce the desired results.

What is to be monitored and controlled—when and how—must be defined. "You get what you measure" or "Expect what you inspect" means the definition of what is to be measured and monitored has a large impact on the final product. What can be done for a particular project must be realistically assessed. Benchmarking is frequently used to develop realistic guidelines. Use of standards from past similar projects to determine a relevant range of achievable possibilities helps focus on realistic achievable standards for the present project.

Increasing acceptable tolerances makes control more achievable

Design details that permit less precision while achieving the desired result make quality control easier and more achievable. "Tolerant fit," which permits more "give and go" in design details, and "robust engineering," which permits significant deviation from the intended result—while still achieving the purpose— must be built into the initial design. The construction manager's input on constructability and value engineering is key to this achievement but must be included early in project planning to be effective. This planning step is virtually cost free but makes conformance easier and therefore lowers project construction cost.

Grades, precision, and accuracy must be monitored and controlled in real time

Those closest to the work know it best and are best able to make ongoing adjustments to achieve needed conformance. This control must start with communicating the desired result to those doing the work. Management procedures to continuously provide current information, including scope changes, must be planned—and this includes information about both the task and how the task relates to other activities. For example, installation of the earthwork or concrete to specified elevations requires provision of the elevations and identification of a benchmark that can be readily checked. (Incorrectly assumed benchmarks are all too common, with disastrous results.)

The types of installation equipment and instruments to check conformance must be specified in early project planning. For example, surveyors from an outside firm could be scheduled at the required intervals or in-house qualified installation personnel with needed instruments could be planned. More advanced equipment with automated grade and position control could be selected, but then timely calibration of this equipment must be planned. Concrete test cylinders could be cast by the installing personnel or by the personnel of an independent testing laboratory—and the number of breaks selected per sampled concrete load (4 days, 7 days, and 28 days) will affect the timeliness of monitoring response. The selected solution must be planned and appropriate cost included for personnel and needed equipment.

Quality planning—particularly of material standards—is influenced by external and internal forces

Quality planning, including the standards to be achieved, monitoring methods, and the specific tasks that must be performed, can be specified in multiple ways as described below.

Government regulation
Specification of quality standards, processes, and procedures can be highly developed in some industries such as nuclear and fossil fuel power generation, refineries, airports, military facilities, transportation including roads, bridges, and tunnels, food processing, and medical facilities. The standards to be achieved—test type and number and frequency and specifications for delivery of results as a condition of approval—may all be specified.

Construction contract
The construction contract may similarly specify grades of materials, tolerances, and testing and certification procedures.

Self-imposed standards
The construction manager will have internal processes and procedures and may have minimum standards that are superior to government or contract regulations.

Cost management planning is integrated with job costing

Cost management usually consists of weekly monitoring of labor and material costs and periodic (biweekly or monthly) monitoring of scope changes. And some construction management contracts specify additional reporting procedures. Cost management relies heavily on established job costing and to a lesser extent on financial accounting. The construction manager's cost management processes and procedures will already be well established and will only be altered slightly for project-specific requirements. These systems are complex, regulated, and integrated and cannot be developed anew quickly enough for each project.

Cost management provides essential cost control but also serves as a "canary in the coal mine," using even minor cost deviation as an early warning of developing problems. Since many will review job costing every week, the early warning will be communicated to many at the same time—making prompt correction more feasible and probable.

Time management planning is integrated with scheduling

Time management is usually accomplished by weekly schedule monitoring and can also be supplemented by techniques such as earned value and control charts described below. Similar to cost management planning, time management processes and procedures are complex and integrated and have a steep learning curve. So the construction manager's established procedures will be used with only slight alteration.

Quality Assurance—Are the Planned Evaluation Methods in Place and in Use?

Monitoring the processes and procedures, but not the work in progress

Quality assurance determines that the planned control measures are in place and use. This is a step before quality monitoring and control described below that actually performs the planned monitoring, inspection, documentation, charting, analysis, and correction.

Quality assurance implements the planned statistical sampling and analysis for prediction and correction. A key element of this analysis is the control chart. The control chart shows the desired value, upper and lower control limits, and the specification limits. The specification limits indicate the boundaries of output acceptability—values exceeding these limits are rejected. The control limits provide early warning signs that the process might be getting out of control—but outputs within these control limits are still acceptable and do not need to be rejected or reworked. Control limits are set by the project manager—and wide but still acceptable limits mean easier and more economical conformance. Control limits of three standard deviations are common.

The process is out of control when a value exceeds a control limit, seven consecutive values are between the upper control limit and the goal (intend value), or seven consecutive values are between the lower control limit and the goal. An out-of-control process must be corrected.

Recognition of the inherent variation of all products and processes—and use of these analytical techniques to determine when this variation exceeds the normal distribution and therefore warrants corrective action—minimizes needed corrective activity. This is the key benefit of statistical process control—early detection from small sample sizes permits prediction and corrective action before defects develop (again, prevention not detection). But normal variation (within established acceptable limits) is tolerated and unnecessary correction effort avoided.

| Steeple erection | *photo 15 of 15* |

Charting can aid understanding
Histograms, Pareto charts, scatter diagrams, and trending

The control chart is a key powerful graphic analysis tool to help determine when corrective action is needed. But even if this chart is not drawn, the idea of statistical sampling and early warning using only numbers can produce the same result.

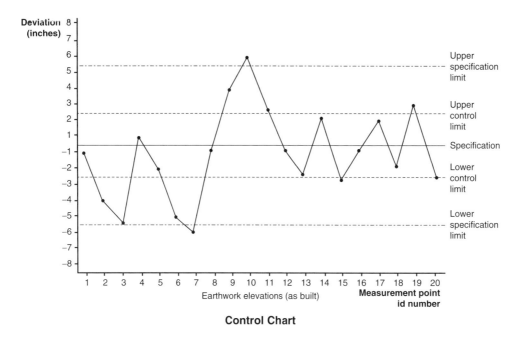

Control Chart

Graphing results can highlight present conditions and trends. The simplest is a histogram, shown below, which uses bar height to indicate occurrence frequency.

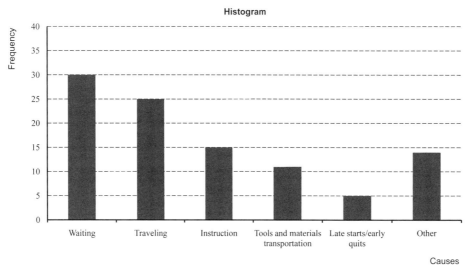

Causes of Non-Productive Time

The Pareto chart is a histogram organized by descending frequency of occurrence supplemented by additional information. Vilfredo Pareto (1848–1923) was the Italian economist who noted that 80% of the wealth (land) was held by 20% of households. This 80/20 rule was later broadly applied to mean that 80% of effects come from 20% of causes.

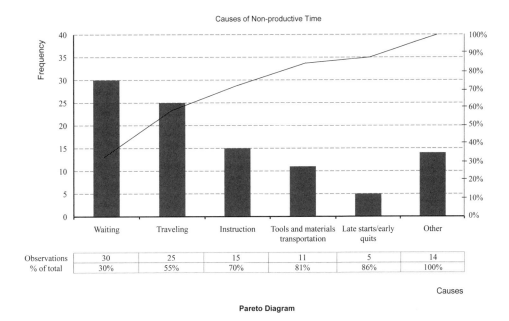

	Waiting	Traveling	Instruction	Tools and materials transportation	Late starts/early quits	Other
Observations	30	25	15	11	5	14
% of total	30%	55%	70%	81%	86%	100%

Causes

Pareto Diagram

Trending diagrams can be used to highlight direction and size of deviations, particularly for communicating to those not directly involved with the day-to-day project operations—such as project owners. But frequently, small data sets can be grasped by numerical analysis without the benefit of a graph.

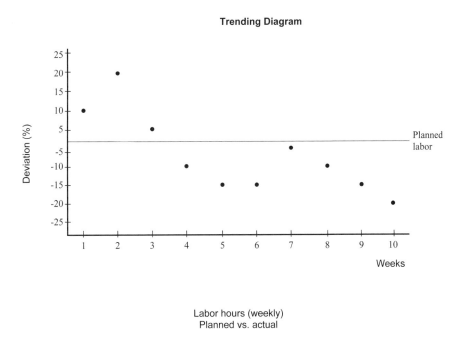

A scatter diagram shown below is more frequently used for larger data sets found in manufacturing. Construction management students may be familiar with scatter diagrams from science and engineering studies. But scatter diagrams are not generally used for analysis of construction projects.

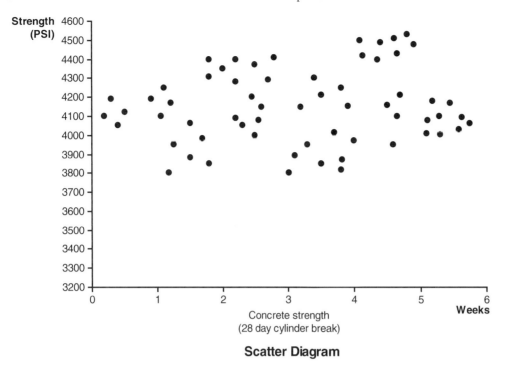

Scatter Diagram

Quality Control—Inspecting, Analyzing, Correcting, Improving

Monitoring the work in progress—and correcting and improving the process

Executing the planned monitoring and control is time consuming but not difficult—as long as the established procedures are realistic and achievable. The scope (and grade), cost, and time monitoring of present conditions determine the location, size, and frequency of variation for immediate correction and longer term improvement.

Determine root causes for focused correction and long-term improvement

The analytical techniques described above—the control chart, histogram, and Pareto chart—as well as schedule management techniques and job costing, described in other chapters, show the size and location of variation needing correction. Frequently, this information can assist determination of the location of the largest few—maybe three—causes. But some causes may be more complicated and can benefit from additional analytical tools.

Ishikawa's fishbone diagram shows cause and effects

Kaoru Ishikawa (1915–1989) was a major proponent and driving force in the quality movement in Japanese industry and worked with and developed the principles of Deming and Juran. Ishikawa used the control charts and other analytical tools described above and also developed a unique tool—the fishbone diagram—to help determine root causes of problems. The fishbone diagram—named because of its resemblance to the side view of a fish skeleton—identifies major and contributory causes of a problem. An example of a fishbone diagram for a construction project is shown below.

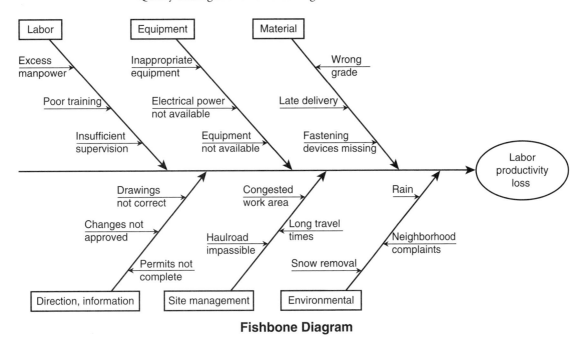

Fishbone Diagram

Even if the diagram is not drawn, the structured identification of major and contributory causes can aid analysis.

Correct immediately, improve long term

The purpose of the processes and procedures described above is to determine the location and size and root causes of variation to prevent defects in a process from occurring. Longer term improvement to reduce the number of potential process defects that must be managed is then sought—continuous process improvement. This changes the monitoring and control function from simply inspection for defects to a function that can and must work upstream to alter root causes. This is a fundamental difference that affects the culture, lines of communication, and authority for a project.

Summary

The quality process in construction project management seeks to manage the normal variation that exists in all materials and processes—to better achieve the planned results. One approach is to use processes and procedures that control the processes—another is to increase tolerances (widen control limits) for easier and less costly conformance. Both approaches may be used together.

The quality process (prevention not detection) is fundamentally different than the "inspection for defects" process and must start in early planning and continue through execution and monitoring and control. This involves a cultural shift that management must lead. The benefit is more reliable achievement of needed and planned results at lower cost.

Review Questions (True or False)

1. Quality means reliable achievement of planned results and usually requires higher grade materials.
2. The ISO defines quality as "the degree to which a set of inherent characteristics fulfils requirements," and defines grade has a "category assigned to products or services having the same functional use but different characteristics."
3. The cost of quality must compare the cost of conformance to the cost of nonconformance.
4. Conformance activities focus heavily on management activities performed by few people quickly

and cheaply, whereas the cost of nonconformance involves some management activities but also construction labor, material, and equipment that requires larger costs and time.

5. Production processes and quality processes both rely most heavily on inspection by quality control departments.

6. Quality processes monitor each step of production to catch and correct potential defects at or before occurrence—emphasizing prevention not detection.

7. Quality processes were developed in manufacturing that has large continuous production runs and data sets, and were later adapted to the construction industry that has shorter runs and therefore smaller data sets.

8. The quality processes of plan, do, check, and act are similar to the project management processes plan, execute, monitor, and control.

9. What is to be monitored and controlled, and when and how, should be consistent for all project types and sizes.

10. Design details built into the initial design that permit less precision while achieving the desired results (tolerant fit) make quality control easier and more achievable.

11. Management must continuously provide correct current information including scope changes and information about the task and its relation to other tasks, as well as provide necessary measurement instruments to check conformance, or the field personnel cannot effectively participate in the quality process.

12. Because of the complexity and effort required for proper execution, job costing and time management are not integrated with the quality process.

13. A key benefit of control charts is that observed work within the control limits provides an early warning signs that the process might be getting out of control but does not require rejection or rework of this observed work.

14. Statistical process control can provide early detection but does require large sample sizes.

15. Histograms, Pareto charts, trending diagrams, and scatter diagram are graphical representations of statistics that can aid understanding of variation.

16. Analysis of root causes, such as the fishbone diagram, can assist immediate correction and long-term improvement.

Test Your Understanding

1. Softwood dimensional lumber (with low costs) is typically used for framing and blocking, and hardwoods (with higher costs) are typically used for trim and millwork. Discuss why use of hardwoods of suitable technical characteristics to frame a single-family house might be considered a lower quality solution.

2. Discuss how job costing, control charts, and earned value (that evaluates time and cost together) can provide early warning signs of deviation from specification of the work in progress.

3. You are mass grading a large site, and the two portions of the site are separated by a wood lot that will remain with no alteration. As you evaluate the grading of the two areas, which are being performed simultaneously, you notice one area is consistently lower than the specified elevations (precise but not accurate) and the other area centers around the specified elevation but is randomly higher and lower (accurate but not precise). Discuss the most likely causes for variation in each of the two areas:

   Operator error

   Machine error

   Improperly calibrated measurement instruments

   Incorrect or uncertain instructions

CHAPTER
3.11

Safety Starts with Management Planning and Continues with Labor Execution

Installation of HVAC main duct runs usually must be scheduled early to permit optimal use of hoisting equipment, increase productivity, and reduce interference with other trades. Development and approval of HVAC ductwork shop drawings must also be an early project task—but one that is frequently overlooked.

Safety Starts with Management Planning and Continues with Labor Execution

Integration into the project management processes is essential for safety success

Construction, if not managed, can be dangerous

Construction can be one of the most dangerous businesses, as shown by the U.S. Bureau of Labor Statistics data below. But the construction industry began to view dangerous operations as unacceptable starting in the middle of the 20th century and started working to improve safety—and these management and labor efforts greatly reduced accidents and fatalities. A good safety record is one of project owner's screening criteria when awarding work to construction managers. And safety is part of the entire construction management process, as described in this chapter.

Industry	Annual Nonfatal Accidents Per 10,000 Workers
Manufacturing	560
Construction	540
Educational, health services	520
Private industry average	420
Financial services	140

Industry	Annual Fatal Accidents Per 10,000 Workers
Agricultural, forestry	2.73
Mining	2.48
Transportation and warehousing	1.59
Construction	1.03
Industry average	.37
Educational, health services	.07
Financial services	.01

And the highest fatality rate by trade

Occupation, Trade	% of Construction Total
Laborer	26
Carpenter	8
Field supervisor	8
Roofer	6
Electrician	6
Construction manager	6
Truck driver	4
Painter	3

The causes of fatal accidents in descending order are:
    Falls
    Crushing (trench, form collapse, machinery)
    Electrocution
    Drowning

Asphyxiation

Burns

And the causes of nonfatal accidents in descending order are:

Abrasions

Punctures

Being struck by an object

Injury is significantly more likely for unskilled and poorly trained workers—and workers new (the first month particularly) to the job site and unfamiliar with the surroundings and equipment. On-road motor vehicle accidents are also a large cause of accidents in all industry classifications.

Motivators for Safety Improvement

Humanitarian concerns, reduced morale, lost productivity, and adverse public relations

Unsafe operations have a human cost. No reasonable person wants fellow employees injured or killed. And the aversion is particularly acute for construction project managers who are guided by higher values and standards of conduct, have longer time horizons, and seek continuous process improvement—values at odds with the consequences of unsafe operations.

Worker perception that operations are unsafe will reduce morale and increase employee turnover, which decreases productivity. Dissatisfied and disgruntled workers will always produce less, and gripe sessions after a major accident or series of minor accidents can temporarily stop all productive work.

Media reporting of accidents can damage a contractor's and a project owner's reputation. Some project owners are so sensitive that one publicized accident can bar the construction manager from future work.

The economic impact of liability, insurance, and fines is huge

Accidents that damage property or employees of other firms have an immediate and longer term monetary cost. Liability insurance, as discussed in more detail in the chapter on insurance, usually requires the construction manager to pay a portion of a claim, and large or frequent claims will increase premiums in future policy periods. Accidents that injure the construction manager's employees will increase the Workers Compensation experience modification for 3 years—which also increases premiums. Multi-year increases in insurance rates can cause contractors to lose profit, business, or close their doors.

Regulatory agencies such as OSHA (Occupational Safety and Health Act) can impose fines for accidents or unsafe operations. Fines typically range from $1,000 to $70,000, but are increased to $500,000 for persistent willful violations—and a single inspection or accident can result in multiple fines. (Fines can also be reduced for first-time violations, persistently safe operation, and smaller firms.) But in all cases, fines directly reduce profit.

Safe operations will be less costly than unsafe operations in the mid and long-term

Safety planning is similar to quality planning in that the cost of conformance is compared to the cost of nonconformance. And higher quality and safer operations have lower mid and long-term costs.

Cost of Conformance	Cost of Nonconformance
Safe equipment acquisition	Insurance premiums increase
Equipment repaired or removed from service when unsafe	Uninsured damages
Safety measures (guardrails, properly grounded temporary electrical)	Schedule delays
Personal protective equipment	Accident investigations

Safety personnel (safety director, safety engineer)	Productivity loss
Training costs—both the cost of training and the cost of workers' (nonworking) time during training	Equipment and material replacement when damaged in an accident
Meetings, record keeping, and documentation	Skilled workers lost
Accident prevention inspections and audits	Lost business
	Fines
	Equipment downtime
	Administrative and legal cost

Costs of conformance are largely general condition costs, which can vary significantly by project type and size but may center around 8% of project value. The cost of nonconformance is largely the other 92% of project value—the cost of the work. And the cost of nonconformance focuses heavily on labor productivity, which is closely related to schedule maintenance—and produces huge project impacts.

Legal and Regulatory Forces

Historical roots of safety regulation

In 1884, Germany enacted the first Worker's Compensation Act, followed by Austria in 1887, England in 1887, and the United States (federal government employees) in 1908. In 1867, Massachusetts was first to address dangerous industrial working conditions, and in 1911, Wisconsin established a state industrial commission to develop industrial health rules and regulations. These imposed responsibility on the employer but not the employee.

Light gauge framing and gypsum drywall installation—Light-gauge framing and gypsum drywall must follow certain trades and proceed and work together with others. HVAC ductwork risers and mains, plumbing risers, waste and larger vents, and electrical risers must be substantially complete before the start of framing. Electrical conduit of 2-inch diameter and smaller for branch wiring, and water piping for plumbing fixtures are partially supported by the light framing and must be scheduled with or slightly after framing. Completion and inspection of all in wall work must precede installation of drywall.

photo 1 of 6

Emergence and development of OSHA in the United States

In 1969, the U.S. federal government passed the Construction Safety Act that approached safety by focusing on unsafe conditions, and required some reporting and training. In 1970, the Williams-Steiger Occupational Safety and Health Act established mandatory safety and health procedures. This act is administered by the U.S. Department of Labor.

The act establishes safety responsibilities as follows:

Sec. 5. (a) Each employer—

1. shall furnish to each of his employees employment and a place of employment which are free from recognized hazards that are causing or are likely to cause death or serious physical harm to his employees;
2. shall comply with occupational safe and healthy standards promulgated under this Act.
   (b) Each employee shall comply with occupational safety and health standards and all rules, regulations, and orders issued pursuant to this act that are applicable to his own action and conduct.

This captures one of the bedrock principles of safety: management's activities are a necessary first step to create the conditions for safety, but safe actions can only be achieved with employees' focused efforts.

In 1971, the Department of Labor issued a CFR (Code of Federal Regulations) 1910 General Standards and CFR 1926 Construction Standards. (General Industry Standards and Maritime Standards were also issued. These standards are different from the construction standards and are a frequent source of complaint about excessive regulation. But the construction standards tend to be consistent with appropriate industry practice—and therefore are not as significant a source of legitimate complaint.)

In 1988, OSHA implemented the Hazardous Communication Standard. This standard required employers to inventory and label hazardous substances and train employees in their safe use. MSDS (material safety data sheets) for each substance must be maintained on site. The definition of hazardous is broad and imperfectly defined, so MSDS for all known hazardous substances and then for the most common other substances are maintained as a precaution.

In 1989, OSHA established a new category of "competent person" defined as "one who is capable of identifying existing and predictable hazards in the surroundings, or working conditions which are unsanitary, hazardous or dangerous to employees, and one who is authorized to take the corrective measures to eliminate them." This designation was originally focused on earthwork operations and required the competent person to be specifically trained in and knowledgeable about soil analysis and use of systems and the applicable requirements of OSHA standards. The concept of competent person then expanded to areas other than earthwork.

In 1994, OSHA started its Focused Inspection Initiation plan to assist responsible contractors and subcontractors who had implemented effective safety programs. This program sought to focus on the OSHA identified leading causes of accidents: falls from elevated areas, struck by object or machine, "caught in between," and electrical hazards.

This brief discussion of the historical development is useful because regulatory approaches to safety continue to change. Early emphasis on unsafe conditions was followed by emphasis on procedures and record keeping, and then emphasis swung back to focus on unsafe conditions and acts. Emphasis on employer and employee responsibilities continues to fluctuate as well. Viewing future fluctuations in this historical context can assist taking the appropriate and prompt reaction.

Other safety regulators

Individual states can administer the OSHA program themselves without continual direct intervention of the U.S. Department of Labor. About half the states have assumed this role. And some state highway departments, the Army Corps of Engineers, and the Navy have also developed safety standards and regulations. Some project owners have their own safety standards as well.

When multiple standards apply to a project, all must be observed—and when in conflict, the highest standard governs. The National Labor Relations Board (NLRB) has ruled that safety is part of the terms and conditions of employment and can become part of contractually binding union work rules —adding yet more safety regulation.

The Federal and State Environmental Protection agencies regulate the safety of activities such as underground tank removal and brown field cleanups. And State Fire Marshals may have safety regulations for flammable storage and Departments of Public Health for food service and some health care facilities.

Responsibility for Safety and Enforcement

Responsibility for safety inspection and liability for accidents can be tricky

Construction managers, general contractors, and subcontractors will always be liable for the consequences of their own actions. This responsibility cannot be delegated or contracted away. (A contract clause that states that any losses sustained by reason of another's failure to abide by safety regulations or a general duty of care can be used.)

Multiemployer work sites, or owners or designers who identify safety requirements make the picture more complex. In 1991, OSHA established four categories of responsibility for multiemployer work sites:

1. *The creating employer* caused hazardous conditions that violated an OSHA standard. The creating employers are always citable.

2. *An exposing employer* has employees exposed to the hazard and is citable only if they fail to take specific action to remove or mitigate hazards.

3. *A correcting employer* is responsible for correcting a hazard if equipment, barriers, or other items for which they are contractually liable are deemed hazardous and the correcting employer has not exercised a reasonable standard of care.

4. *The controlling employer* has general supervisory authority over the work site including the power to correct safety and health violations itself or requires others to correct them. Control can be defined either by contract or by practice. Although the controlling employer must make periodic inspections and implement an effective system for promptly correcting hazards and enforce other employers' compliance with OSHA requirements, they are not held to as high a standard as the creating employer.

These categories of responsibility require some clarification: the construction manager or general contractor has a general duty for safety of all operations on site and a specific duty for the activities of his employees. All parties are responsible for the consequences of their own action but must also take reasonable measures in response to the actions of others. Significant ambiguity still exists about the definition of "reasonable."

The responsibility of designers and owners can add further complexity

Designers usually try to specify that "construction means and methods" are solely the responsibility of the contractor. However, even with this contractual clause, if in the normal course of business, designers happen to encounter a serious safety hazard they must take appropriate action.

However, designers and owners may also contractually require compliance to safety regulations. For example, Article 10 of the AIA (American Institute of Architects) general conditions (Appendix E) describes the contract responsibilities for job site safety and incorporates OSHA requirements by reference in Article 10.2.2. Since compliance is a contractual requirement, and the designer has the responsibility to inspect the work of the contract, the designer has a duty to inspect safety—and has some liability. Similar ambiguities exist when management layers such as an owner's agent, construction manager, and general contractor are all assigned to the same project. These ambiguities might well be clarified with refinements to the contract.

Light gauge framing and gypsum drywall installation *photo 2 of 6*

Light gauge framing and gypsum drywall installation *photo 3 of 6*

OSHA administers a bureaucratic model focusing on policy, procedures, and records

OSHA publishes a list of the 100 most cited construction violations. The top 10 most frequently cited violations from this list (in descending order) are the following:

1. Written hazardous communication program
2. Employee training—hazardous communication
3. MSDS for hazardous chemicals
4. OSHA poster
5. Accessible copies of MSDS
6. Safety training/recognition of unsafe conditions
7. Guarding open-sided floors
8. Head protection
9. Ground fault protection
10. Electrical grounding

The first six most frequently cited violations deal with record keeping and administrative procedures. Correction of unsafe conditions starts with item 7, guarding open-sided floors. And the most frequently cited violations correspond poorly to the most frequent causes of accidents.

A bureaucratic approach can establish and enforce minimum standards, but the construction manager must seek additional methods of improving safety and achieving excellence. Because OSHA is the law and there are heavy fines, OSHA standards must be followed. But the professional construction manager includes OSHA conformance and then goes beyond these standards as described below.

Project Safety Management Planning and Implementation

Attitudes—both management and trade personnel—can be a problem

People, particularly men and even more particularly young men, feel that accidents will never happen to them—only to other people. "I know what I'm doing," "I will be careful," "it is only for a little while" are common attitudes. And those with many years of trade experience can become complacent as well.

Managers can and must lead by example to communicate safety values to trade personnel. Some guides for top managers are given below:

1. Know the safety records of field managers and use this information when making personnel decisions.
2. Communicate about safety, cost, and schedule together during job visits.
3. Include safety cost in the job costing system—the cost of conformance, such as training and personal protective equipment, and the cost of nonconformance, such as losses not covered by insurance.
4. Include safety planning in the selection of scaffolding, hoisting equipment, and concrete forming.
5. Insist that newly hired employees receive appropriate training.

Once management understands that the long-term costs of safe operations are less than those of unsafe operations, safety becomes integrated with other parts of job management. And safety ceases to be a separate stand-alone subject, and demands for high production and fast performance of the scheduled work are minimized. It is not that high production and profit are sacrificed for safety, but that profit is achieved by integrating safety into project planning.

Large-scale environmental problems should remain the owner's responsibility

Project owners have an obligation to deliver the work site free from any preexisting environmental hazards such as asbestos, lead paint, PCBs, radioactive material, and other hazardous chemicals and mold. A phase I environmental report will typically be required at the time of land acquisition or securing a construction loan, or maybe specifically required of the project owner during the construction manager's contract negotiations. The phase I will note any potentially environmentally hazardous conditions, and the phase II will document the remediation procedures required. Cleanup will be by others unless the construction manager is specifically licensed, trained, and insured to perform this work. The contract should confirm these normal procedures.

The planned project approach and selected equipment can enhance safety

The construction manager must ensure that owned and leased equipment is equipped with the necessary safety features and maintained in good repair. Increasingly, equipment from reputable commercial suppliers to the commercial–industrial construction market will have the appropriate features, but maintaining this equipment in good repair is needed.

Selection of the general conditions equipment such as material and man hoists and cranes can assist safe operations by moving and storing material to maintain an unencumbered site with good housekeeping. And approaches to potentially dangerous activities such as large-scale concrete forming can be planned with safety in mind—with locations for tie offs or guardrails integrated with the forming systems.

Large benefits can also be planned by keeping an unencumbered site with appropriate organization and cleanup. Also, resource leveling (scheduling work to maintain constant crew sizes) can be used to ensure optimal trade density and manage crew size variation and the resulting frequent turnover. Again, productivity and safe operations can be achieved simultaneously.

Job site Safety Planning, Policies, and Procedures

Conditions and acts, accidents, and injuries to be addressed

Safety hazards can be caused either by unsafe conditions, which are heavily the responsibility of management as described above, and also the trade personnel, or by unsafe acts, which are primarily the responsibility of the trade personnel. Safe conditions are a precondition to safe acts, but unsafe acts account for about 80% of injuries and accidents.

Accidents and injuries can be health related, such as heat exhaustion or stroke, frostbite or hypothermia, hearing damage, and radiation and toxic chemical exposure. Injuries can also result from the causes described at the beginning of this chapter.

A job hazard analysis is a job-site focused risk register

The previous chapter on risk discussed global project risks, and identifying safety as one of the possible risks. The risk register used for global risk is adapted to the job-specific tasks and is called the job hazard analysis. It identifies the task, potential hazard, and hazard mitigation measures as shown below.

Construction Task	Potential Hazards	Hazard Mitigation Measures
Foundation wall excavation	Trench collapse	1. Trench shields over 5-foot depth 2. Storm drainage control to maintain desired soil moisture content
Dump trucks leaving site	Automobile traffic	1. Full-time flagman on street 2. Schedule some hauling during low traffic hours
Form and pour footing	Man access to trench	Ladders in two locations
Brick ledges and utility blockouts in concrete foundation wall	Materials and saws in congested work area	Fabricate blockouts at grade level

Staffing and training must be planned and maintained

The number of staff responsible for safety can vary significantly by the size of the construction project. The largest firms will have a safety director or safety officer in charge in the home office—not assigned to a specific project. The project superintendent has overall site safety responsibility, and larger projects will have a safety engineer and possibly support personnel for routine inspections. A foreman will typically conduct safety enforcement surrounding his work area, and the required periodic training for his crew, such as toolbox safety meetings.

All supervisory personnel from the foreman level and above (and for some companies working for demanding owners—all personnel) must complete periodic training in some of the following areas:

> OSHA safety course
>
> First aid
>
> Scaffolding
>
> Confined spaces
>
> Other courses as required by the nature of operations

Materials storage must be planned as well

Fuel must be stored in approved containers designed for the purpose. Flammable gases such as oxygen and acetylene must have bottles chained and restrained to avoid damaging or breaking control valves. And chemicals must be stored in approved containers. Management must purchase these appropriate storage devices, and the tradesman must use them as intended.

Equipment must be selected appropriately and maintained and used as intended

Equipment that addresses the most frequent injuries must receive particular attention: scaffolding, ladders, guardrails, and hoisting must be selected appropriately and continuously maintained. And this includes replacement of guardrails that are temporarily removed—an ongoing frustrating field management task.

Electrical power must be distributed properly throughout the site to minimize the use of extension cords—and must be properly grounded. This involves both correct purchase of the temporary service for the site and maintaining cords and GFIs in working order and promptly removing damaged temporary electrical distribution components, such as extension cords.

Personal protective gear includes the following:

> Hard hats
>
> Goggles
>
> Face shields
>
> Ear protection—either plugs or earmuffs
>
> Safety or steel toe shoes gloves
>
> Respirators
>
> Harnesses

Provision of personal protective gear is primarily management's responsibility, but site supervisors must enforce needed use.

Policy procedures and record keeping

Policies, procedures, and record keeping are essential for personnel management and are also the focus of OSHA citations. Essential requirements are listed below.

Job site safety meetings (tool box, tailgate) mandated by regulation—usually at least every 2 weeks. Keeping these meetings interesting enough to retain employees' attention is a challenge—"We have heard it all before" and "I know what I'm doing" are common attitudes. Meeting should be short—usually 10–20 minutes and should focus on the following:

1. Recent accidents or near-misses
2. Equipment or activities that have just come or will shortly come to the job site
3. Continuous enforcement of standing safety rules such as:
   a. Keep the job site clean. Deposit rubbish immediately in designated containers
   b. Replace removed guardrails immediately after use
   c. Keep bottled gases secured at all times
   d. Maintain ladders and scaffolds in good working order
   e. Maintain extension cords, GFIs, and related temporary electrical devices in good working order

A record of the meeting date, time, and attendees should be retained by the construction manager.

Safety inspections—daily, weekly, and audits—of increasing detail

Hazardous communication program
   a. Prepare a hazardous communication program that contains policies and procedures, a hazardous substance list, the employee training program, and MSDS
   b. Establish a labeling system and ensure all containers are properly identified
   c. Conduct training concerning the program and exposure hazards

Safety policy and programs

These can be custom developed and extremely detailed at larger companies addressing hazards specific to their project types, or can be purchased from firms specializing in this service. Key elements are that they exist, are widely available especially at the job site, and are understood and frequently reinforced.

The safety program should include:
   a. Statement of company policy
   b. The company's safety organization and assigned responsibilities
   c. Safety and first aid training and personal protection
   d. Fire prevention
   e. Safety record keeping
   f. Job site inspection
   g. Accident and hazard reporting
   h. Safety rules
   i. Identified safety-related disciplinary measures and incentives

In the middle of the 20th century, alcoholic beverages on and around the job site were acceptable. As late as the 1990s, some union contracts specified that tradesman had the right to drink beer on the job. Now the overwhelming consensus is that alcohol and illegal drugs must be strictly prohibited at the job site. Mandatory and random alcohol and drug testing can be enforced. Some unions have taken the position that they regulate the conditions of work and have resisted such testing—but this resistance is fast diminishing.

Safety inspections and audits

The construction manager has a duty to monitor the work and document these periodic inspections—daily and weekly. And less frequent but more intensive safety audit can also be performed, sometimes in cooperation with the construction manager's insurance carrier's compliance personnel.

The key documents that must be maintained are:
1. Safety program and safety rules on site
2. MSDS on site
3. Documentation record keeping is also key and must include the following:
4. OSHA poster title "Job Safety and Health Protection"

5. OSHA safety log (a log must be maintained even if the job site has had no accidents or incidents)
6. Incidents that are work related must be recorded if they result in any of the following:
    a. Death
    b. Days away from work
    c. Restricted duty
    d. Medical treatment or first aid
    e. Loss of consciousness
    f. A serious injury or illness diagnosed by a physician or other licensed health care professional
7. Accident and incident reports
8. Emergency phone numbers—police, fire, medical

The safety records must be maintained at the location where "the employee usually reports to work," which is usually the job site. Record maintenance on very small job sites can be a challenge.

Handling an Accident or OSHA Inspection

Accidents are managed for regulatory conformance and process improvement

The purpose of accident investigation is:
1. Determine what happened
2. Determine why it happened
3. Develop legally required documentation
4. Process improvement—determine alterations in policy or procedures that could minimize probable reoccurrence.

The procedures for accident investigation include the following:
1. Clear the scene of nonessential personnel, and barricade the area
2. Ensure that any unsafe conditions are stabilized, at least temporarily, and managed
3. Leave the accident scene undisturbed
4. Photograph and/or videotape the scene
5. Individually interview, as close to the time of accident as possible, those involved or those personally witnessed the accident or events surrounding the accident. Maintain a written record of the interview, including interviewee name, work classification, employer, time and date of interview, and interviewee's location and activities at the time of the accident.

A fatal accident must be reported to OSHA within 8 hours of occurrence. (And OSHA records must be maintained for 5 years.) Some owners will require copies of accident reports, and copies of reports of any accident that is, or could possibly become, an insurable event. These should be provided to the construction manager's insurance agent.

OSHA inspection

OSHA has the right to make unannounced job site inspections. (Technically, the employer must approve the inspection. But if refused, the inspectors can return with a search warrant and a bad attitude.) Inspections can be triggered by a tip or complaint or may be part of OSHA's planned inspection program, which inspects a small sample of job sites each year.

An inspection has four parts:
1. An opening conference with the employer.
2. Selection of a representative of the employer and employees to accompany the inspector. (An employer and employee representative both have the right to accompany the inspector during the inspection.)

3. A walk around inspection during which the inspector is allowed to talk to employees.
4. A closing conference during which the inspector discusses his findings that might be health or safety violations. Actual citations, if any, will be issued by mail weeks or months later.

If a clear violation exists, the employer should correct the condition immediately prior to receiving a citation. If a citation is issued, the employer must post the citation and a notice of employee's rights on the job site. The employer must contest a citation within 15 working days or the citation becomes final.

How good is good enough—what level of safety should be sought

Improvements in safety occurred over the last 60 years, in part urged by OSHA, but also by management realization that safe operations are desirable and achievable. But the extreme position taken by some that human life is valuable so no accident is tolerable is not reasonable. Normal variation and human error make this unachievable—even a highly skilled, trained and focused athlete can trip on a crack in the sidewalk. But aligning safety with other goals—cost, schedule, and quality—seeks continuous improvement not perfection, and is achievable. The Bureau of Labor Statistics found that fatal construction accidents per 100,000 employees declined 23.1% from 1992 to 2006—for all types of firms. Professional construction management firms can and should obtain larger improvements.

Summary

Construction, without proper management, can be dangerous business. Safety improvement involves commitment and actions by management to provide safe conditions and then needed action by trade labor (with management urging and support) to act safely. Management provides the necessary preconditions, but safe acts require focused trade labor attention.

Safety is an integrated part of project planning and is included in the approach to project, equipment, and contracts. Safety planning is similar to risk management and the quality process and shares the same impact: the mid and long-term costs of conformance are lower than the costs of nonconformance. High production with safe operations lowers costs while managing schedule.

Sound management practices and regulation require certain work conditions, training, and record keeping—and these needed activities require attention both on the management and site level. A professional construction manager views these needed activities as a minimum and seeks a higher level of safety performance.

Review Questions (True or False)

1. Construction is the most dangerous industry in America, leading in both nonfatal and fatal accidents.
2. Falls, crushing, electrocution, abrasions, punctures, and "being struck by an object" are the leading causes of both fatal and nonfatal accidents.
3. Worker perception that operations are unsafe reduces morale, which increases turnover and decreases productivity.
4. Incidents that injure or kill workers can increase workers' compensation premiums for up to 2 years.
5. The money cost of safety is the cost of nonconformance less the cost of conformance. Safer operations lower mid and long-term costs.
6. The cost of nonconformance centers around general conditions that may be around 8% of project value, and the cost of conformance centers around the other 92%—the cost of the work.
7. Management's activities are needed to create safe conditions, but safe actions can only be achieved with the employees' focused efforts. Unsafe actions cause about 80% of the number of incidents.

8. OSHA produces safety regulations and inspects job site safety. OSHA is part of the NLRB.

9. Legally, all parties are responsible for their own actions but must also take reasonable measures in response to the actions of others.

10. Project owners and designers have no involvement with or responsibility for safety.

11. Large-scale environmental problems usually should remain the owner's responsibility. The contractor should become involved in environmental remediation only if specifically licensed, trained, and insured to perform this type of work.

12. The planned approach and equipment selection can both increase safety and reduce labor costs.

13. Selection of the appropriate equipment and provision of personal protective equipment is usually the employer's responsibility. Although appropriate use is primarily the workers' responsibility, it must be reinforced by management personnel.

14. A statement of safety policy includes safety personnel and training, inspections, accident and hazard reporting, and record keeping, as well as safety rules and disciplinary measures and incentives.

15. Accidents and incidents of all types and consequences must be immediately entered into the safety log and also reported to OSHA within 8 hours of occurrence.

16. Safety records must be maintained at the location where the employee usually reports to work, which is usually the job site.

17. Both an employer and employee representative have the right to be present during an OSHA inspection, and the inspector has the right to talk to employees.

Test Your Understanding

1. Visit a job site, even if from the curb, and perform a job hazard analysis showing construction tasks, potential hazards, and hazard mitigation procedures. Include four work items such as trenching or excavation, rough framing or structural steel erection, concrete placement or roofing. Discuss whether, in your opinion, the responses used at this job site are appropriate and effective.

2. In either print or Internet job postings, find advertised construction safety positions. From the job description, evaluate which of the safety-related activities discussed in this chapter would be performed by the applicant, and which would be a performed by other company personnel such as foremen and superintendents.

CHAPTER
3.12

Claims Management Also Starts in Planning and Continues in Execution

Rough and final grading requires removal of temporary facilities and equipment.

Claims Management Also Starts in Planning and Continues in Execution

Manage to avoid claims, then promptly and fairly resolve claims that do develop

Claims Management and Dispute/Resolution—an Attitude and a Process

The best way to resolve a dispute is to avoid it. Project planning, again, is key—if the workable approach defines the scope well, and the schedule and cost are reasonable and achievable, and the right team is in place, a workable approach is possible. Successful execution then removes most of the reasons for disputes.

Removal of incentives that make disputes profitable is an essential early step. Mutual waiver of consequential damages by all parties is a start. Consequential damages are claims, which are independent of the actual performance on the project. An examples from a contractor might be: "The owner slowed me down. I didn't finish on time, and I couldn't take on other projects. I want the money I would have earned on those projects." Or an owner might claim: "The contractor didn't finish on time. I've lost business, and I want the contractor to pay me for all the profit I could have received from that business."

The second early action is to require each party to pay their own legal fees. With these two exclusions, dispute claims are focused on the costs in the project and therefore smaller. Pie-in-the-sky claims for big damages are minimized—and attorney costs are reduced.

Yet, disputes—most involving unresolved change order requests—will still happen, and these claims must be processed. The goal is to prevent claims where possible, minimize the effects of those that do occur, and resolve claims quickly for the lowest cost and least project impact.

What Is and Is Not a Claim

The definition of claim

A project event (or perceived event) that was not specifically anticipated and included in the project plan, and therefore contract documents, can produce a claim. Events that were anticipated but not fully defined in the project plan (allowances and unit costs) that are not promptly resolved can also produce claims.

A claim is usually a request or demand for adjustment in cost and/or time, but less frequently for specific performance such as certifications, warrantees, or additional bonds or insurance. Claims most frequently seek cost adjustment (one element of the triple constraint of scope, cost, and time) and less frequently time. But the impact of time on claims and claims management is huge. The time of claim identification, notification, and processing hugely affects claim resolution—prompt notification and rapid resolution lower costs and minimize project impacts. The impact of time both on scheduled completion (that can have interactive effects on many project aspects) and on labor productivity is also huge. And these impacts of time are most difficult for the owner and designers to understand—and for the claimant to prove.

The usual sources of claims

The usual sources of claims between parties are:

Scope related
- Plans and specifications contain errors or omissions, ambiguities, or improper coordination
- Site conditions are materially different than the conditions described in the contract documents, including unforeseen subsurface conditions

334

- Uncovered existing conditions in a renovation project are materially different than the conditions described in the contract documents

Time and management related
- Disruptions, delays, or acceleration of the work
- Unusually severe weather conditions
- Failure to obtain permits when needed
- Failure to agree promptly on change order pricing
- Slow or unresponsive approval of shop drawings and submittals
- Failure to respond promptly and accurately to questions or problems
- Inadequate administration of responsibilities by the owners, architects, engineers, construction managers, subcontractors, and vendors

Contract or performance related
- Unwillingness or inability to execute the work as specified
- Breaches of contract

Claims most frequently move up: vendor claims against subcontractor, subcontractor claims against construction manager, and construction manager claims against owner. But claims can be by the owner against the construction manager—they are usually less frequent but more severe.

What is not a claim

Claims, as described below, are processed, evaluated, and resolved in a more rigorous manner than routine project activities—so distinguishing what is and is not a claim helps minimize administrative effort. Owner directed scope changes for which the time and cost impact can be fully resolved and a change order issued promptly are not claims. Similarly, unit costs and allowances in the contract that are promptly resolved and converted to change orders are not claims. But time is key—if resolution is not prompt, the same activities become claims.

Although insurance uses the word "claim," insurance claims are not considered claims in the construction management sense. Workers' compensation claims, liability, and collision claims for automobile accidents and other property or liability incidents, if properly covered by insurance, are not claims. Only if a party believes that the insurance coverage or the processing of the insurance claim does not conform to the contract requirements does the insurance claim convert to a project claim.

Similarly, matters of payment such as owner to construction manager and construction manager to subcontractors and vendors only become a claim when not in accordance with the contract.

The Context, Guidelines, and Rules of Claims

The project scope and approach, as defined by the contract, are meant to be interpreted by a reasonable person customarily involved in the construction industry. Judgments and interpretations must be performed within this context—and cannot use overly specific and legalistic arguments to obtain unreasonable advantage.

Customary guidelines that also have wide legal acceptance are the following:

The documents must be read as a whole
The AIA (American Institute of Architects) and AGC (Association of General Contractors) model contracts are carefully crafted with many parts interconnected and cross-referenced. Drawings, specifications, and general conditions are similarly interconnected. The intent and answers to specific questions can only be determined through review of all of these parts.

The drafter of the documents has a higher burden of responsibility
The drafter of a document, such as architect or engineer, had access to more information, was allowed more time, and was assumed to have a higher level of relevant expertise than the executor, such as the construction manager, subcontractors, and vendors. Therefore, the executors are entitled to rely on the documents and do not need to take extraordinary measures, such as independent review of design calculations to verify the completeness, accuracy, and competence of the documents.

The contract documents supersede all previous documents and discussions
It is common for one party in a dispute to claim that their original bid proposal qualified or excluded a work item—but this is not acceptable. The contract documents and contract must specifically itemize and define the agreement between the parties. If some elements of the bid constitute a part of the agreement, these elements must be included as a modification, such as a rider to the contract.

The documents must be interpreted in the normal context of the trade
Common sense and common usage in the project area must be applied, not some academic or highly technical interpretation.

Specific terms govern over general terms
The order of precedence from specific to general is listed below.
> The agreement (contract)
> Specifications
> Drawings

A further breakdown within these three categories is:
> Change orders
> The agreement (contract)
> Agenda
> Supplementary or special conditions
> General conditions of the contract
> Technical specifications
> Standard boilerplate specifications
> Contract drawings

And the contract drawings have the order of precedence of:
> Numerical dimensions govern over scaled dimensions
> Detailed drawings govern over general drawings
> Change order drawings govern over contract drawings
> Contract drawings govern over standard drawings
> Contract drawings govern over shop drawings

This accepted order of precedence is used to resolve differences between the documents, but excessively legalistic determination should not be attempted—the documents should be viewed as a whole.

A clarification of the precedence of contract drawings and shop drawing must be made. Some shop drawings, such as precast concrete and some types of structural steel, can contain very detailed engineering calculations (sometimes sealed by a professional engineer). These very detailed drawings, which are far more specific than the contract drawings, define the work to be executed. Approval by the architect or engineer is a key step that confirms that the shop drawings show the design intent of the contract.

These guidelines are well accepted and serve as a guide for those seeking effective construction project management and project success. However, for each of these rules there are technical exceptions that can be identified and exploited—usually by claim consultants and specialized attorneys. The efforts of these consultants and attorneys are expensive and time consuming but can be necessary and appropriate—but only rarely. These technicalities are beyond the scope of this text. Here we focus on claim avoidance and prompt resolution of claims that do occur.

Claim Prevention Can Minimize the Number and Impact of Claims

The best way to win a fight is to avoid it

The scope and approach must be reasonable and achievable

The scope and approach must be reasonable and achievable with the customs of the subcontractors and vendors in the project area. Demands for the unreasonable or unfeasible—that will probably cause claims—must be identified and eliminated. Work breakdown structures and work packages must be normal and customary in the project area, so available subcontractors and vendors can perform within their normal experience, expertise, and financial capability.

The project scope, as defined by the contract, first must be verified as complete and the approach constructable. This involves detailed counting, measuring, and then costing all components of the project organized into a standardized format, such as the CSI (Construction Specification Institute) specification divisions. This counting and measuring is "building the project on paper and in your head" and can assist evaluation of completeness and reasonableness—and provide costing for later analysis of subcontractor proposals and claims.

The construction managers must work with subcontractors to confirm that they share this perception of the scope—so that misconceptions or omissions that will later give rise to claims are identified early. This usually involves a comparison of quantities for key work items and discussion of intended approach, such as staffing, crew size, and major equipment to be used.

The construction managers must then evaluate the subcontractors' capacity to perform the work. This involves their financial capacity to manage the needed cash flow, usually by review of their financial statements. It also involves review of their insurance coverage in place and their experience modification and loss ratios to find possible changes to their coverage or rates that could cause problems during the project.

The contract documents, usually the general conditions supplemented by the contract itself, define the rules for processing changes and claims. The model contracts typically have places for the parties to enter their agreed markup percentages for additions and deductive changes, and specify the procedures and the timing of claim identification, notification, and resolution. Allowable home office overhead and markup, field overhead, and overhead on the lower tier subcontractors are also defined—but frequently imperfectly. Model contracts serve as an industry-accepted equitable solution. Attempts to modify these accepted solutions with excessively burdensome one-sided demands can increase both the number and size of claims.

Claim Identification, Quantification, and Documentation

Early identification, notification, and quantification are key to successful resolution

As the construction manager attempts to avoid claims, conditions that may later produce claims are identified early. Notification of these conditions must be provided by the construction manager to the owner, or subcontractor to the construction manager. If these conditions do develop into a claim, formal notification and adequate proof must be provided—to allow the other party opportunity to correct. The method and timing of notification are specified in the contract and must be strictly observed. However, some wiggle room is possible—the claimant may state that they could not yet fully determine all the conditions related to the claim.

Prompt documentation and processing is essential

When a claim is presented, it must be acknowledged and entered into a claim log. Then, the merits of the claim must be evaluated against the contract to determine if there are legitimate grounds for the claim. Then, the claim must be quantified, even if it appears weak. Even meritless claims can linger and cause disproportionate problems.

Cost and schedule must both be evaluated

Cost should first be evaluated against the construction manager's estimate of that work item. And the estimating method for the claim should be consistent with the original method used for the project. If the work covered by the claim has been performed, actual job cost records, such as payroll, material, and subcontractor invoices, can be checked—but caution is required. Segregation of claim activities from contract activities requires judgement and may be difficult to prove and evaluate. Changes tend to be priced at full retail—far higher than the wholesale cost of the original estimate.

Evaluation of schedule claims is more difficult. One method evaluates the "as-planned" schedules against the "as-built" schedules. This is feasible for the construction manager who developed the original schedule, but may be unfeasible for a subcontractor or vendor who does not have full access to this original schedule. Job records of directions given may affect the schedule—man-hours expended and documentation of the material and equipment delivery — can also be examined.

But this analysis can quickly become complicated since both the claimant may be partially at fault and there can be significant interactive effects of multiple causes. The claim can be further complicated by the claims for additional field and home office overhead. This includes compensation for equipment rental, supervisory personnel, and lost opportunities to obtain other profitable work. And claims for productivity reduction caused by owner-directed schedule acceleration can be huge. As discussed elsewhere in the text, labor productivity is one of the key variations in cost and profitability. If all the costs of lost productivity and profit are sought, the claim can be huge—and extremely difficult to prove.

Large HVAC equipment frequently must be placed early in the project to avoid interference with other trades and optimize use of hoisting equipment. (Note the hoisted air handler that can be seen through the structural steel and light-gauge framing.) This may require preorder of long lead time equipment before award of all subcontracts.

Nonexcusable, excusable, and compensable delays

Nonexcusable delays are caused by factors within the contractor's reasonable control. In plain language, "it is the contractor's fault," and additional time or cost cannot be justified.

Excusable delays are caused by factors not within the contractor's reasonable control but also not as a result of the owner's actions or failure to act. Additional time, but not additional costs, can be justified. A common example of this type is unusually adverse weather—but what is unusual must be defined and supported. Although there is no universally accepted definition, a reasonable example might be conditions 20% worse than the 5 and 10-year average for the project area (as defined by U. S. Weather Bureau records).

Compensable delays are caused by the owner's failure to act in accordance with the contract requirements, or the owner's direct action, such as issuance of a stop order. Both additional time and cost can be justified.

Resolving the Claim

The hearing must be fair

As described above, the contractual basis of the claim, and the cost and time must all be evaluated, and responsibilities assessed. This careful analysis alone communicates to the claimant that consideration is being given. And if his analysis indicates the claim is fully or partially invalid, convincing reasonable evidence can support this conclusion. The response of some owners and designers is "We've done nothing wrong and so none of this is our responsibility," or they take a very narrow legalistic view to defeat the claim on a technicality that will escalate the claim, and may produce other claims as well. Multiple parties may be partially responsible and so a more modest equitable solution may be negotiated.

A prompt resolution is contractually required and produces better results

Contracts specify the time of notification and resolution of claims—usually action must be taken within 5, 10, 15, but no more than 30 days. The short durations are particularly important because the project progress will continue and performing needed workout of sequence can produce additional claims. Continued work on the project is contractually required despite the claim. (Work can usually be suspended only for the owner's failure to make contractually required payments.) Although the contractor must keep working, the attitude of "you guys just keep going, and we'll work it out at the end of the job" will usually cause the contractor to seek revenge in other areas. But since the contractor has large fixed overhead and large ongoing project costs, and the owner and designers may have lower overhead or not keep records in a way that identifies the impact of this overhead, this sense of urgency can be particularly difficult to communicate.

Using job site records, designers and possibly outside experts may assist resolution

The job site records, as described above, can show what should have occurred and what actually occurred. The model contracts also include adjudication by the designers—the AIA contract specifies the architect and the AGC contract specifies the architect or other designated owner consultants. Outside consultants and experts can be engaged for more complicated claims.

This analysis produces either a change order documenting the agreed change in time and cost or a rejection of the claim. Dispute resolution is required if the claimant wishes to contest the rejection.

Placement of the HVAC roof top unit optimizes the start of the interior ductwork installation. The normal and highly preferred installation sequence starts with the large main ductwork at the unit and then proceeds to the smaller branch ductwork.

Make the Courts the Last Resort for Dispute Resolution

Expensive, time consuming, painful, embarrassing, and unsatisfactory

Litigation has proved to be a highly inefficient, time consuming, and expensive method of dispute resolution for construction. This is caused, first, because attorneys are not educated or skilled in construction, but they must learn (at your expense) enough to at least grasp the nature of the items in dispute. Second, most construction disputes involve money and accounting, and most attorneys have extraordinarily poor numerical skills. Many are unable to figure a tip on a restaurant bill without the aid of a calculator. Also, construction project management involves a significant amount of shared understanding, trust, personal integrity, and common sense, and these are alien to legal proceedings that use rules of evidence and procedure.

In construction litigation, few feel justice was done. The cost of the proceedings, including legal fees, can erode or eliminate any compensation ultimately received. For this reason, the industry has moved toward alternative dispute resolution. These procedures are now required in the model AGC and AIA contracts used on most commercial projects. These require a sequence of mediation, arbitration, and then litigation.

Negotiation is always sought first

Negotiation is always the first step in attempting to resolve a claim. The process of negotiation is described extensively above.

Mediation—a fast way to reach a common sense, real-world resolution

A dose of reality promotes speedy settlement

Mediation is a very abbreviated process of common sense evidence presentation and forced structured discussion between the parties in a dispute. The procedures are specified, usually by the American Arbitration Association, and involve a mediator and the parties in the dispute. The mediator is typically knowledgeable about construction and construction disputes. Each side presents their side of the story in their own way in person. The mediator can meet with the sides individually or together. The purpose is to (1) eliminate all frivolous matters related to anger, (2) distill the dispute down to the essential facts, and (3) convince each party of the strengths and weaknesses of their position, and the probable outcome.

Many straight forward construction disputes can be settled in one day. A few days may be required for more complicated disputes, or disputes for which one of the parties is not properly prepared.

Both parties must agree. The mediator cannot impose a decision, but if a decision is reached, it is legally enforceable.

Arbitration—half-way between mediation and litigation
Similar to mediation, but the decision is usually binding

If mediation does not reach a settlement, arbitration is the next step. This is similar to mediation except one or more arbitrators, depending on the size of the amount claimed, will be present. The difference is the arbitrators will make a binding decision that is legally enforceable. Clever or persistent lawyers can still attempt to litigate this decision, but judges with heavy caseloads may not respond enthusiastically. (Note: this describes arbitration within the construction industry. Arbitration for organized labor and professional sports teams, which is frequently in the news, is entirely different.)

Litigation
The end of the line

Litigation uses a highly formalized set of rules and procedures and is divorced from the common sense rules by which construction people lead their lives and conduct their businesses. Rules about types and timing of evidence permitted mean that the facts as they actually occurred may be disallowed. A new set of "facts" manufactured by outside "expert witnesses" makes progress slow and expensive.

One to three years may be necessary to complete the smallest most straightforward case. More complex matters can last for decades. The cost of proceedings can range from 6-month wages for the smallest matter to more than a person will earn in an entire lifetime for medium-size cases. In addition, litigation may be noticed by the news media, which can be highly undesirable for the public relations of a contractor or owner. For these reasons, efforts to minimize litigation for construction disputes have been increasingly accepted by both owners and contractors.

(Although minimizing attorneys' involvement in the dispute resolution process is now well accepted, this should not be interpreted to mean attorneys have no place in the construction world. Attorneys still have an important and sometimes essential role in other areas, such as establishing and altering corporate business structures and managing real estate transactions.)

Summary

Claims management focuses first on claim prevention. A well-defined scope, approach, cost, and schedule, and constructible contract documents are an essential beginning. Then subcontractors and vendors who share these understandings and are technically and financially capable of execution must be selected. And effective execution as planned can then minimize claims.

Claims that occur must be identified early, required notification given, and must be quantified and analyzed. Prompt resolution is required by contract and to achieve the lowest cost and minimal project impacts. The review must be reasonable and in the normal context of the trade, viewing contract documents as a whole and must not be overly legalistic or technical.

Claims not settled promptly must move to dispute resolution. The effective order of steps adopted by the most widely used model contracts specifies the order of: negotiation, mediation, arbitration, and litigation. This is also the ascending order of time and cost of resolution.

Review Questions (True or False)

1. Claims management seeks to prevent claims were possible, minimize the effects of those that do occur, and resolve claims quickly for the lowest cost and project impact.

2. Mutual waiver of consequential damages and requiring each party to pay their own legal fees reduces the incentive for and impact of claims.

3. A claim is an event not specifically anticipated and included in the project plan. Claims indicate a failure of one party, such as deficient drawings or poor contract administration, so the failing party should become responsible for the claim impact.

4. Owner-directed scope changes, and resolution of contract unit prices and allowances for which agreement can be reached promptly are not claims.

5. Insurance claims should always be handled through the claims resolution process.

6. Contract documents must be read as a whole and interpreted in the normal context of the trade.

7. When evaluating a claim, documents specifically itemized in the contract must be considered, and in the industry accepted order of precedence.

8. Claims avoidance must start with an approach and scope that is reasonable and achievable, followed by confirmation that subcontractors understand and are willing and capable of executing this scope.

9. Claims that at first appear to have little or no merit should be denied until convincing proof is presented.

10. A new claim should first be entered into a claim log, and then the cost and schedule impact determined even before the merits of the claim are fully evaluated.

11. Not excusable, excusable, and compensable delays all can justify both additional time and cost.

12. A prompt and fair claim hearing is both contractually required and will produce lower claim costs.

13. The order of claim dispute resolution in many model contracts is: negotiation, mediation, arbitration, and litigation.

Test Your Understanding

1. For a complete building renovation with many unforeseen conditions, discuss early purchasing decisions that could minimize claims and the impact of claims with reference to:
   Purchasing smaller more focused work packages
   Unit costs
   Allowances
   Construction manager–subcontractor risk sharing
   Analyzing unforeseen conditions and agreeing to possible responses
   Establishing more detailed claims resolution procedures for different types and sizes of claims

2. For equally competent contract documents, which delivery system is most likely to minimize the number, costs, and impacts of claims: hard bid, construction management for fee (not at risk), construction management at risk with a GMP (guaranteed maximum price), and unit costs. Then, discuss how the claims potential of different project types affects selection of the optimal delivery system.

3. For an office tenant build out project, a fan-powered variable volume box was shown on the mechanical drawings with related control wiring, but the power feed did not appear on the electrical drawings. The electrical contractor has requested additional compensation, but no additional time, for this power feed. Using the steps outlined in this chapter, describe how you would process this claim.

CHAPTER
3.13

Project Close Out—Completion, Documentation, Lessons Learned, and then Sales

Final grading and landscaping require full demobilization of temporary offices and removal of equipment. Simultaneous completion of all major work items required for this demobilization is a significant management task.

Project Close Out—Completion, Documentation, Lessons Learned, and then Sales

Completes the project and builds for the future

Closeout is an essential and beneficial last step

Completion of the physical work and documentation of completion are required by common sense and contract—and is needed to gain formal owner acceptance. But this last step is frequently not given sufficient attention—both in the construction project management literature and in practice.

Closeout also involves documenting lessons learned to improve the construction manager's capabilities for future projects. Completion of one project makes the construction manager an expert on that exact type of project. And these lessons learned can be used on future similar projects or parts of very different projects. Closeout, when viewed in this way, is part of the construction manager's continuous process improvement. And closeout can also be used as a sales tool—communicating lessons learned and capabilities demonstrated to the owner can leverage the relationship into future projects. But these valuable steps are overlooked by many.

Completing, Commissioning, and Documenting the Physical Work

Completing the Physical Work

Completing the physical work is best thought of as a project in itself. The needed tasks must be identified—and a plan for execution developed and implemented. A construction manager spearheads this effort with a "punch list"— identifying all work items to be completed, repaired, or replaced. A master list is distributed to the affected parties for execution, and frequently sub-lists of deficiencies by room are posted in each room. Persistent monitoring and control of completion is a time-consuming ongoing task.

Commissioning of systems—heavily mechanical, electrical, life safety

The commissioning process selectively changes out temporary construction components to permanent components—and performs the necessary adjustments and certifications to place the systems in permanent operation. Commissioning is performed near project completion—when all the conditions are as close to final as possible.

Temporary filters and fluids used in mechanical systems during construction are replaced and systems sanitized. The inclusion of these new filters and fluids, and any specified spares for attic stock, must be negotiated when awarding the original contract. This is a frequent omission, and the cost is frequently borne by the construction manager. (Relamping electrical fixtures may be similarly required.)

Testing and balancing of the HVAC and hydronic heating and cooling systems is one of the first parts of the commissioning process. The correct equipment, capacity, power, and rotation of pumps and fans are verified, and the air output at each point of the distribution ductwork is measured and adjusted to specifications and to balance with the corresponding points of the return ductwork. A similar process is used for hydronic systems.

Fire alarm systems and related life safety devices such as HVAC duct detectors and electronic hold opens for doors, as well as related building automation and security systems are evaluated. Signal strength and battery capacity are verified and then real-life system performance is tested, which can become quite complex and interactive. For example, a fire alarm test may require testing pull stations, smoke detectors, and duct detectors, under both permanent and emergency power. And the interactive effect of fire alarm

| Light gauge framing and gypsum drywall installation | *photo 4 of 6* |

activation on shutdown of mechanical units and elevators and selective electronic door activation must be verified—which can produce thousands of interactions. Commissioning is also performed for elevators, communication systems, emergency power backup, and fire protection systems.

Commissioning is performed in part by the installing contractor but may also be supplemented by outside independent testing laboratories. For example, contracts may frequently specify that an outside independent testing laboratory perform HVAC test and balance. When the installing subcontractor knows that commissioning of this system is a condition of acceptance, there is a strong incentive for continuous process improvement—correcting small defects or deviations when first noticed. This early detection heavily involves the experience and knowledge of the installing tradesman. Delegating the entire commissioning process to outside agencies—particularly as part of the LEEDS certification process—has become fashionable recently. This adds another layer of management, removes the subcontractor's motivation for continuous improvement, and disregards the knowledge and experience of the installing tradesman.

The commissioning process also involves training of the owner's facility operating and maintenance personnel. Traditionally, this involved training sessions of about 2 hours per system component—a boiler, or emergency power generator. But as building components increasingly become microprocessor controlled utilizing proprietary software, training sessions lasting several weeks at a remote locations may be required. This training must be scheduled so that the owner's personnel are fully capable of assuming operating control at turnover.

Removal of Temporary Facilities and Construction Cleanup Must Be Planned

Removal of temporary facilities, such as offices, hoisting and storage structures, haul roads and fences, and related restoration, must be planned to match the overall demobilization. Timing of these necessary tasks also has a psychological effect on the owner's acceptance of the project—signaling completion and turnover and acceptance is imminent.

The extent of construction cleaning is specified in the contract. It always involves removal of debris and materials not part of the permanent construction, followed by "broom cleaning." It can also involve final janitorial cleaning and sanitation of systems. This janitorial cleaning is almost always performed by outside janitorial firms with lower wage rate structures—and more skilled cleaning personnel with appropriate materials and equipment. Construction trade personnel usually do not perform janitorial cleaning efficiently or effectively.

Documentation of the physical work executed must also be managed

Documentation of the work as executed benefits both the owner's operations and maintenance and the construction manager's process improvement—and is frequently required by contract. Placing notations of alterations on the original design drawings—"as builts"—documents these changes. Mechanical, electrical, and some strong architectural or structural subcontractors will perform the "as builts" for their portion of the work, but the construction manager must take the lead and coordinate all submittals and perform "as builts" when subcontractor participation is absent.

Traditionally, "as builts" have been a manual markup of design drawings, but increasingly electronic markups are sought, which can produce a troublesome concern that must be managed. Architects view the drawings as an "instrument of service" and their copyrighted property, so some are unwilling to provide electronic backgrounds for "as builts." This can require the construction manager to redraw the entire project—an unnecessary, costly, and pointless burden. Negotiating use of electronic background drawings for "as-built" development must be negotiated with the owner's participation and concurrence.

Operating and maintenance manuals are prepared by the vendor manufacturing the equipment or system and include the physical characteristics of the component or system and instructions for maintenance. Competent vendors provide these manuals as normal operating procedure, and so fulfilling this requirement is usually not troublesome if requested early. Closeout requirements are best negotiated prior to contract award and should be included in the subcontract agreement.

Documentation of regulatory and payment conformance is discussed further below because these activities are usually performed substantially later, and possibly by different personnel after completion of the physical work. But it should be noted that commissioning and turnover of final documents tend to be viewed by subcontractors as completion of their work, and a start of their warranty period. But the start of the warranty for components and the entire project must be identical (unless phased acceptance was agreed)—regardless of the time of commissioning. Synchronization of these subcontractor and owner time periods must be specifically negotiated at the time of contract award—or exceptions negotiated between the construction manager and owner.

Demobilizing from this site—requires managing attitudes and expectations

Experienced project managers know that getting started well and getting completely finished demand significant management attention and effort. These management efforts have a significant people management dimension.

The earlier chapter on productivity identified the causes of nonproductive time for the project in a full production mode as:

Waiting 29%

Traveling 13%

Instruction 8%

Tools and material transportation 7%

Late starts, early quits 6%

Personal breaks 5%

| Light gauge framing and gypsum drywall installation | *photo 5 of 6* |

Project completion has fewer tasks dispersed over large areas, each requiring specific instructions, so productivity plummets. This poor productivity cannot be eliminated but can be managed by shortening the duration of the completion activities. The type of personality most capable of executing large volumes of work in a full production mode will tend to be least capable of performing fewer, fussier tasks. A supervisor who recently completed installation of 3,000 doors will seldom give full and efficient attention to repairing 3 doors.

Also, a project team may feel camaraderie and may be reluctant to separate. This is accentuated if all staff members do not have another immediate assignment. Everyone knows their services at the project must come to an end, so their expectations must be managed. Some of the more capable may jump ship early and others may attempt to drag out completion. If personnel have a start date for another project assignment with the same company, these difficulties are minimized.

A very common approach is to maintain a substantial staff to complete nearly all items and then reduce to a skeletal crew. When the skeletal crew is terminated, staff in the home office complete the few remaining details.

Owner and Regulatory Acceptance and Project Turnover

Owner acceptance procedures specified by contract

When the construction manager believes the work is complete, the contract usually requires issuance of a contractor's certificate of completion. The certificate will contain wording such as:

"I know of my own personal knowledge, and do hereby certify, that the work of the contract described above has been performed, and materials used and installed in every particular, in accordance with, and in conformity to, the contract drawings and specifications. The contract work is now complete in all parts and requirements, and is ready for final inspection."

Although provision of this certification is a normal and customary contract requirement, curiously it is frequently omitted with no architect or owner objection.

The owner and the design consultants then prepare a punch list—a specific identification of every omission or deficiency requiring correction. As long as these deficiencies are of a minor nature and can be expected to be promptly corrected, the punch list will be accompanied by a Certificate of Substantial Completion. If the deficiencies are more substantial, issuance of the certificate will be delayed until correction of these deficiencies.

Certificate of Substantial Completion

Substantial completion is defined by the American Institute of Architects as follows:

"Substantial completion is the stage in the progress of the work when the work or a designated portion thereof is sufficiently complete in accordance with the contract documents that the owner can occupy or utilize the work for its intended use."

The date of substantial completion has two significant consequences: it is the end of the time of execution of the work and therefore the end of calculation of any time-related damages, and it is the start of the warranty.

Project turnover transfers possession and responsibility for maintenance

Turnover transfers the physical possession of the premises from the construction manager to the owner. This involves first changing construction lock cores and delivering the permanent keys to the owner. (Or, equivalent change for electronic locks.) At this point, the care, custody, and control of the site transfer from the construction manager to the owner, including responsibility for security, operations and maintenance. Construction management personnel must then reenter the site as visitors to the owner.

The construction manager's ongoing project insurance, such as builders' risk, is terminated at this time, and any additional insurance required by contract is placed. The owners must similarly insure the project for their use. Sophisticated owners may place this insurance routinely, but project owners must be advised to place the insurance at the right time. Responsibility for payment of utility bills is also transferred at this time.

Projects with phased and partial occupancy need special attention. Phased remodeling of an existing facility or occupancy of portions of a project before completion of the full project requires corresponding adjustments in insurance coverages and warranty periods. One solution is for the project owner to carry the insurance on the entire existing building and an installation floater for the work in progress. Other insurance possibilities exist but must protect both the owner's completed work and the contractor's installed but unpaid work.

Acceptance of the work and identification of substantial completion must correspond to the occupancy—so may be as detailed as one Certificate of Substantial Completion for each floor of the building. And once a mechanical system is placed in service, even if it may serve areas of the building not yet completed, the warranty for that mechanical system must begin. Matching insurance coverage, substantial completion, and warranty periods to the work as executed is common sense, but must be carefully addressed or disastrous gaps may result.

Certificate of Final Completion

Contracts usually require a Certificate of Final Completion, similar to a Certificate of Substantial Completion, except no deficiencies are noted. However, in common practice, a certificate of final completion is rarely issued. The construction manager finishes the punch list items, submits all required documentations, and requests final payment.

Government Acceptance Specified by Regulation and Law

The government body issuing the building permit, usually the city, also usually issues a Certificate of Occupancy—documenting that the building is complete for city purposes and may be occupied. The city requirements focus on life safety, drainage, and interaction with city property, but not suitability for the owner's use. So Certificate of Occupancy requirements may be quite different from the owner's needs and the contract specifications—with fewer or more, and more lenient or more rigorous or just different requirements. Occupancy does not prove owner acceptance.

The construction manager requests occupancy inspection when tasks of interest to the city are complete. The inspectors from each department of the building department and also the fire and other city departments such as streets and sanitation will inspect—this can involve up to 20 inspectors. System demonstration of life safety systems, such as wet fire protection sprinkler systems and emergency backup power, will be performed.

Usually, as-built surveys of the building indicating dimensions from property lines, elevations of finished floor and frequently the top of rim, and invert elevation of all drainage structures performed by a registered surveyor, not the contractor's personnel, are required. For development of raw land involving roads, drainage structures, and storm water management systems, as-built surveys are a condition of city release of the construction manager's very substantial cash guarantee deposits.

Certain other types of occupancies require additional government inspections. Medical facilities, such as hospitals and outpatient medical centers, require Department of Public Health detailed inspection and volumes of test data on each and every building component and system. Food service establishments require a similar but less burdensome review.

Nursing homes, child day care centers, and schools require review from other government departments involved with long-term care, childcare and education. Facilities with significant environmental impact, such as refineries and power plants, require a very detailed environmental agency review and certification of the outputs of the facility's processes. Approval by these government agencies is required

| Light gauge framing and gypsum drywall installation | *photo 6 of 6* |

before occupancy—so must be planned in the early stages of the project, and lines of communication with these regulatory agencies opened, so timely conformance becomes probable.

Payments and Agreements to Finalize the Project

Finalizing cost—unit costs, quantities, allowances, penalties, and change orders

To receive final payment, the final contract sum must be determined. For contracts involving unit prices, final quantities must be determined and resulting final prices agreed. Similar calculations, adjustments, and agreements must be made for contracts with allowances or penalties. And in all cases, change orders for all agreed work must be executed. After this finalization, both the owner and construction manager waive the right to seek further adjustments to the contract sum. A corresponding analysis, adjustment, and agreement must be performed between the construction manager and each subcontractor and vendor.

A final bill, in sworn statement form, is then presented to the owner. Before the final bill will be paid, the construction manager must submit evidence (final lien waivers) that all subcontractors and vendors have been fully paid. Since final payment involves release of retention—that can be up to 10% of the project value—final subcontractor payment before payment by the owner can be a significant cash flow burden on the construction manager. This can be managed by requesting mid-project retention reduction from 10% to 5%.

It can also be managed by direct title company payment to the subcontractors—transferring the burden of proof of subcontractor payment from the construction manager to the title company. This title company payment of the final amounts directly to the subcontractors eliminates the construction manager's cash flow burden.

A light-gauge framing and drywall subcontractor can increase productivity by installing their work earlier in the project—but this dramatically reduces the productivity of other trades and slows the overall project progress. It is best to clarify scheduling before awarding the subcontract to avoid this possibility.

The construction manager can also require the subcontractors to furnish lien waivers in advance of payment, sometimes labeled "not valid until receipt of funds." But this procedure (of marginal legality) is not well received by subcontractors or owners and is frequently rejected by finance and title companies.

If the construction manager provided a payment and performance bond on the project, final payment will not be released until the surety consents to the release. This is both for the surety to ensure that all needed payments have been made to subcontractors and also to determine the final contract sum for premium adjustment. Bond premiums for payment and performance bonds are charged on a percent of total project cost, including approved change orders. So, an increased contract sum will require an increased bond premium.

Documentation of regulatory conformance and final payments

The methods of documentation for regulatory and payment conformance are described above. It should be noted that there can be substantial delays, particularly in regulatory conformance, so the final payment may not be issued until after the on-site project offices have been demobilized. In this case, personnel working in the home office will handle the final documentation.

Improving the Construction Manager's Capabilities

One of the most valuable aspects of project closeout is improvement of the construction manager's capabilities to win and more efficiently execute future projects. A well executed project makes a construction manager an expert on that very project that can enhance reputation and lead to more business. So it is essential that this reputation be backed up with performance.

Contractually required documents become a construction manager's process asset

As-built drawings, shop drawings, color selections, and key and valve schedules document the executed work and can produce great efficiencies if this work needs to be serviced or renovated—a huge competitive advantage for future work. Sophisticated project owners with facility management departments will maintain and use these documents effectively—but this is rare. Most owners lack personnel to effectively understand these drawings or to manipulate electronic files—and have no storage facilities for drawings and therefore frequently lose them. A construction manager who meticulously maintains these documents will receive the first call when additional work is contemplated.

Lessons learned can improve the construction manager's approach to future projects

Best practices in planning, construction means and methods, products, and construction systems used can be described and archived for future use. The mistakes made and lessons learned must also be identified—not everything will work out well and mistakes should not be repeated. This process must be formalized in writing and included in the project archive—knowledgeable personnel may not be available when later needed, so good memories alone are not enough.

Cost structures, schedule templates, and planning checklists should also be archived with notes of what worked well and problems that developed. The procurement process should be described as well. The results of decisions about work breakdown structures and distribution of work among subcontractors, and whether to "make or buy"—self-perform or subcontract should be evaluated and documented. Subcontractor's performance should be analyzed for success and areas of needed improvement. And the performance of the subcontractors and vendors should be noted to assist the selection evaluation for future projects.

The owner's psychological acceptance—relationship building for future projects

The owner's formal acceptance of the project required by contract was described above. Psychological acceptance of the project that forms a favorable opinion of the construction manager must also be sought. This usually involves an informal interview, possibly in a social setting, of the senior project manager or company officer with a senior member of the owner's firm. This is a qualitative evaluation of the overall impression of the project performance.

This is also a veiled sales call—letting the owner know that the construction manager is available for future work. The demonstrated capacity to perform work to the owner's satisfaction, as well as the templates and lessons learned that will improve this performance, can provide an owner preference for the construction manager's services. It is quite common for the owner to identify current needs and future project possibilities in this exit interview—a huge competitive advantage and sales opportunity for the construction manager.

Summary

Project closeout involves four tasks: (1) completing the physical work and (2) documentation to gain owner and regulatory acceptance, (3) documenting the lessons learned to improve the construction manager's capabilities, (4) gain the owner's psychological acceptance and promote future business.

Project completion and documentation is specified by contract, regulation, and law. But effective and timely closeout requires that needed requirements and procedures are planned and built in at the start of the project. The closeout of the project is best considered a subproject that must be planned, executed, and monitored and controlled to manage the productivity and people management dimensions that occur at project conclusion. Improving the project manager's capabilities for future projects using the archived lessons learned is an essential last step for construction project management and continuous process improvement. The construction manager's effectively execution of these close out steps can create an enhanced reputation and owner relationships that wins new projects.

Review Questions (True or False)

1. Close out involves completion of the physical work and documentation of completion to gain formal owner and government acceptance. It also involves improving the construction manager's capabilities for future projects and developing owner relationships.
2. The construction manager spearheads the physical completion of the work by identifying all work items to be completed, repaired, or replaced in a punch list.
3. Commissioning of systems that are heavily mechanical, electrical, and life safety must be performed by professional engineers.
4. Removal of temporary facilities such as offices, hoisting, and storage structures is a necessary demobilization task, and also signal to the project owners that completion and turnover are imminent.
5. Although operating and maintenance manuals can be competently prepared by the vendors manufacturing the products, as-built drawings must be prepared by the construction manager to ensure needed quality control.
6. Completion of punch list items involves fewer tasks dispersed over large areas requiring specific instructions, so productivity will suffer. The number and capabilities and tendencies of the staff assigned to these punch list tasks must be managed to maximize productivity.
7. Model contract forms frequently require the architect to perform the punch list, but in practice, punch lists are usually prepared by the construction manager.

8. Substantial completion defines the end of the time of execution of the work and the start of warranty.

9. Project turnover transfers possession of the premises and responsibility for maintenance and insurance from the construction manager to the owner.

10. It is both a contractual requirement and normal practice to execute a certificate of final completion for all projects.

11. A certificate of occupancy certifies that both government agencies and the owner consider the project finally complete.

12. The cost of unit price work, penalties, and scope changes must be agreed and documented by change order to establish a final contract sum.

13. The construction manager must provide convincing documentation of final payment of all bills as a condition of closeout. But retention of 5-10% still required on these subcontractor payments is a significant cash flow management problem that must be managed.

14. Contractually required closeout documentation, such as as-built drawings, shop drawings, color selections, and valve schedules, becomes the property of the owner and the construction manager must turnover all originals.

15. Lessons learned about best practices and mistakes to be avoided (with supporting documentation) become a valuable construction manager asset for continuous improvement.

16. The construction manager's closeout interview with the owner can be used to develop a relationship for future projects.

Test your Understanding

1. Project closeout is required for all projects, but the timing and scope of the effort will vary by project type. A 1-million sf warehouse and a 100,000 sf hospital each has the same cost. Discuss how the closeout procedures listed below will differ in effort and timing for the two project types.
Removal of temporary structures
Termination of staff, including superintendents, discipline superintendents, project engineers, and accountants
Scheduling of government and regulatory agencies' final inspections

2. Staff reduction during the completion of the punch list and closeout procedures must be planned to optimize productivity and morale. Discuss how staff reduction possibilities will differ in times of high work volume where all staff members will have new assignments, and low work volumes when some of the staff must be laid off.

3. You are documenting the lessons learned from your project. What on going project records would you evaluate to find the lessons learned in the categories listed below?
Cost estimates and achieved job costs
Planned and achieved schedule
The work breakdown structure and assignment of tasks to subcontractors
Communications planned and communication problems
Project office staffing

A. Acord Form

ACORD®	CERTIFICATE OF LIABILITY INSURANCE		DATE (MM/DD/YYYY)

PRODUCER

ABC Agency
123 Any Avenue
My Town, My State 00000

THIS CERTIFICATE IS ISSUED AS A MATTER OF INFORMATION ONLY AND CONFERS NO RIGHTS UPON THE CERTIFICATE HOLDER. THIS CERTIFICATE DOES NOT AMEND, EXTEND OR ALTER THE COVERAGE AFFORDED BY THE POLICIES BELOW.

INSURERS AFFORDING COVERAGE	NAIC #
INSURER A: XYZ Insurance	12345
INSURER B: QRS Insurance Company	54321
INSURER C: WC Insurance Company	98765
INSURER D:	
INSURER E:	

INSURED

John Q. Public
1234 Any Street
My Town, My State 00000

COVERAGES

THE POLICIES OF INSURANCE LISTED BELOW HAVE BEEN ISSUED TO THE INSURED NAMED ABOVE FOR THE POLICY PERIOD INDICATED. NOTWITHSTANDING ANY REQUIREMENT, TERM OR CONDITION OF ANY CONTRACT OR OTHER DOCUMENT WITH RESPECT TO WHICH THIS CERTIFICATE MAY BE ISSUED OR MAY PERTAIN, THE INSURANCE AFFORDED BY THE POLICIES DESCRIBED HEREIN IS SUBJECT TO ALL THE TERMS, EXCLUSIONS AND CONDITIONS OF SUCH POLICIES. AGGREGATE LIMITS SHOWN MAY HAVE BEEN REDUCED BY PAID CLAIMS.

INSR LTR	ADD'L INSRD	TYPE OF INSURANCE	POLICY NUMBER	POLICY EFFECTIVE DATE (MM/DD/YYYY)	POLICY EXPIRATION DATE (MM/DD/YYYY)	LIMITS	
A		GENERAL LIABILITY [X] COMMERCIAL GENERAL LIABILITY [ ] CLAIMS MADE [X] OCCUR	L1234567	01/01/2009	01/01/2010	EACH OCCURRENCE	$ 5
						DAMAGE TO RENTED PREMISES (Ea occurrence)	$ 10
						MED EXP (Any one person)	$ 5
						PERSONAL & ADV INJURY	$ 5
						GENERAL AGGREGATE	$ 25
		GEN'L AGGREGATE LIMIT APPLIES PER: [ ] POLICY [ ] PROJECT [ ] LOC				PRODUCTS - COMP/OP AGG	$
B		AUTOMOBILE LIABILITY [X] ANY AUTO [ ] ALL OWNED AUTOS [ ] SCHEDULED AUTOS [ ] HIRED AUTOS [ ] NON-OWNED AUTOS	A7654321	01/01/2009	07/01/2009	COMBINED SINGLE LIMIT (Ea accident)	$
						BODILY INJURY (Per person)	$ 5
						BODILY INJURY (Per accident)	$ 10
						PROPERTY DAMAGE (Per accident)	$ 5
		GARAGE LIABILITY [ ] ANY AUTO				AUTO ONLY - EA ACCIDENT	$
						OTHER THAN EA ACC	$
						AUTO ONLY: AGG	$
		EXCESS / UMBRELLA LIABILITY [ ] OCCUR [ ] CLAIMS MADE [ ] DEDUCTIBLE [ ] RETENTION $				EACH OCCURRENCE	$
						AGGREGATE	$
							$
							$
							$
C		WORKERS COMPENSATION AND EMPLOYERS' LIABILITY ANY PROPRIETOR/PARTNER/EXECUTIVE OFFICER/MEMBER EXCLUDED? [N] (Mandatory in NH) If yes, describe under SPECIAL PROVISIONS below	WC000001	02/01/2009	03/01/2010	[X] WC STATUTORY LIMITS [ ] OTHER	
						E.L. EACH ACCIDENT	$ 100
						E.L. DISEASE - EA EMPLOYEE	$ 100
						E.L. DISEASE - POLICY LIMIT	$ 300
		OTHER					

DESCRIPTION OF OPERATIONS / LOCATIONS / VEHICLES / EXCLUSIONS ADDED BY ENDORSEMENT / SPECIAL PROVISIONS

CERTIFICATE HOLDER	CANCELLATION
ABC Company 9876 Any Lane Any Town, Any State 00000	SHOULD ANY OF THE ABOVE DESCRIBED POLICIES BE CANCELLED BEFORE THE EXPIRATION DATE THEREOF, THE ISSUING INSURER WILL ENDEAVOR TO MAIL 30 DAYS WRITTEN NOTICE TO THE CERTIFICATE HOLDER NAMED TO THE LEFT, BUT FAILURE TO DO SO SHALL IMPOSE NO OBLIGATION OR LIABILITY OF ANY KIND UPON THE INSURER, ITS AGENTS OR REPRESENTATIVES. AUTHORIZED REPRESENTATIVE

ACORD 25 (2009/01)

© 1988-2009 ACORD CORPORATION. All rights reserved.

The ACORD name and logo are registered marks of ACORD

IMPORTANT

If the certificate holder is an ADDITIONAL INSURED, the policy(ies) must be endorsed. A statement on this certificate does not confer rights to the certificate holder in lieu of such endorsement(s).

If SUBROGATION IS WAIVED, subject to the terms and conditions of the policy, certain policies may require an endorsement. A statement on this certificate does not confer rights to the certificate holder in lieu of such endorsement(s).

DISCLAIMER

This Certificate of Insurance does not constitute a contract between the issuing insurer(s), authorized representative or producer, and the certificate holder, nor does it affirmatively or negatively amend, extend or alter the coverage afforded by the policies listed thereon.

ACORD 25 (2009/01)

This small sample of AIA and AGC contract documents illustrates the format, scope, and complexity of widely accepted model documents—carefully crafted and comprehensive formats with "fill in the blanks" for project specifics. (The forms can be purchased as paper copies or in licensed electronic format.) These and other organizations have other similar contract forms for different project sizes and delivery methods, as well as related forms for project management tasks such as request for information, change orders, and substantial completion.

A single copy of all commonly used model documents would form a stack of paper about 8 inches high, but this should not be intimidating. Only one or at most three contract suites of forms will be appropriate for a construction manager's typical projects. Once the selected forms are well understood, little additional management time is needed for each project.

The AIA granted permission for use of their documents in this book. The AGC granted permission for use of their documents in this book under copyright license 0179.

B. AIA sample documents

▓AIA® Document G701™ – 2001

Change Order

PROJECT: *(Name and address)*   CHANGE ORDER NUMBER: OWNER ☐

                                       DATE: ARCHITECT ☐

                                       ARCHITECT'S PROJECT NUMBER: CONTRACTOR ☐

TO CONTRACTOR: *(Name and address)*   FIELD ☐

                                       CONTRACT DATE: OTHER ☐

                                       CONTRACT FOR:

The Contract is changed as follows:
(Include, where applicable, any undisputed amount attributable to previously executed Construction Change Directives)

The original (Contract Sum) (Guaranteed Maximum Price) was $ _____

The net change by previously authorized Change Orders $ _____

The (Contract Sum) (Guaranteed Maximum Price) prior to this Change Order was $ _____

The (Contract Sum) (Guaranteed Maximum Price) will be (increased) (decreased) (unchanged)

by this Change Order in the amount of $ _____

The new (Contract Sum) (Guaranteed Maximum Price) including this Change Order will be $ _____

The Contract Time will be (increased) (decreased) (unchanged) by   (   ) days

The date of Substantial Completion as of the date of this Change Order therefore is

(Note: This Change Order does not include changes in the Contract Sum, Contract Time or Guaranteed Maximum Price which have been authorized by Construction Change Directive until the cost and time have been agreed upon by both the Owner and Contractor, in which case a Change Order is executed to supersede the Construction Change Directive.)

NOT VALID UNTIL SIGNED BY THE ARCHITECT, CONTRACTOR AND OWNER.

ARCHITECT *(Firm name)*	CONTRACTOR *(Firm name)*	OWNER *(Firm name)*
ADDRESS	ADDRESS	ADDRESS
BY *(Signature)*	BY *(Signature)*	BY *(Signature)*
(Typed name)	*(Typed name)*	*(Typed name)*
DATE	DATE	DATE

CAUTION: You should sign an original AIA Contract Document, on which this text appears in RED. An original assures that changes will not be obscured.

▓AIA® Document A107™ – 2007 Exhibit A

Determination of the Cost of the Work

for the following PROJECT:
(Name, location and brief description)

THE OWNER:
(Name, address and other information)

THE CONTRACTOR:
(Name, address and other information)

THE ARCHITECT:
(Name, address and other information)

ARTICLE A.1 CONTROL ESTIMATE

§ A.1.1 Where the Contract Sum is the Cost of the Work, plus the Contractor's Fee without a Guaranteed Maximum Price pursuant to Section 3.3 of the Agreement, the Contractor shall prepare and submit to the Owner, in writing, a Control Estimate within 14 days of executing this Agreement. The Control Estimate shall include the estimated Cost of the Work plus the Contractor's Fee. The Control Estimate shall be used to monitor actual costs and the timely performance of the Work. The Contractor shall update the Control Estimate with each Application for Payment as needed to reflect Changes in the Work.

§ A.1.2 The Control Estimate shall include

  .1   the documents enumerated in Article 6 of the Agreement, including all Addenda thereto and the Conditions of the Contract;

  .2   a list of the clarifications and assumptions made by the Contractor in the preparation of the Control Estimate, including assumptions under A.1.4, to supplement the information provided by the Owner and contained in the Drawings and Specifications;

  .3   a statement of the estimated Cost of the Work organized by trade categories or systems and the Contractor's Fee;

  .4   a project schedule indicating proposed Subcontractors, activity sequences and durations, milestone dates for receipt and approval of pertinent information, schedule of shop drawings and samples, procurement and delivery of materials or equipment requiring long-lead time, and the Owner's occupancy requirements showing portions of the Project having occupancy priority; and

  .5   contingencies for further development of design and construction as required by Section A.1.4.

§ A.1.3 The Contractor shall meet with the Owner and Architect to review the Control Estimate. In the event that the Owner or Architect discovers any inconsistencies or inaccuracies in the information presented, they shall promptly notify the Contractor, who shall make appropriate adjustments to the Control Estimate. When the Control Estimate is acceptable to the Owner, the Owner shall acknowledge it in writing. The Owner's acceptance of the Control Estimate does not imply that the Control Estimate constitutes a Guaranteed Maximum Price.

§ A.1.4 To the extent that the Drawings and Specifications are anticipated to require further development by the Architect, the Contractor shall provide in the Control Estimate for such further development consistent with the Contract Documents and reasonably inferable therefrom. Such further development does not include changes in scope, systems, kinds and quality of materials, finishes or equipment, all of which, if required, shall be incorporated in a revised Control Estimate by mutual agreement of the parties.

§ A.1.5 The Contractor shall develop and implement a detailed system of cost control that will provide the Owner and Architect with timely information as to the anticipated total Cost of the Work. The cost control system shall compare the Control Estimate with the actual cost for activities in progress and estimates for uncompleted tasks and proposed changes. This information shall be reported to the Owner, in writing, no later than the Contractor's first Application for Payment and shall be revised and submitted with each Application for Payment.

ARTICLE A.2   COSTS TO BE REIMBURSED
§ A.2.1 COST OF THE WORK
§ A.2.1.1 The term Cost of the Work shall mean costs necessarily incurred by the Contractor in the proper performance of the Work. Such costs shall be at rates not higher than the standard paid at the place of the Project except with prior consent of the Owner. The Cost of the Work shall include only the items set forth in this Article A.2.

§ A.2.1.2 Where any cost is subject to the Owner's prior approval, the Contractor shall obtain this approval prior to incurring the cost. The parties shall endeavor to identify any such costs prior to executing the Agreement.

§ A.2.2 LABOR COSTS
§ A.2.2.1 Wages of construction workers directly employed by the Contractor to perform the construction of the Work at the site or, with the Owner's prior approval, at off-site workshops.

§ A.2.2.2 Wages or salaries of the Contractor's supervisory and administrative personnel when stationed at the site with the Owner's prior approval.
(If it is intended that the wages or salaries of certain personnel stationed at the Contractor's principal or other offices shall be included in the Cost of the Work, identify below the personnel to be included, whether for all or only part of their time, and the rates at which their time will be charged to the Work.)

§ A.2.2.3 Wages and salaries of the Contractor's supervisory or administrative personnel engaged at factories, workshops or on the road, in expediting the production or transportation of materials or equipment required for the Work, but only for that portion of their time required for the Work.

§ A.2.2.4 Costs paid or incurred by the Contractor for taxes, insurance, contributions, assessments and benefits required by law or collective bargaining agreements and, for personnel not covered by such agreements, customary benefits such as sick leave, medical and health benefits, holidays, vacations and pensions, provided such costs are based on wages and salaries included in the Cost of the Work under Section A.2.2.

§ A.2.2.5 Bonuses, profit sharing, incentive compensation and any other discretionary payments paid to anyone hired by the Contractor or paid to any Subcontractor or vendor, with the Owner's prior approval.

§ A.2.3 SUBCONTRACT COSTS
Payments made by the Contractor to Subcontractors in accordance with the requirements of their subcontracts.

§ A.2.4 COSTS OF MATERIALS AND EQUIPMENT INCORPORATED IN THE COMPLETED CONSTRUCTION
§ A.2.4.1 Costs, including transportation and storage, of materials and equipment incorporated or to be incorporated in the completed construction.

§ A.2.4.2 Costs of materials described in the preceding Section A.2.4.1 in excess of those actually installed to allow for reasonable waste and spoilage. Unused excess materials, if any, shall become the Owner's property at the completion of the Work or, at the Owner's option, shall be sold by the Contractor. Any amounts realized from such sales shall be credited to the Owner as a deduction from the Cost of the Work.

§ A.2.5 COSTS OF OTHER MATERIALS AND EQUIPMENT, TEMPORARY FACILITIES AND RELATED ITEMS

§ A.2.5.1 Costs of transportation, storage, installation, maintenance, dismantling and removal of materials, supplies, temporary facilities, machinery, equipment and hand tools not customarily owned by construction workers that are provided by the Contractor at the site and fully consumed in the performance of the Work. Costs of materials, supplies, temporary facilities, machinery, equipment and tools that are not fully consumed shall be based on the cost or value of the item at the time it is first used on the Project site less the value of the item when it is no longer used at the Project site. Costs for items not fully consumed by the Contractor shall mean fair market value.

§ A.2.5.2 Rental charges for temporary facilities, machinery, equipment and hand tools not customarily owned by construction workers that are provided by the Contractor at the site and costs of transportation, installation, minor repairs, dismantling and removal. The total rental cost of any Contractor-owned item may not exceed the purchase price of any comparable item. Rates of Contractor-owned equipment and quantities of equipment shall be subject to the Owner's prior approval.

§ A.2.5.3 Costs of removal of debris from the site of the Work and its proper and legal disposal.

§ A.2.5.4 Costs of document reproductions, facsimile transmissions and long-distance telephone calls, postage and parcel delivery charges, telephone service at the site and reasonable petty cash expenses of the site office.

§ A.2.5.5 Costs of materials and equipment suitably stored off the site at a mutually acceptable location, with the Owner's prior approval.

§ A.2.6 MISCELLANEOUS COSTS

§ A.2.6.1 Premiums for that portion of insurance and bonds required by the Contract Documents that can be directly attributed to this Contract. Self-insurance for either full or partial amounts of the coverages required by the Contract Documents, with the Owner's prior approval.

§ A.2.6.2 Sales, use or similar taxes imposed by a governmental authority that are related to the Work and for which the Contractor is liable.

§ A.2.6.3 Fees and assessments for the building permit and for other permits, licenses and inspections for which the Contractor is required by the Contract Documents to pay.

§ A.2.6.4 Fees of laboratories for tests required by the Contract Documents, except those related to defective or nonconforming Work for which reimbursement is excluded by Article 18 of the Agreement or by other provisions of the Contract Documents, and which do not fall within the scope of Section A.2.7.3.

§ A.2.6.5 Royalties and license fees paid for the use of a particular design, process or product required by the Contract Documents; the cost of defending suits or claims for infringement of patent rights arising from such requirement of the Contract Documents; and payments made in accordance with legal judgments against the Contractor resulting from such suits or claims and payments of settlements made with the Owner's consent. However, such costs of legal defenses, judgments and settlements shall not be included in the calculation of the Contractor's Fee or subject to the Guaranteed Maximum Price. If such royalties, fees and costs are excluded by the last sentence of Section 9.13 of the Agreement or other provisions of the Contract Documents, then they shall not be included in the Cost of the Work.

§ A.2.6.6 Costs for electronic equipment and software, directly related to the Work with the Owner's prior approval.

§ A.2.6.7 Deposits lost for causes other than the Contractor's negligence or failure to fulfill a specific responsibility in the Contract Documents.

§ A.2.6.8 Legal, mediation and arbitration costs, including attorneys' fees, other than those arising from disputes between the Owner and Contractor, reasonably incurred by the Contractor after the execution of this Agreement in the performance of the Work and with the Owner's prior approval, which shall not be unreasonably withheld.

§ A.2.6.9 Subject to the Owner's prior approval, expenses incurred in accordance with the Contractor's standard written personnel policy for relocation and temporary living allowances of the Contractor's personnel required for the Work.

§ A.2.6.10 That portion of the reasonable expenses of the Contractor's supervisory or administrative personnel incurred while traveling in discharge of duties connected with the Work.

§ A.2.7 OTHER COSTS AND EMERGENCIES
§ A.2.7.1 Other costs incurred in the performance of the Work if, and to the extent, approved in advance in writing by the Owner.

§ A.2.7.2 Costs incurred in taking action to prevent threatened damage, injury or loss in case of an emergency affecting the safety of persons and property.

§ A.2.7.3 Costs of repairing or correcting damaged or nonconforming Work executed by the Contractor, Subcontractors or suppliers, provided that such damaged or nonconforming Work was not caused by negligence or failure to fulfill a specific responsibility of the Contractor and only to the extent that the cost of repair or correction is not recovered by the Contractor from insurance, sureties, Subcontractors, suppliers, or others.

§ A.2.8 RELATED PARTY TRANSACTIONS
§ A.2.8.1 For purposes of Section A.2.8, the term "related party" shall mean a parent, subsidiary, affiliate or other entity having common ownership or management with the Contractor; any entity in which any stockholder in, or management employee of, the Contractor owns any interest in excess of ten percent in the aggregate; or any person or entity which has the right to control the business or affairs of the Contractor. The term "related party" includes any member of the immediate family of any person identified above.

§ A.2.8.2 If any of the costs to be reimbursed arise from a transaction between the Contractor and a related party, the Contractor shall notify the Owner of the specific nature of the contemplated transaction, including the identity of the related party and the anticipated cost to be incurred, before any such transaction is consummated or cost incurred. If the Owner, after such notification, authorizes the proposed transaction, then the cost incurred shall be included as a cost to be reimbursed, and the Contractor shall procure the Work, equipment, goods or service from the related party, as a Subcontractor, according to the terms of Article A.5. If the Owner fails to authorize the transaction, the Contractor shall procure the Work, equipment, goods or service from some person or entity other than a related party according to the terms of Article A.5.

ARTICLE A.3   COSTS NOT TO BE REIMBURSED
§ A.3.1 The Cost of the Work shall not include the items listed below:
- .1   Salaries and other compensation of the Contractor's personnel stationed at the Contractor's principal office or offices other than the site office, except as specifically provided in Section A2.2.2;
- .2   Expenses of the Contractor's principal office and offices other than the site office;
- .3   Overhead and general expenses, except as may be expressly included in Article A.2;
- .4   The Contractor's capital expenses, including interest on the Contractor's capital employed for the Work;
- .5   Except as provided in Section A.2.7.3 of this Agreement, costs due to the negligence or failure of the Contractor, Subcontractors and suppliers or anyone directly or indirectly employed by any of them or for whose acts any of them may be liable to fulfill a specific responsibility of the Contract;
- .6   Any cost not specifically and expressly described in Article A.2; and
- .7   Costs, other than costs included in Change Orders approved by the Owner, that would cause the Guaranteed Maximum Price to be exceeded.

ARTICLE A.4   DISCOUNTS, REBATES AND REFUNDS
§ A.4.1 Cash discounts obtained on payments made by the Contractor shall accrue to the Owner if (1) before making the payment, the Contractor included them in an Application for Payment and received payment from the Owner, or (2) the Owner has deposited funds with the Contractor with which to make payments; otherwise, cash discounts shall accrue to the Contractor. Trade discounts, rebates, refunds and amounts received from sales of surplus materials and equipment shall accrue to the Owner, and the Contractor shall make provisions so that they can be obtained.

§ A.4.2 Amounts that accrue to the Owner in accordance with Section A.4.1 shall be credited to the Owner as a deduction from the Cost of the Work.

ARTICLE A.5   SUBCONTRACTS AND OTHER AGREEMENTS
§ A.5.1 Those portions of the Work that the Contractor does not customarily perform with the Contractor's own personnel shall be performed under subcontracts or by other appropriate agreements with the Contractor. The Owner

may designate specific persons from whom, or entities from which, the Contractor shall obtain bids. The Contractor shall obtain bids from Subcontractors and from suppliers of materials or equipment fabricated especially for the Work and shall deliver such bids to the Architect. The Owner shall then determine, with the advice of the Contractor and the Architect, which bids will be accepted. The Contractor shall not be required to contract with anyone to whom the Contractor has reasonable objection.

§ A.5.2 When a the Contractor has provided a Guaranteed Maximum Price, and a specific bidder (1) is recommended to the Owner by the Contractor; (2) is qualified to perform that portion of the Work; and (3) has submitted a bid that conforms to the requirements of the Contract Documents without reservations or exceptions, but the Owner requires that another bid be accepted, then the Contractor may require that a Change Order be issued to adjust the Guaranteed Maximum Price by the difference between the bid of the person or entity recommended to the Owner by the Contractor and the amount of the subcontract or other agreement actually signed with the person or entity designated by the Owner.

§ A.5.3 Subcontracts or other agreements shall conform to the applicable payment provisions of this Agreement, and shall not be awarded on the basis of cost plus a fee without the prior consent of the Owner. If the subcontract is awarded on a cost-plus a fee basis, the Contractor shall provide in the subcontract for the Owner to receive the same audit rights with regard to the Subcontractor as the Owner receives with regard to the Contractor in Article A.6, below.

ARTICLE A.6 ACCOUNTING RECORDS

§ A.6.1 The Contractor shall keep full and detailed records and accounts related to the cost of the Work and exercise such controls as may be necessary for proper financial management under this Contract and to substantiate all costs incurred. The accounting and control systems shall be satisfactory to the Owner. The Owner and the Owner's auditors shall, during regular business hours and upon reasonable notice, be afforded access to, and shall be permitted to audit and copy, the Contractor's records and accounts, including complete documentation supporting accounting entries, books, correspondence, instructions, drawings, receipts, subcontracts, Subcontractor's proposals, purchase orders, vouchers, memoranda and other data relating to this Contract. The Contractor shall preserve these records, for a period of three years after final payment, or for such longer period as may be required by law.

§ A.6.2 When the Contractor believes that all the Work required by the Agreement has been fully performed, the Contractor shall deliver to the Owner's auditors a final accounting of the Cost of the Work.

§ A.6.3 The Owner's auditors will review and report in writing on the Contractor's final accounting within 30 days after delivery of the final accounting to the Architect by the Contractor. Based upon such Cost of the Work as the Owner's auditors report to be substantiated by the Contractor's final accounting, and provided the other conditions of Section 4.2.1 of the Agreement have been met, the Architect will, within seven days after receipt of the written report of the Owner's auditors, either issue to the Owner a final Certificate for Payment with a copy to the Contractor, or notify the Contractor and Owner in writing of the Architect's reasons for withholding a certificate as provided in Section 15.2.3 of the Agreement. The Architect is not responsible for verifying the accuracy of the Contractor's final accounting.

§ A.6.4 If the Owner's auditors report the Cost of the Work as substantiated by the Contractor's final accounting to be less than claimed by the Contractor, the Contractor shall be entitled to request mediation of the dispute without a further decision of the Architect. A request for mediation shall be made by the Contractor within 30 days after the Contractor's receipt of a copy of the Architect's final Certificate for Payment. If the Contractor fails to request mediation within this 30-day period, the substantiated amount reported by the Owner's auditors shall become binding on the Contractor. Pending a final resolution of the disputed amount, the Owner shall pay the Contractor the amount, if any, determined by the Owner's auditors to be due the Contractor.

§ A.6.5 If, subsequent to final payment and at the Owner's request, the Contractor incurs costs in connection with the correction of defective or non-conforming work as described in Article A.2, Costs to be Reimbursed, and not excluded by Article A.3, Costs Not to be Reimbursed, the Owner shall reimburse the Contractor such costs and the Contractor's Fee applicable thereto on the same basis as if such costs had been incurred prior to final payment, but not in excess of the Guaranteed Maximum Price, if any. If the Contractor has participated in savings, the amount of such savings shall be recalculated and appropriate credit given to the Owner in determining the net amount to be paid by the Owner to the Contractor.

Document A107™ – 2007

Standard Form of Agreement Between Owner and Contractor *for a Project of Limited Scope*

AGREEMENT made as of the   day of
in the year
(In words, indicate day, month and year)

BETWEEN the Owner:
(Name, address and other information)

This document has important legal consequences. Consultation with an attorney is encouraged with respect to its completion or modification.

and the Contractor:
(Name, address and other information)

for the following Project:
(Name, location and detailed description)

The Architect:
(Name, address and other information)

The Owner and Contractor agree as follows.

TABLE OF ARTICLES

ARTICLE 1 THE WORK OF THIS CONTRACT

The Contractor shall execute the Work described in the Contract Documents, except as specifically indicated in the Contract Documents to be the responsibility of others.

ARTICLE 2 DATE OF COMMENCEMENT AND SUBSTANTIAL COMPLETION

§ 2.1 The date of commencement of the Work shall be the date of this Agreement unless a different date is stated below or provision is made for the date to be fixed in a notice to proceed issued by the Owner.

(Insert the date of commencement, if it differs from the date of this Agreement or, if applicable, state that the date will be fixed in a notice to proceed.)

§ 2.2 The Contract Time shall be measured from the date of commencement.

§ 2.3 The Contractor shall achieve Substantial Completion of the entire Work not later than
(   ) days from the date of commencement, or as follows:
(Insert number of calendar days. Alternatively, a calendar date may be used when coordinated with the date of commencement. If appropriate, insert requirements for earlier Substantial Completion of certain portions of the Work.)

, subject to adjustments of this Contract Time as provided in the Contract Documents.
(Insert provisions, if any, for liquidated damages relating to failure to achieve Substantial Completion on time or for bonus payments for early completion of the Work.)

ARTICLE 3   CONTRACT SUM
§ 3.1 The Owner shall pay the Contractor the Contract Sum in current funds for the Contractor's performance of the Contract. The Contract Sum shall be one of the following:
(Check the appropriate box.)

☐   Stipulated Sum, in accordance with Section 3.2 below

☐   Cost of the Work plus the Contractor's Fee, in accordance with Section 3.3 below

☐   Cost of the Work plus the Contractor's Fee with a Guaranteed Maximum Price, in accordance with Section 3.4 below

(Based on the selection above, complete Section 3.2, 3.3 or 3.4 below.)

§ 3.2 The Stipulated Sum shall be   Dollars
($), subject to additions and deletions as provided in the Contract Documents.

§ 3.2.1 The Stipulated Sum is based upon the following alternates, if any, which are described in the Contract Documents and are hereby accepted by the Owner:
(State the numbers or other identification of accepted alternates. If the bidding or proposal documents permit the Owner to accept other alternates subsequent to the execution of this Agreement, attach a schedule of such other alternates showing the amount for each and the date when that amount expires.)

§ 3.2.2 Unit prices, if any:
(Identify and state the unit price, and state the quantity limitations, if any, to which the unit price will be applicable.)

Item	Units and Limitations	Price per Unit

§ 3.2.3 Allowances included in the stipulated sum, if any:
(Identify allowance and state exclusions, if any, from the allowance price.)

Item	Allowance

§ 3.3 COST OF THE WORK PLUS CONTRACTOR'S FEE
§ 3.3.1 The Cost of the Work is as defined in Exhibit A, Determination of the Cost of the Work.

§ 3.3.2 The Contractor's Fee:
(State a lump sum, percentage of Cost of the Work or other provision for determining the Contractor's Fee and the method of adjustment to the Fee for changes in the Work.)

§ 3.4 COST OF THE WORK PLUS CONTRACTOR'S FEE WITH A GUARANTEED MAXIMUM PRICE
§ 3.4.1 The Cost of the Work is as defined in Exhibit A, Determination of the Cost of the Work.

§ 3.4.2 The Contractor's Fee:
(State a lump sum, percentage of Cost of the Work or other provision for determining the Contractor's Fee and the method of adjustment to the Fee for changes in the Work.)

§ 3.4.3 GUARANTEED MAXIMUM PRICE
§ 3.4.3.1 The sum of the Cost of the Work and the Contractor's Fee is guaranteed by the Contractor not to exceed
Dollars ($), subject to additions and
deductions by changes in the Work as provided in the Contract Documents. Such maximum sum is referred to in the
Contract Documents as the Guaranteed Maximum Price. Costs which would cause the Guaranteed Maximum Price to be
exceeded shall be paid by the Contractor without reimbursement by the Owner.
(Insert specific provisions if the Contractor is to participate in any savings.)

§ 3.4.3.2 The Guaranteed Maximum Price is based on the following alternates, if any, which are described in the Contract
Documents and are hereby accepted by the Owner:

§ 3.4.3.3 Unit Prices, if any:
(Identify and state the unit price, and state the quantity limitations, if any, to which the unit price will be applicable.)

Item	Units and Limitations	Price per Unit

§ 3.4.3.4 Allowances included in the Guaranteed Maximum Price, if any:
(Identify and state the amounts of any allowances, and state whether they include labor, materials, or both.)

Item	Allowance

§ 3.4.3.5 Assumptions, if any, on which the Guaranteed Maximum Price is based:

ARTICLE 4 PAYMENTS
§ 4.1 PROGRESS PAYMENTS
§ 4.1.1 Based upon Applications for Payment submitted to the Architect by the Contractor and Certificates for Payment issued by the Architect, the Owner shall make progress payments on account of the Contract Sum to the Contractor as provided below and elsewhere in the Contract Documents.

§ 4.1.2 The period covered by each Application for Payment shall be one calendar month ending on the last day of the month, or as follows:

§ 4.1.3 Provided that an Application for Payment is received by the Architect not later than the
day of a month, the Owner shall make payment of the certified amount to the Contractor not later than the
    day of the   month. If an Application for Payment is received by the
Architect after the date fixed above, payment shall be made by the Owner not later than   days
after the Architect receives the Application for Payment.
(Federal, state or local laws may require payment within a certain period of time.)

§ 4.1.4 Retainage, if any, shall be withheld as follows:

§ 4.1.5 Payments due and unpaid under the Contract shall bear interest from the date payment is due at the rate stated below, or in the absence thereof, at the legal rate prevailing from time to time at the place where the Project is located.
(Insert rate of interest agreed upon, if any.)

§ 4.2 FINAL PAYMENT
§ 4.2.1 Final payment, constituting the entire unpaid balance of the Contract Sum, shall be made by the Owner to the Contractor when

    .1 the Contractor has fully performed the Contract except for the Contractor's responsibility to correct Work as provided in Section 18.2, and to satisfy other requirements, if any, which extend beyond final payment;

    .2 the contractor has submitted a final accounting for the Cost of the Work, where payment is on the basis of the Cost of the Work with or without a guaranteed maximum price; and

    .3 a final Certificate for Payment has been issued by the Architect.

§ 4.2.2 The Owner's final payment to the Contractor shall be made no later than 30 days after the issuance of the Architect's final Certificate for Payment, or as follows:

ARTICLE 5 DISPUTE RESOLUTION
§ 5.1 BINDING DISPUTE RESOLUTION
For any claim subject to, but not resolved by, mediation pursuant to Section 21.3, the method of binding dispute resolution shall be as follows:
(Check the appropriate box. If the Owner and Contractor do not select a method of binding dispute resolution below, or do not subsequently agree in writing to a binding dispute resolution method other than litigation, claims will be resolved in a court of competent jurisdiction.)

☐ Arbitration pursuant to Section 21.4 of this Agreement

☐ Litigation in a court of competent jurisdiction

☐ Other *(Specify)*

ARTICLE 6 ENUMERATION OF CONTRACT DOCUMENTS
§ 6.1 The Contract Documents are defined in Article 7 and, except for Modifications issued after execution of this Agreement, are enumerated in the sections below.

§ 6.1.1 The Agreement is this executed AIA Document A107–2007, Standard Form of Agreement Between Owner and Contractor for a Project of Limited Scope.

§ 6.1.2 The Supplementary and other Conditions of the Contract:

Document	Title	Date	Pages

§ 6.1.3 The Specifications:
(Either list the Specifications here or refer to an exhibit attached to this Agreement.)

Section	Title	Date	Pages

§ **6.1.4** The Drawings:
(Either list the Drawings here or refer to an exhibit attached to this Agreement.)

Number	Title	Date

§ **6.1.5** The Addenda, if any:

Number	Date	Pages

Portions of Addenda relating to bidding requirements are not part of the Contract Documents unless the bidding requirements are enumerated in this Article 6.

§ **6.1.6** Additional documents, if any, forming part of the Contract Documents:
.1   Exhibit A, Determination of the Cost of the Work, if applicable.
.2   AIA Document E201™–2007, Digital Data Protocol Exhibit, if completed, or the following:

.3   Other documents:
(List here any additional documents that are intended to form part of the Contract Documents.)

ARTICLE 7   GENERAL PROVISIONS
§ 7.1 THE CONTRACT DOCUMENTS
The Contract Documents are enumerated in Article 6 and consist of this Agreement (including, if applicable, Supplementary and other Conditions of the Contract), Drawings, Specifications, Addenda issued prior to the execution of this Agreement, other documents listed in this Agreement and Modifications issued after execution of this Agreement. A Modification is (1) a written amendment to the Contract signed by both parties, (2) a Change Order, (3) a Construction Change Directive or (4) a written order for a minor change in the Work issued by the Architect. The intent of the Contract Documents is to include all items necessary for the proper execution and completion of the Work by the Contractor. The Contract Documents are complementary, and what is required by one shall be as binding as if required by all; performance by the Contractor shall be required to the extent consistent with the Contract Documents and reasonably inferable from them as being necessary to produce the indicated results.

§ 7.2 THE CONTRACT
The Contract Documents form the Contract for Construction. The Contract represents the entire and integrated agreement between the parties hereto and supersedes prior negotiations, representations or agreements, either written or oral. The Contract may be amended or modified only by a Modification. The Contract Documents shall not be construed to create a contractual relationship of any kind between any persons or entities other than the Owner and the Contractor.

§ 7.3 THE WORK

The term "Work" means the construction and services required by the Contract Documents, whether completed or partially completed, and includes all other labor, materials, equipment and services provided or to be provided by the Contractor to fulfill the Contractor's obligations. The Work may constitute the whole or a part of the Project.

§ 7.4 INSTRUMENTS OF SERVICE

Instruments of Service are representations, in any medium of expression now known or later developed, of the tangible and intangible creative work performed by the Architect and the Architect's consultants under their respective professional services agreements. Instruments of Service may include, without limitation, studies, surveys, models, sketches, drawings, specifications, and other similar materials.

§ 7.5 OWNERSHIP AND USE OF DRAWINGS, SPECIFICATIONS AND OTHER INSTRUMENTS OF SERVICE

§ 7.5.1 The Architect and the Architect's consultants shall be deemed the authors and owners of their respective Instruments of Service, including the Drawings and Specifications, and will retain all common law, statutory and other reserved rights, including copyrights. The Contractor, Subcontractors, Sub-subcontractors, and material or equipment suppliers shall not own or claim a copyright in the Instruments of Service. Submittal or distribution to meet official regulatory requirements or for other purposes in connection with this Project is not to be construed as publication in derogation of the Architect's or Architect's consultants' reserved rights.

§ 7.5.2 The Contractor, Subcontractors, Sub-subcontractors and material or equipment suppliers are authorized to use and reproduce the Instruments of Service provided to them solely and exclusively for execution of the Work. All copies made under this authorization shall bear the copyright notice, if any, shown on the Instruments of Service. The Contractor, Subcontractors, Sub-subcontractors, and material or equipment suppliers may not use the Instruments of Service on other projects or for additions to this Project outside the scope of the Work without the specific written consent of the Owner, Architect and the Architect's consultants.

§ 7.6 TRANSMISSION OF DATA IN DIGITAL FORM

If the parties intend to transmit Instruments of Service or any other information or documentation in digital form, they shall endeavor to establish necessary protocols governing such transmission, unless otherwise provided in the Agreement or in the Contract Documents.

ARTICLE 8   OWNER
§ 8.1 INFORMATION AND SERVICES REQUIRED OF THE OWNER

§ 8.1.1 The Owner shall furnish all necessary surveys and a legal description of the site.

§ 8.1.2 The Contractor shall be entitled to rely on the accuracy of information furnished by the Owner but shall exercise proper precautions relating to the safe performance of the Work.

§ 8.1.3 Except for permits and fees that are the responsibility of the Contractor under the Contract Documents, including those required under Section 9.6.1, the Owner shall secure and pay for other necessary approvals, easements, assessments and charges required for the construction, use or occupancy of permanent structures or for permanent changes in existing facilities.

§ 8.2 OWNER'S RIGHT TO STOP THE WORK

If the Contractor fails to correct Work which is not in accordance with the requirements of the Contract Documents, or repeatedly fails to carry out the Work in accordance with the Contract Documents, the Owner may issue a written order to the Contractor to stop the Work, or any portion thereof, until the cause for such order is eliminated; however, the right of the Owner to stop the Work shall not give rise to a duty on the part of the Owner to exercise this right for the benefit of the Contractor or any other person or entity.

§ 8.3 OWNER'S RIGHT TO CARRY OUT THE WORK

If the Contractor defaults or neglects to carry out the Work in accordance with the Contract Documents, and fails within a ten-day period after receipt of written notice from the Owner to commence and continue correction of such default or neglect with diligence and promptness, the Owner, without prejudice to any other remedy the Owner may have, may correct such deficiencies and may deduct the reasonable cost thereof, including Owner's expenses and compensation for the Architect's services made necessary thereby, from the payment then or thereafter due the Contractor.

ARTICLE 9 CONTRACTOR
§ 9.1 REVIEW OF CONTRACT DOCUMENTS AND FIELD CONDITIONS BY CONTRACTOR
§ 9.1.1 Execution of the Contract by the Contractor is a representation that the Contractor has visited the site, become generally familiar with local conditions under which the Work is to be performed and correlated personal observations with requirements of the Contract Documents.

§ 9.1.2 Because the Contract Documents are complementary, the Contractor shall, before starting each portion of the Work, carefully study and compare the various Contract Documents relative to that portion of the Work, as well as the information furnished by the Owner pursuant to Section 8.1.1, shall take field measurements of any existing conditions related to that portion of the Work and shall observe any conditions at the site affecting it. These obligations are for the purpose of facilitating coordination and construction by the Contractor and are not for the purpose of discovering errors, omissions, or inconsistencies in the Contract Documents; however, the Contractor shall promptly report to the Architect any errors, inconsistencies, or omissions discovered by or made known to the Contractor as a request for information in such form as the Architect may require. It is recognized that the Contractor's review is made in the Contractor's capacity as a contractor and not as a licensed design professional unless otherwise specifically provided in the Contract Documents.

§ 9.1.3 The Contractor is not required to ascertain that the Contract Documents are in accordance with applicable laws, statutes, ordinances, codes, rules and regulations, or lawful orders of public authorities, but the Contractor shall promptly report to the Architect any nonconformity discovered by or made known to the Contractor as a request for information in such form as the Architect may require.

§ 9.2 SUPERVISION AND CONSTRUCTION PROCEDURES
§ 9.2.1 The Contractor shall supervise and direct the Work, using the Contractor's best skill and attention. The Contractor shall be solely responsible for and have control over construction means, methods, techniques, sequences and procedures, and for coordinating all portions of the Work under the Contract, unless the Contract Documents give other specific instructions concerning these matters.

§ 9.2.2 The Contractor shall be responsible to the Owner for acts and omissions of the Contractor's employees, Subcontractors and their agents and employees, and other persons or entities performing portions of the Work for or on behalf of the Contractor or any of its Subcontractors.

§ 9.3 LABOR AND MATERIALS
§ 9.3.1 Unless otherwise provided in the Contract Documents, the Contractor shall provide and pay for labor, materials, equipment, tools, construction equipment and machinery, water, heat, utilities, transportation, and other facilities and services necessary for proper execution and completion of the Work whether temporary or permanent and whether or not incorporated or to be incorporated in the Work.

§ 9.3.2 The Contractor shall enforce strict discipline and good order among the Contractor's employees and other persons carrying out the Work. The Contractor shall not permit employment of unfit persons or persons not skilled in tasks assigned to them.

§ 9.3.3 The Contractor may make a substitution only with the consent of the Owner, after evaluation by the Architect and in accordance with a Modification.

§ 9.4 WARRANTY
The Contractor warrants to the Owner and Architect that materials and equipment furnished under the Contract will be of good quality and new unless the Contract Documents require or permit otherwise. The Contractor further warrants that the Work will conform to the requirements of the Contract Documents and will be free from defects, except for those inherent in the quality of the Work the Contract Documents require or permit. Work, materials, or equipment not conforming to these requirements may be considered defective. The Contractor's warranty excludes remedy for damage or defect caused by abuse, alterations to the Work not executed by the Contractor, improper or insufficient maintenance, improper operation or normal wear and tear under normal usage.

§ 9.5 TAXES
The Contractor shall pay sales, consumer, use and other similar taxes that are legally enacted when bids are received or negotiations concluded, whether or not yet effective or merely scheduled to go into effect.

§ 9.6 PERMITS, FEES, NOTICES, AND COMPLIANCE WITH LAWS

§ 9.6.1 Unless otherwise provided in the Contract Documents, the Contractor shall secure and pay for the building permit as well as other permits, fees, licenses and inspections by government agencies necessary for proper execution and completion of the Work that are customarily secured after execution of the Contract and legally required at the time bids are received or negotiations concluded.

§ 9.6.2 The Contractor shall comply with and give notices required by applicable laws, statutes, ordinances, codes, rules, and regulations, and lawful orders of public authorities applicable to performance of the Work. If the Contractor performs Work knowing it to be contrary to applicable laws, statutes, ordinances, codes, rules and regulations, or lawful orders of public authorities, the Contractor shall assume appropriate responsibility for such Work and shall bear the costs attributable to correction.

§ 9.7 ALLOWANCES

The Contractor shall include in the Contract Sum all allowances stated in the Contract Documents. The Owner shall select materials and equipment under allowances with reasonable promptness. Allowance amounts shall include the costs to the Contractor of materials and equipment delivered at the site and all required taxes, less applicable trade discounts. Allowance amounts shall not include the Contractor's costs for unloading and handling at the site, labor, installation, overhead, and profit.

§ 9.8 CONTRACTOR'S CONSTRUCTION SCHEDULES

§ 9.8.1 The Contractor, promptly after being awarded the Contract, shall prepare and submit for the Owner's and Architect's information a Contractor's construction schedule for the Work. The schedule shall not exceed time limits current under the Contract Documents, shall be revised at appropriate intervals as required by the conditions of the Work and Project, shall be related to the entire Project to the extent required by the Contract Documents, and shall provide for expeditious and practicable execution of the Work.

§ 9.8.2 The Contractor shall perform the Work in general accordance with the most recent schedule submitted to the Owner and Architect.

§ 9.9 SUBMITTALS

§ 9.9.1 The Contractor shall review for compliance with the Contract Documents and submit to the Architect Shop Drawings, Product Data, Samples and similar submittals required by the Contract Documents in coordination with the Contractor's construction schedule and in such sequence as to allow the Architect reasonable time for review. By submitting Shop Drawings, Product Data, Samples and similar submittals, the Contractor represents to the Owner and Architect that the Contractor has (1) reviewed and approved them; (2) determined and verified materials, field measurements and field construction criteria related thereto, or will do so; and (3) checked and coordinated the information contained within such submittals with the requirements of the Work and of the Contract Documents. The Work shall be in accordance with approved submittals.

§ 9.9.2 Shop Drawings, Product Data, Samples and similar submittals are not Contract Documents.

§ 9.10 USE OF SITE

The Contractor shall confine operations at the site to areas permitted by applicable laws, statutes, ordinances, codes, rules and regulations, lawful orders of public authorities, and the Contract Documents and shall not unreasonably encumber the site with materials or equipment.

§ 9.11 CUTTING AND PATCHING

The Contractor shall be responsible for cutting, fitting or patching required to complete the Work or to make its parts fit together properly.

§ 9.12 CLEANING UP

The Contractor shall keep the premises and surrounding area free from accumulation of waste materials or rubbish caused by operations under the Contract. At completion of the Work, the Contractor shall remove waste materials, rubbish, the Contractor's tools, construction equipment, machinery and surplus material from and about the Project.

§ 9.13 ROYALTIES, PATENTS AND COPYRIGHTS

The Contractor shall pay all royalties and license fees. The Contractor shall defend suits or claims for infringement of copyrights and patent rights and shall hold the Owner and Architect harmless from loss on account thereof, but shall not be responsible for such defense or loss when a particular design, process or product of a particular manufacturer or manufacturers is required by the Contract Documents or where the copyright violations are contained in Drawings, Specifications or other documents prepared by the Owner or Architect. However, if the Contractor has reason to believe that the required design, process or product is an infringement of a copyright or a patent, the Contractor shall be responsible for such loss unless such information is promptly furnished to the Architect.

§ 9.14 ACCESS TO WORK
The Contractor shall provide the Owner and Architect access to the Work in preparation and progress wherever located.

§ 9.15 INDEMNIFICATION
§ 9.15.1 To the fullest extent permitted by law, the Contractor shall indemnify and hold harmless the Owner, Architect, Architect's consultants and agents and employees of any of them from and against claims, damages, losses and expenses, including but not limited to attorneys' fees, arising out of or resulting from performance of the Work, provided that such claim, damage, loss or expense is attributable to bodily injury, sickness, disease or death, or to injury to or destruction of tangible property (other than the Work itself), but only to the extent caused by the negligent acts or omissions of the Contractor, a Subcontractor, anyone directly or indirectly employed by them or anyone for whose acts they may be liable, regardless of whether or not such claim, damage, loss or expense is caused in part by a party indemnified hereunder. Such obligation shall not be construed to negate, abridge, or reduce other rights or obligations of indemnity which would otherwise exist as to a party or person described in this Section 9.15.1.

§ 9.15.2 In claims against any person or entity indemnified under this Section 9.15 by an employee of the Contractor, a Subcontractor, anyone directly or indirectly employed by them or anyone for whose acts they may be liable, the indemnification obligation under Section 9.15.1 shall not be limited by a limitation on amount or type of damages, compensation or benefits payable by or for the Contractor or Subcontractor under workers' compensation acts, disability benefit acts or other employee benefit acts.

ARTICLE 10   ARCHITECT
§ 10.1 The Architect will provide administration of the Contract and will be an Owner's representative during construction, until the date the Architect issues the final Certificate for Payment. The Architect will have authority to act on behalf of the Owner only to the extent provided in the Contract Documents, unless otherwise modified in writing in accordance with other provisions of the Contract.

§ 10.2 The Architect will visit the site at intervals appropriate to the stage of the construction to become generally familiar with the progress and quality of the portion of the Work completed, and to determine in general, if the Work observed is being performed in a manner indicating that the Work, when fully completed, will be in accordance with the Contract Documents. However, the Architect will not be required to make exhaustive or continuous on-site inspections to check the quality or quantity of the Work. The Architect will not have control over, charge of, or responsibility for, the construction means, methods, techniques, sequences or procedures, or for safety precautions and programs in connection with the Work, since these are solely the Contractor's rights and responsibilities under the Contract Documents.

§ 10.3 On the basis of the site visits, the Architect will keep the Owner reasonably informed about the progress and quality of the portion of the Work completed, and report to the Owner (1) known deviations from the Contract Documents and from the most recent construction schedule submitted by the Contractor, and (2) defects and deficiencies observed in the Work. The Architect will not be responsible for the Contractor's failure to perform the Work in accordance with the requirements of the Contract Documents. The Architect will not have control over or charge of and will not be responsible for acts or omissions of the Contractor, Subcontractors, or their agents or employees, or any other persons or entities performing portions of the Work.

§ 10.4 Based on the Architect's evaluations of the Work and of the Contractor's Applications for Payment, the Architect will review and certify the amounts due the Contractor and will issue Certificates for Payment in such amounts.

§ 10.5 The Architect has authority to reject Work that does not conform to the Contract Documents and to require inspection or testing of the Work.

§ 10.6 The Architect will review and approve or take other appropriate action upon the Contractor's submittals such as Shop Drawings, Product Data and Samples, but only for the limited purpose of checking for conformance with information given and the design concept expressed in the Contract Documents.

§ 10.7 The Architect will interpret and decide matters concerning performance under, and requirements of, the Contract Documents on written request of either the Owner or Contractor. The Architect will make initial decisions on all claims, disputes and other matters in question between the Owner and Contractor but will not be liable for results of any interpretations or decisions rendered in good faith.

§ 10.8 The Architect's decisions on matters relating to aesthetic effect will be final if consistent with the intent expressed in the Contract Documents.

§ 10.9 Duties, responsibilities and limitations of authority of the Architect as set forth in the Contract Documents shall not be restricted, modified or extended without written consent of the Owner, Contractor and Architect. Consent shall not be unreasonably withheld.

ARTICLE 11 SUBCONTRACTORS
§ 11.1 A Subcontractor is a person or entity who has a direct contract with the Contractor to perform a portion of the Work at the site.

§ 11.2 Unless otherwise stated in the Contract Documents or the bidding requirements, the Contractor, as soon as practicable after award of the Contract, shall furnish in writing to the Owner through the Architect the names of the Subcontractors or suppliers for each of the principal portions of the Work. The Contractor shall not contract with any Subcontractor or supplier to whom the Owner or Architect has made reasonable written objection within ten days after receipt of the Contractor's list of Subcontractors and suppliers. If the proposed but rejected Subcontractor was reasonably capable of performing the Work, the Contract Sum and Contract Time shall be increased or decreased by the difference, if any, occasioned by such change, and an appropriate Change Order shall be issued before commencement of the substitute Subcontractor's Work. The Contractor shall not be required to contract with anyone to whom the Contractor has made reasonable objection.

§ 11.3 Contracts between the Contractor and Subcontractors shall (1) require each Subcontractor, to the extent of the Work to be performed by the Subcontractor, to be bound to the Contractor by the terms of the Contract Documents, and to assume toward the Contractor all the obligations and responsibilities, including the responsibility for safety of the Subcontractor's Work, which the Contractor, by the Contract Documents, assumes toward the Owner and Architect, and (2) allow the Subcontractor the benefit of all rights, remedies and redress against the Contractor that the Contractor, by these Contract Documents, has against the Owner.

ARTICLE 12 CONSTRUCTION BY OWNER OR BY SEPARATE CONTRACTORS
§ 12.1 The Owner reserves the right to perform construction or operations related to the Project with the Owner's own forces, and to award separate contracts in connection with other portions of the Project or other construction or operations on the site under conditions of the contract identical or substantially similar to these, including those portions related to insurance and waiver of subrogation. If the Contractor claims that delay or additional cost is involved because of such action by the Owner, the Contractor shall make such claim as provided in Article 21.

§ 12.2 The Contractor shall afford the Owner and separate contractors reasonable opportunity for introduction and storage of their materials and equipment and performance of their activities, and shall connect and coordinate the Contractor's activities with theirs as required by the Contract Documents.

§ 12.3 The Owner shall be reimbursed by the Contractor for costs incurred by the Owner which are payable to a separate contractor because of delays, improperly timed activities or defective construction of the Contractor. The Owner shall be responsible to the Contractor for costs incurred by the Contractor because of delays, improperly timed activities, damage to the Work or defective construction of a separate contractor.

ARTICLE 13 CHANGES IN THE WORK
§ 13.1 By appropriate Modification, changes in the Work may be accomplished after execution of the Contract. The Owner, without invalidating the Contract, may order changes in the Work within the general scope of the Contract consisting of additions, deletions or other revisions, with the Contract Sum and Contract Time being adjusted accordingly. Such changes in the Work shall be authorized by written Change Order signed by the Owner, Contractor and Architect, or by written Construction Change Directive signed by the Owner and Architect.

§ 13.2 Adjustments in the Contract Sum and Contract Time resulting from a change in the Work shall be determined by mutual agreement of the parties or, in the case of a Construction Change Directive signed only by the Owner and Architect, by the Contractor's cost of labor, material, equipment, and reasonable overhead and profit, unless the parties agree on another method for determining the cost or credit. Pending final determination of the total cost of a Construction Change Directive, the Contractor may request payment for Work completed pursuant to the Construction Change Directive. The Architect will make an interim determination of the amount of payment due for purposes of certifying the Contractor's monthly Application for Payment. When the Owner and Contractor agree on adjustments to the Contract Sum and Contract Time arising from a Construction Change Directive, the Architect will prepare a Change Order.

§ 13.3 The Architect will have authority to order minor changes in the Work not involving adjustment in the Contract Sum or extension of the Contract Time and not inconsistent with the intent of the Contract Documents. Such changes shall be effected by written order and shall be binding on the Owner and Contractor. The Contractor shall carry out such written orders promptly.

§ 13.4 If concealed or unknown physical conditions are encountered at the site that differ materially from those indicated in the Contract Documents or from those conditions ordinarily found to exist, the Contract Sum and Contract Time shall be equitably adjusted as mutually agreed between the Owner and Contractor; provided that the Contractor provides notice to the Owner and Architect promptly and before conditions are disturbed.

ARTICLE 14 TIME
§ 14.1 Time limits stated in the Contract Documents are of the essence of the Contract. By executing the Agreement the Contractor confirms that the Contract Time is a reasonable period for performing the Work.

§ 14.2 Unless otherwise provided, Contract Time is the period of time, including authorized adjustments, allotted in the Contract Documents for Substantial Completion of the Work.

§ 14.3 The term "day" as used in the Contract Documents shall mean calendar day unless otherwise specifically defined.

§ 14.4 The date of Substantial Completion is the date certified by the Architect in accordance with Section 15.4.3.

§ 14.5 If the Contractor is delayed at any time in the commencement or progress of the Work by changes ordered in the Work, by labor disputes, fire, unusual delay in deliveries, abnormal adverse weather conditions not reasonably anticipatable, unavoidable casualties or any causes beyond the Contractor's control, or by other causes which the Architect determines may justify delay, then the Contract Time shall be extended by Change Order for such reasonable time as the Architect may determine, subject to the provisions of Article 21.

ARTICLE 15 PAYMENTS AND COMPLETION
§ 15.1 APPLICATIONS FOR PAYMENT
§ 15.1.1 Where the Contract is based on a Stipulated Sum or the Cost of the Work with a Guaranteed Maximum Price, the Contractor shall submit to the Architect, before the first Application for Payment, a schedule of values, allocating the entire Contract Sum to the various portions of the Work, prepared in such form and supported by such data to substantiate its accuracy as the Architect may require. This schedule, unless objected to by the Architect, shall be used in reviewing the Contractor's Applications for Payment.

§ 15.1.2 With each Application for Payment where the Contract Sum is based upon the Cost of the Work, or the Cost of the Work with a Guaranteed Maximum Price, the Contractor shall submit payrolls, petty cash accounts, receipted invoices or invoices with check vouchers attached, and any other evidence required by the Owner to demonstrate that cash disbursements already made by the Contractor on account of the Cost of the Work equal or exceed (1) progress payments already received by the Contractor, less (2) that portion of those payments attributable to the Contractor's Fee; plus (3) payrolls for the period covered by the present Application for Payment.

§ 15.1.3 Payments shall be made on account of materials and equipment delivered and suitably stored at the site for subsequent incorporation in the Work. If approved in advance by the Owner, payment may similarly be made for materials and equipment stored, and protected from damage, off the site at a location agreed upon in writing.

§ 15.1.4 The Contractor warrants that title to all Work covered by an Application for Payment will pass to the Owner no later than the time of payment. The Contractor further warrants that upon submittal of an Application for Payment all Work for which Certificates for Payment have been previously issued and payments received from the Owner shall, to the best of the Contractor's knowledge, information and belief, be free and clear of liens, claims, security interests or other encumbrances adverse to the Owner's interests.

§ 15.2 CERTIFICATES FOR PAYMENT
§ 15.2.1 The Architect will, within seven days after receipt of the Contractor's Application for Payment, either issue to the Owner a Certificate for Payment, with a copy to the Contractor, for such amount as the Architect determines is properly due, or notify the Contractor and Owner in writing of the Architect's reasons for withholding certification in whole or in part as provided in Section 15.2.3.

§ 15.2.2 The issuance of a Certificate for Payment will constitute a representation by the Architect to the Owner, based on the Architect's evaluations of the Work and the data comprising the Application for Payment, that, to the best of the Architect's knowledge, information and belief, the Work has progressed to the point indicated and that the quality of the Work is in accordance with the Contract Documents. The foregoing representations are subject to an evaluation of the Work for conformance with the Contract Documents upon Substantial Completion, to results of subsequent tests and inspections, to correction of minor deviations from the Contract Documents prior to completion and to specific qualifications expressed by the Architect. The issuance of a Certificate for Payment will further constitute a representation that the Contractor is entitled to payment in the amount certified. However, the issuance of a Certificate for Payment will not be a representation that the Architect has (1) made exhaustive or continuous on-site inspections to check the quality or quantity of the Work, (2) reviewed construction means, methods, techniques, sequences or procedures, (3) reviewed copies of requisitions received from Subcontractors and material suppliers and other data requested by the Owner to substantiate the Contractor's right to payment, or (4) made examination to ascertain how or for what purpose the Contractor has used money previously paid on account of the Contract Sum.

§ 15.2.3 The Architect may withhold a Certificate for Payment in whole or in part, to the extent reasonably necessary to protect the Owner, if in the Architect's opinion the representations to the Owner required by Section 15.2.2 cannot be made. If the Architect is unable to certify payment in the amount of the Application, the Architect will notify the Contractor and Owner as provided in Section 15.2.1. If the Contractor and the Architect cannot agree on a revised amount, the Architect will promptly issue a Certificate for Payment for the amount for which the Architect is able to make such representations to the Owner. The Architect may also withhold a Certificate for Payment or, because of subsequently discovered evidence, may nullify the whole or a part of a Certificate for Payment previously issued, to such extent as may be necessary in the Architect's opinion to protect the Owner from loss for which the Contractor is responsible, including loss resulting from acts and omissions described in Section 9.2.2, because of

.1 defective Work not remedied;
.2 third party claims filed or reasonable evidence indicating probable filing of such claims unless security acceptable to the Owner is provided by the Contractor;
.3 failure of the Contractor to make payments properly to Subcontractors or for labor, materials or equipment;
.4 reasonable evidence that the Work cannot be completed for the unpaid balance of the Contract Sum;
.5 damage to the Owner or a separate contractor;
.6 reasonable evidence that the Work will not be completed within the Contract Time and that the unpaid balance would not be adequate to cover actual or liquidated damages for the anticipated delay; or
.7 repeated failure to carry out the Work in accordance with the Contract Documents.

§ 15.2.4 When the above reasons for withholding certification are removed, certification will be made for amounts previously withheld.

§ 15.3 PROGRESS PAYMENTS
§ 15.3.1 The Contractor shall pay each Subcontractor, no later than seven days after receipt of payment, the amount to which the Subcontractor is entitled, reflecting percentages actually retained from payments to the Contractor on account of the Subcontractor's portion of the Work. The Contractor shall, by appropriate agreement with each Subcontractor, require each Subcontractor to make payments to sub-subcontractors in similar manner.

§ 15.3.2 Neither the Owner nor Architect shall have an obligation to pay or see to the payment of money to a Subcontractor except as may otherwise be required by law.

§ 15.3.3 A Certificate for Payment, a progress payment, or partial or entire use or occupancy of the Project by the Owner shall not constitute acceptance of Work not in accordance with the Contract Documents.

§ 15.4 SUBSTANTIAL COMPLETION

§ 15.4.1 Substantial Completion is the stage in the progress of the Work when the Work or designated portion thereof is sufficiently complete in accordance with the Contract Documents so that the Owner can occupy or utilize the Work for its intended use.

§ 15.4.2 When the Contractor considers that the Work, or a portion thereof which the Owner agrees to accept separately, is substantially complete, the Contractor shall prepare and submit to the Architect a comprehensive list of items to be completed or corrected prior to final payment. Failure to include an item on such list does not alter the responsibility of the Contractor to complete all Work in accordance with the Contract Documents.

§ 15.4.3 Upon receipt of the Contractor's list, the Architect will make an inspection to determine whether the Work or designated portion thereof is substantially complete. When the Architect determines that the Work or designated portion thereof is substantially complete, the Architect will issue a Certificate of Substantial Completion which shall establish the date of Substantial Completion, establish responsibilities of the Owner and Contractor for security, maintenance, heat, utilities, damage to the Work and insurance, and fix the time within which the Contractor shall finish all items on the list accompanying the Certificate. Warranties required by the Contract Documents shall commence on the date of Substantial Completion of the Work or designated portion thereof unless otherwise provided in the Certificate of Substantial Completion.

§ 15.4.4 The Certificate of Substantial Completion shall be submitted to the Owner and Contractor for their written acceptance of responsibilities assigned to them in such Certificate. Upon such acceptance and consent of surety, if any, the Owner shall make payment of retainage applying to such Work or designated portion thereof. Such payment shall be adjusted for Work that is incomplete or not in accordance with the requirements of the Contract Documents.

§ 15.5 FINAL COMPLETION AND FINAL PAYMENT

§ 15.5.1 Upon receipt of the Contractor's written notice that the Work is ready for final inspection and acceptance and upon receipt of a final Application for Payment, the Architect will promptly make such inspection and, when the Architect finds the Work acceptable under the Contract Documents and the Contract fully performed, the Architect will promptly issue a final Certificate for Payment stating that to the best of the Architect's knowledge, information and belief, and on the basis of the Architect's on-site visits and inspections, the Work has been completed in accordance with terms and conditions of the Contract Documents and that the entire balance found to be due the Contractor and noted in the final Certificate is due and payable. The Architect's final Certificate for Payment will constitute a further representation that conditions stated in Section 15.5.2 as precedent to the Contractor's being entitled to final payment have been fulfilled.

§ 15.5.2 Final payment shall not become due until the Contractor has delivered to the Owner a complete release of all liens arising out of this Contract or receipts in full covering all labor, materials and equipment for which a lien could be filed, or a bond satisfactory to the Owner to indemnify the Owner against such lien. If such lien remains unsatisfied after payments are made, the Contractor shall refund to the Owner all money that the Owner may be compelled to pay in discharging such lien, including costs and reasonable attorneys' fees.

15.5.3 The making of final payment shall constitute a waiver of claims by the Owner except those arising from

    .1   liens, claims, security interests or encumbrances arising out of the Contract and unsettled;
    .2   failure of the Work to comply with the requirements of the Contract Documents; or
    .3   terms of special warranties required by the Contract Documents.

§ 15.5.4 Acceptance of final payment by the Contractor, a Subcontractor or material supplier shall constitute a waiver of claims by that payee except those previously made in writing and identified by that payee as unsettled at the time of final Application for Payment.

ARTICLE 16   PROTECTION OF PERSONS AND PROPERTY
§ 16.1 SAFETY PRECAUTIONS AND PROGRAMS
The Contractor shall be responsible for initiating, maintaining and supervising all safety precautions and programs in connection with the performance of the Contract. The Contractor shall take reasonable precautions for safety of, and shall provide reasonable protection to prevent damage, injury or loss to

- .1   employees on the Work and other persons who may be affected thereby;
- .2   the Work and materials and equipment to be incorporated therein, whether in storage on or off the site, under care, custody or control of the Contractor or the Contractor's Subcontractors or Sub-subcontractors; and
- .3   other property at the site or adjacent thereto, such as trees, shrubs, lawns, walks, pavements, roadways, structures and utilities not designated for removal, relocation or replacement in the course of construction.

The Contractor shall comply with and give notices required by applicable laws, statutes, ordinances, codes, rules and regulations, and lawful orders of public authorities bearing on safety of persons and property and their protection from damage, injury or loss. The Contractor shall promptly remedy damage and loss to property caused in whole or in part by the Contractor, a Subcontractor, a sub-subcontractor, or anyone directly or indirectly employed by any of them, or by anyone for whose acts they may be liable and for which the Contractor is responsible under Sections 16.1.2 and 16.1.3, except for damage or loss attributable to acts or omissions of the Owner or Architect or by anyone for whose acts either of them may be liable, and not attributable to the fault or negligence of the Contractor. The foregoing obligations of the Contractor are in addition to the Contractor's obligations under Section 9.15.

§ 16.2 HAZARDOUS MATERIALS
§ 16.2.1 The Contractor is responsible for compliance with the requirements of the Contract Documents regarding hazardous materials. If the Contractor encounters a hazardous material or substance not addressed in the Contract Documents, and if reasonable precautions will be inadequate to prevent foreseeable bodily injury or death to persons resulting from a material or substance, including but not limited to asbestos or polychlorinated biphenyl (PCB), encountered on the site by the Contractor, the Contractor shall, upon recognizing the condition, immediately stop Work in the affected area and report the condition to the Owner and Architect in writing. When the material or substance has been rendered harmless, Work in the affected area shall resume upon written agreement of the Owner and Contractor. By Change Order, the Contract Time shall be extended appropriately and the Contract Sum shall be increased in the amount of the Contractor's reasonable additional costs of shutdown, delay and start-up.

§ 16.2.2 To the fullest extent permitted by law, the Owner shall indemnify and hold harmless the Contractor, Subcontractors, Architect, Architect's consultants and agents and employees of any of them from and against claims, damages, losses and expenses, including but not limited to attorneys' fees, arising out of or resulting from performance of the Work in the affected area, if in fact, the material or substance presents the risk of bodily injury or death as described in Section 16.2.1 and has not been rendered harmless, provided that such claim, damage, loss or expense is attributable to bodily injury, sickness, disease or death, or to injury to or destruction of tangible property (other than the Work itself), except to the extent that such damage, loss or expense is due to the fault or negligence of the party seeking indemnity.

§ 16.2.3 If, without negligence on the part of the Contractor, the Contractor is held liable by a government agency for the cost of remediation of a hazardous material or substance solely by reason of performing Work as required by the Contract Documents, the Owner shall indemnify the Contractor for all cost and expense thereby incurred.

ARTICLE 17   INSURANCE AND BONDS
§ 17.1 The Contractor shall purchase from, and maintain in a company or companies lawfully authorized to do business in the jurisdiction in which the Project is located, insurance for protection from claims under workers' compensation acts and other employee benefit acts which are applicable, claims for damages because of bodily injury, including death, and claims for damages, other than to the Work itself, to property which may arise out of or result from the Contractor's operations and completed operations under the Contract, whether such operations be by the Contractor or by a Subcontractor or anyone directly or indirectly employed by any of them. This insurance shall be written for not less than limits of liability specified in the Contract Documents or required by law, whichever coverage is greater, and shall include contractual liability insurance applicable to the Contractor's obligations under Section 9.15. Certificates of Insurance acceptable to the Owner shall be filed with the Owner prior to commencement of the Work. Each policy shall contain a provision that the policy will not be canceled or allowed to expire until at least 30 days' prior written notice has been given to the Owner. The Contractor shall cause the commercial liability coverage required by the Contract

Documents to include: (1) the Owner, the Architect and the Architect's Consultants as additional insureds for claims caused in whole or in part by the Contractor's negligent acts or omissions during the Contractor's operations; and (2) the Owner as an additional insured for claims caused in whole or in part by the Contractor's negligent acts or omissions during the Contractor's completed operations.

§ 17.2 OWNER'S LIABILITY INSURANCE
The Owner shall be responsible for purchasing and maintaining the Owner's usual liability insurance.

§ 17.3 PROPERTY INSURANCE
§ 17.3.1 Unless otherwise provided, the Owner shall purchase and maintain, in a company or companies lawfully authorized to do business in the jurisdiction in which the Project is located, property insurance on an "all-risk" or equivalent policy form, including builder's risk, in the amount of the initial Contract Sum, plus the value of subsequent modifications and cost of materials supplied and installed by others, comprising total value for the entire Project at the site on a replacement cost basis without optional deductibles. Such property insurance shall be maintained, unless otherwise provided in the Contract Documents or otherwise agreed in writing by all persons and entities who are beneficiaries of such insurance, until final payment has been made as provided in Section 15.5 or until no person or entity other than the Owner has an insurable interest in the property required by this Section 17.3.1 to be covered, whichever is later. This insurance shall include interests of the Owner, the Contractor, Subcontractors and sub-subcontractors in the Project.

§ 17.3.2 The Owner shall file a copy of each policy with the Contractor before an exposure to loss may occur. Each policy shall contain a provision that the policy will not be canceled or allowed to expire, and that its limits will not be reduced, until at least 30 days' prior written notice has been given to the Contractor.

§ 17.3.3 The Owner and Contractor waive all rights against (1) each other and any of their subcontractors, sub-subcontractors, agents and employees, each of the other, and (2) the Architect, Architect's consultants, separate contractors described in Article 12, if any, and any of their subcontractors, sub-subcontractors, agents and employees for damages caused by fire or other causes of loss to the extent covered by property insurance obtained pursuant to Section 17.3 or other property insurance applicable to the Work, except such rights as they have to proceeds of such insurance held by the Owner as fiduciary. The Owner or Contractor, as appropriate, shall require of the Architect, Architect's consultants, separate contractors described in Article 12, if any, and the subcontractors, sub-subcontractors, agents and employees of any of them, by appropriate agreements, written where legally required for validity, similar waivers each in favor of other parties enumerated herein. The policies shall provide such waivers of subrogation by endorsement or otherwise. A waiver of subrogation shall be effective as to a person or entity even though that person or entity would otherwise have a duty of indemnification, contractual or otherwise, did not pay the insurance premium directly or indirectly, and whether or not the person or entity had an insurable interest in the property damaged.

§ 17.3.4 A loss insured under the Owner's property insurance shall be adjusted by the Owner as fiduciary and made payable to the Owner as fiduciary for the insureds, as their interests may appear, subject to requirements of any applicable mortgagee clause. The Contractor shall pay Subcontractors their just shares of insurance proceeds received by the Contractor, and by appropriate agreements, written where legally required for validity, shall require Subcontractors to make payments to their sub-subcontractors in similar manner.

§ 17.4 PERFORMANCE BOND AND PAYMENT BOND
§ 17.4.1 The Owner shall have the right to require the Contractor to furnish bonds covering faithful performance of the Contract and payment of obligations arising thereunder as stipulated in bidding requirements or specifically required in the Contract Documents on the date of execution of the Contract.

§ 17.4.2 Upon the request of any person or entity appearing to be a potential beneficiary of bonds covering payment of obligations arising under the Contract, the Contractor shall promptly furnish a copy of the bonds or shall authorize a copy to be furnished.

ARTICLE 18 CORRECTION OF WORK
§ 18.1 The Contractor shall promptly correct Work rejected by the Architect or failing to conform to the requirements of the Contract Documents, whether discovered before or after Substantial Completion and whether or not fabricated, installed or completed. Costs of correcting such rejected Work, including additional testing and inspections, the cost of uncovering and replacement, and compensation for the Architect's services and expenses made necessary thereby, shall

be at the Contractor's expense, unless compensable under Section A.2.7.3 in Exhibit A, Determination of the Cost of the Work.

§ **18.2** In addition to the Contractor's obligations under Section 9.4, if, within one year after the date of Substantial Completion of the Work or designated portion thereof or after the date for commencement of warranties established under Section 15.4.3, or by terms of an applicable special warranty required by the Contract Documents, any of the Work is found to be not in accordance with the requirements of the Contract Documents, the Contractor shall correct it promptly after receipt of written notice from the Owner to do so unless the Owner has previously given the Contractor a written acceptance of such condition. The Owner shall give such notice promptly after discovery of the condition. During the one-year period for correction of Work, if the Owner fails to notify the Contractor and give the Contractor an opportunity to make the correction, the Owner waives the rights to require correction by the Contractor and to make a claim for breach of warranty.

§ **18.3** If the Contractor fails to correct nonconforming Work within a reasonable time, the Owner may correct it in accordance with Section 8.3.

§ **18.4** The one-year period for correction of Work shall be extended with respect to portions of Work first performed after Substantial Completion by the period of time between Substantial Completion and the actual completion of that portion of the Work.

§ **18.5** The one-year period for correction of Work shall not be extended by corrective Work performed by the Contractor pursuant to this Article 18.

ARTICLE 19   MISCELLANEOUS PROVISIONS
§ 19.1 ASSIGNMENT OF CONTRACT
Neither party to the Contract shall assign the Contract without written consent of the other, except that the Owner may, without consent of the Contractor, assign the Contract to a lender providing construction financing for the Project if the lender assumes the Owner's rights and obligations under the Contract Documents. The Contractor shall execute all consents reasonably required to facilitate such assignment.

§ 19.2 GOVERNING LAW
The Contract shall be governed by the law of the place where the Project is located, except, that if the parties have selected arbitration as the method of binding dispute resolution, the Federal Arbitration Act shall govern Section 21.4.

§ 19.3 TESTS AND INSPECTIONS
Tests, inspections and approvals of portions of the Work required by the Contract Documents or by applicable laws, statutes, ordinances, codes, rules and regulations or lawful orders of public authorities shall be made at an appropriate time. Unless otherwise provided, the Contractor shall make arrangements for such tests, inspections and approvals with an independent testing laboratory or entity acceptable to the Owner, or with the appropriate public authority, and shall bear all related costs of tests, inspections and approvals. The Contractor shall give the Architect timely notice of when and where tests and inspections are to be made so that the Architect may be present for such procedures. The Owner shall bear costs of (1) tests, inspections or approvals that do not become requirements until after bids are received or negotiations concluded, and (2) of tests, inspections or approvals where building codes or applicable laws or regulations prohibit the Owner from delegating the costs to the Contractor.

§ 19.4 COMMENCEMENT OF STATUTORY LIMITATION PERIOD
The Owner and Contractor shall commence all claims and causes of action, whether in contract, tort, breach of warranty or otherwise, against the other arising out of or related to the Contract in accordance with the requirements of the final dispute resolution method selected in the Agreement within the period specified by applicable law, but in any case not more than 10 years after the date of Substantial Completion of the Work. The Owner and Contractor waive all claims and causes of action not commenced in accordance with this Section 19.4.

ARTICLE 20   TERMINATION OF THE CONTRACT
§ 20.1 TERMINATION BY THE CONTRACTOR
If the Architect fails to certify payment as provided in Section 15.2.1 for a period of 30 days through no fault of the Contractor, or if the Owner fails to make payment as provided in Section 4.1.3 for a period of 30 days, the Contractor may, upon seven additional days' written notice to the Owner and the Architect, terminate the Contract and recover

from the Owner payment for Work executed, including reasonable overhead and profit, costs incurred by reason of such termination, and damages.

§ 20.2 TERMINATION BY THE OWNER FOR CAUSE

§ 20.2.1 The Owner may terminate the Contract if the Contractor

.1   repeatedly refuses or fails to supply enough properly skilled workers or proper materials;
.2   fails to make payment to Subcontractors for materials or labor in accordance with the respective agreements between the Contractor and the Subcontractors;
.3   repeatedly disregards applicable laws, statutes, ordinances, codes, rules and regulations or lawful orders of a public authority; or
.4   otherwise is guilty of substantial breach of a provision of the Contract Documents.

§ 20.2.2 When any of the above reasons exists, the Owner, upon certification by the Architect that sufficient cause exists to justify such action, may, without prejudice to any other remedy the Owner may have and after giving the Contractor seven days' written notice, terminate the Contract and take possession of the site and of all materials, equipment, tools, and construction equipment and machinery thereon owned by the Contractor and may finish the Work by whatever reasonable method the Owner may deem expedient. Upon request of the Contractor, the Owner shall furnish to the Contractor a detailed accounting of the costs incurred by the Owner in finishing the Work.

§ 20.2.3 When the Owner terminates the Contract for one of the reasons stated in Section 20.2.1, the Contractor shall not be entitled to receive further payment until the Work is finished.

§ 20.2.4 If the unpaid balance of the Contract Sum exceeds costs of finishing the Work, including compensation for the Architect's services and expenses made necessary thereby, and other damages incurred by the Owner and not expressly waived, such excess shall be paid to the Contractor. If such costs and damages exceed the unpaid balance, the Contractor shall pay the difference to the Owner. The amount to be paid to the Contractor or Owner, as the case may be, shall be certified by the Architect, upon application, and this obligation for payment shall survive termination of the Contract.

§ 20.3 TERMINATION BY THE OWNER FOR CONVENIENCE

The Owner may, at any time, terminate the Contract for the Owner's convenience and without cause. The Contractor shall be entitled to receive payment for Work executed, and costs incurred by reason of such termination, along with reasonable overhead and profit on the Work not executed.

ARTICLE 21   CLAIMS AND DISPUTES

§ 21.1 Claims, disputes and other matters in question arising out of or relating to this Contract, including those alleging an error or omission by the Architect but excluding those arising under Section 16.2, shall be referred initially to the Architect for decision. Such matters, except those waived as provided for in Section 21.8 and Sections 15.5.3 and 15.5.4, shall, after initial decision by the Architect or 30 days after submission of the matter to the Architect, be subject to mediation as a condition precedent to binding dispute resolution.

§ 21.2 If a claim, dispute or other matter in question relates to or is the subject of a mechanic's lien, the party asserting such matter may proceed in accordance with applicable law to comply with the lien notice or filing deadlines.

§ 21.3 The parties shall endeavor to resolve their disputes by mediation which, unless the parties mutually agree otherwise, shall be administered by the American Arbitration Association in accordance with their Construction Industry Mediation Procedures in effect on the date of the Agreement. A request for mediation shall be made in writing, delivered to the other party to this Agreement, and filed with the person or entity administering the mediation. The request may be made concurrently with the binding dispute resolution but, in such event, mediation shall proceed in advance of binding dispute resolution proceedings, which shall be stayed pending mediation for a period of 60 days from the date of filing, unless stayed for a longer period by agreement of the parties or court order. If an arbitration is stayed pursuant to this Section, the parties may nonetheless proceed to the selection of the arbitrator(s) and agree upon a schedule for later proceedings.

§ 21.4 If the parties have selected arbitration as the method for binding dispute resolution in the Agreement, any claim, subject to, but not resolved by, mediation shall be subject to arbitration which, unless the parties mutually agree otherwise, shall be administered by the American Arbitration Association, in accordance with the Construction Industry Arbitration Rules in effect on the date of this Agreement. Demand for arbitration shall be made in writing, delivered to

Init.

/

AIA Document A107™ – 2007. Copyright © 1936, 1951, 1958, 1961, 1963, 1966, 1970, 1974, 1978, 1987, 1997 and 2007 by The American Institute of Architects. **WARNING:** This AIA® Document is protected by U.S. Copyright Law and International Treaties. Unauthorized reproduction or distribution of this AIA® Document, or any portion of it, may result in severe civil and criminal penalties, and will be prosecuted to the maximum extent possible under the law. Purchasers are permitted to reproduce ten (10) copies of this document when completed. To report copyright violations of AIA Contract Documents, e-mail The American Institute of Architects' legal counsel, copyright@aia.org.

19

the other party to the Contract, and filed with the person or entity administering the arbitration. The award rendered by the arbitrator or arbitrators shall be final, and judgment may be entered upon it in accordance with applicable law in any court having jurisdiction thereof.

§ 21.5 Either party, at its sole discretion, may consolidate an arbitration conducted under this Agreement with any other arbitration to which it is a party provided that (1) the arbitration agreement governing the other arbitration permits consolidation; (2) the arbitrations to be consolidated substantially involve common questions of law or fact; and (3) the arbitrations employ materially similar procedural rules and methods for selecting arbitrator(s).

§ 21.6 Any party to an arbitration may include by joinder persons or entities substantially involved in a common question of law or fact whose presence is required if complete relief is to be accorded in arbitration provided that the party sought to be joined consents in writing to such joinder. Consent to arbitration involving an additional person or entity shall not constitute consent to arbitration of a Claim not described in the written Consent.

§ 21.7 The foregoing agreement to arbitrate and other agreements to arbitrate with an additional person or entity duly consented to by parties to the Agreement shall be specifically enforceable under applicable law in any court having jurisdiction thereof.

§ 21.8 CLAIMS FOR CONSEQUENTIAL DAMAGES
The Contractor and Owner waive claims against each other for consequential damages arising out of or relating to this Contract. This mutual waiver includes

    .1   damages incurred by the Owner for rental expenses, for losses of use, income, profit, financing, business and reputation, and for loss of management or employee productivity or of the services of such persons; and

    .2   damages incurred by the Contractor for principal office expenses including the compensation of personnel stationed there, for losses of financing, business and reputation, and for loss of profit except anticipated profit arising directly from the Work.

This mutual waiver is applicable, without limitation, to all consequential damages due to either party's termination in accordance with Article 20. Nothing contained in this Section 21.8 shall be deemed to preclude an award of liquidated damages, when applicable, in accordance with the requirements of the Contract Documents.

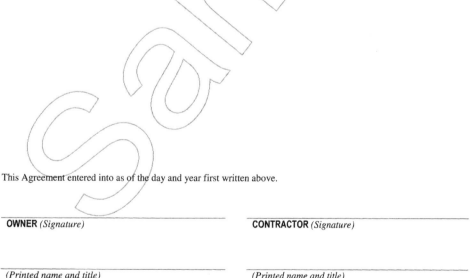

This Agreement entered into as of the day and year first written above.

_____
OWNER *(Signature)*

_____
CONTRACTOR *(Signature)*

_____
(Printed name and title)

_____
(Printed name and title)

Init.

/

20

AIA® Document G702™ – 1992

Application and Certificate for Payment

TO OWNER:

FROM CONTRACTOR:

PROJECT:

VIA ARCHITECT:

APPLICATION NO:

PERIOD TO:

CONTRACT FOR:

CONTRACT DATE:

PROJECT NOS:

Distribution to:

OWNER ☐
ARCHITECT ☐
CONTRACTOR ☐
FIELD ☐
OTHER ☐

CONTRACTOR'S APPLICATION FOR PAYMENT

Application is made for payment, as shown below, in connection with the Contract.
Continuation Sheet, AIA Document G703, is attached.

1. ORIGINAL CONTRACT SUM .... $

2. Net change by Change Orders .... $

3. CONTRACT SUM TO DATE (Line 1 ± 2) .... $

4. TOTAL COMPLETED & STORED TO DATE (Column G on G703) .... $

5. RETAINAGE:
   a. _____ % of Completed Work
      (Column D + E on G703) $
   b. _____ % of Stored Material
      (Column F on G703) $

   Total Retainage (Lines 5a + 5b or Total in Column I of G703) .... $

6. TOTAL EARNED LESS RETAINAGE .... $
   (Line 4 Less Line 5 Total)

7. LESS PREVIOUS CERTIFICATES FOR PAYMENT .... $
   (Line 6 from prior Certificate)

8. CURRENT PAYMENT DUE .... $

9. BALANCE TO FINISH, INCLUDING RETAINAGE .... $
   (Line 3 less Line 6)

CHANGE ORDER SUMMARY	ADDITIONS	DEDUCTIONS
Total changes approved in previous months by Owner	$	$
Total approved this Month	$	$
TOTALS	$	$
NET CHANGES by Change Order		$

The undersigned Contractor certifies that to the best of the Contractor's knowledge, information and belief the Work covered by this Application for Payment has been completed in accordance with the Contract Documents, that all amounts have been paid by the Contractor for Work for which previous Certificates for Payment were issued and payments received from the Owner, and that current payment shown herein is now due.

CONTRACTOR:

By: _____ Date: _____

State of:
County of:
Subscribed and sworn to before
me this _____ day of _____
Notary Public:
My Commission expires:

ARCHITECT'S CERTIFICATE FOR PAYMENT

In accordance with the Contract Documents, based on on-site observations and the data comprising this application, the Architect certifies to the Owner that to the best of the Architect's knowledge, information and belief the Work has progressed as indicated, the quality of the Work is in accordance with the Contract Documents, and the Contractor is entitled to payment of the AMOUNT CERTIFIED.

AMOUNT CERTIFIED _____ $ _____
(Attach explanation if amount certified differs from the amount applied. Initial all figures on this Application and on the Continuation Sheet that are changed to conform with the amount certified.)

ARCHITECT:

By: _____ Date: _____

This Certificate is not negotiable. The AMOUNT CERTIFIED is payable only to the Contractor named herein. Issuance, payment and acceptance of payment are without prejudice to any rights of the Owner or Contractor under this Contract

C. AGC sample documents

for the following changes in the Work:

The Owner agrees to pay for all changes in the Work performed by the Contractor under this Change Order according to the terms of the Agreement. The amount paid by the Owner shall be full compensation for all Work requested and for all effects of this document on the Work. The change, if any, in the Contract Price shall be computed according to one of the following methods.

    __ 1. No Change

    __ 2. Costs Plus a Fee   _____

    __ 3. Unit Price   _____

    __ 4. Lump Sum of $ _____

Unless Item 1 or 4 is marked, the Contractor shall submit promptly to Owner such itemized labor and material breakdowns as Owner may require for Work performed or deleted from the Agreement by this Change Order. The Contractor shall include the cost of such change in its next application for payment in a separate line item.

The change, if any, in the Contract Time resulting from the Work requested by the Change Order shall be determined according to the terms of the Agreement and allows for __ an additional __ deletion of
_____ (_____) Days.

CONTRACTOR:

....

By: _____

Title: _____

Date: _____

OWNER:

....

By: _____

Title: _____

Date: _____

2

CONTRACTOR,

PROJECT:

ARCHITECT/ENGINEER:

1. THE WORK   Contractor shall furnish construction administration and management services and use Contractor's diligent efforts to perform the Work in an expeditious manner consistent with the Contract Documents. Contractor shall provide all labor, materials, equipment and services necessary to complete the Work, as described in Exhibit A, all of which shall be provided in full accord with and reasonably inferable from the Contract Documents as being necessary to produce the indicated results.

2. CONTRACT PRICE   As full compensation for performance by Contractor of the Work, Owner shall pay Contractor the lump sum price of _____ Dollars ($_____). The lump sum price is hereinafter referred to as the Contract Price, which shall be subject to increase or decrease as provided in this Agreement.

3. EXHIBITS   The following Exhibits are incorporated by reference and made part of this Agreement:

    EXHIBIT A: The Work, _____ pages.

    EXHIBIT B: Contract Documents (Attach a complete listing by title, date and number of pages.)

    EXHIBIT C: Progress Schedule, _____ pages.

    EXHIBIT D: Alternates and Unit Prices, include dates when alternates and unit prices no longer apply, _____ pages.

    EXHIBIT __: Other, _____ pages.

4. ETHICS   The Owner and the Contractor shall perform their obligations with integrity, ensuring at a minimum that: a) Conflicts of interest shall be avoided or disclosed promptly to the other Party; and b) The Contractor and the Owner warrant that they have not and shall not pay nor receive any contingent fees or gratuities to or from the other Party, including its agents, officers and employees, subcontractors or others for whom they may be liable, to secure preferential treatment.

5. CONTRACTOR'S RESPONSIBILITIES   Contractor shall be responsible for supervision and coordination of the Work, including the construction means, methods, techniques, sequences and procedures utilized, unless the Contract Documents give other specific instructions.

    5.1 Except for permits and fees that are the responsibility of the Owner pursuant to this Agreement, Contractor shall obtain and pay for all necessary permits, licenses and renewals pertaining to the Work.

    5.2 Contractor shall pay all applicable taxes legally enacted when bids are received or negotiations concluded for the Work provided by Contractor.

    5.3 In the event that Owner elects to perform work at the Worksite directly or by others retained by Owner, Contractor and Owner shall coordinate the activities of all forces at the Worksite and shall agree upon fair and reasonable schedules and operational procedures for Worksite activities. Owner shall require each separate contractor to cooperate with Contractor and assist with the coordination

2

of activities and the review of construction schedules and operations. The Contract Price and Contract Time shall be equitably adjusted, as mutually agreed by the Parties, for changes made necessary by the coordination of construction activities, and the construction schedule shall be revised accordingly.

5.4 In order to facilitate its responsibilities for completion of the Work in accordance with and as reasonably inferable from the Contract Documents, prior to commencing the Work, Contractor shall examine and compare the drawings and specifications with information furnished by Owner pursuant to Paragraph 6.2; relevant field measurements made by Contractor; and any visible conditions at the Worksite affecting the Work.

5.5 WARRANTY

5.5.1 The Work shall be executed in accordance with the Contract Documents in a workmanlike manner. Contractor warrants that all materials and equipment shall be new unless otherwise specified, of good quality, in conformance with the Contract Documents, and free from defective workmanship and materials. Contractor further warrants that the Work will be free from material defects not intrinsic in the design or materials required in the Contract Documents. Contractor's warranty does not include remedies for defects or damages caused by normal wear and tear during normal usage, use for a purpose for which the Project was not intended, improper or insufficient maintenance, modifications performed by Owner or others retained by Owner, or abuse.

5.5.2 If, prior to the Date of Substantial Completion and within one year after the date of Substantial Completion of the Work, any portion of the Work is found to be not in conformance with the Contract Documents ("Defective Work"), Owner shall promptly notify Contractor in writing. Unless Owner provides written acceptance of the condition, Contractor shall promptly correct the Defective Work at its own cost and time and bear the expense of additional services required for correction of any Defective Work for which it is responsible.

5.6 SAFETY Contractor shall have overall responsibility for safety precautions and programs in the performance of the Work, except that Contractor's subcontractors shall also be responsible for the safety of persons or property in the performance of their work; and for compliance with the provisions of applicable laws and regulations. Contractor shall seek to avoid injury, loss or damage to persons or property by taking reasonable steps to protect its employees and other persons at the Worksite; materials and equipment stored at on-site or off-site locations for use in the Work; and property located at the site and adjacent to Work areas, whether or not the property is part of the Work.

5.7 HAZARDOUS MATERIALS A Hazardous Material is any substance or material identified now or in the future as hazardous under any federal, state or local law or regulation, or any other substance or material which may be considered hazardous or otherwise subject to statutory or regulatory requirement governing handling, disposal and/or clean-up. Contractor shall not be obligated to commence or continue work until any Hazardous Material discovered at the Worksite has been removed, or rendered or determined to be harmless by Owner as certified by an independent testing laboratory and approved by the appropriate government agency. If Contractor incurs additional costs and/or is delayed due to the presence or remediation of Hazardous Material, Contractor shall be entitled to an equitable adjustment in the Contract Price and/or the Contract Time.

5.8 MATERIALS BROUGHT TO THE WORKSITE Contractor shall be responsible for the proper delivery, handling, application, storage, removal and disposal of all materials and substances brought to the Worksite by Contractor in accordance with the Contract Documents and used or

3

consumed in the performance of the Work.

5.9 SUBMITTALS Contractor shall submit to Owner and, if directed, to its Architect/Engineer for review and approval all shop drawings, samples, product data and similar submittals required by the Contract Documents. Submittals may be submitted in electronic form if required in accordance with ConsensusDOCS 200.2 and Paragraph 6.4. Contractor shall be responsible to Owner for the accuracy and conformity of its submittals to the Contract Documents. Contractor shall prepare and deliver its submittals to Owner in a manner consistent with the Schedule of the Work and in such time and sequence so as not to delay the performance of the Work or the work of Owner and others retained by Owner. When Contractor delivers its submittals to Owner, Contractor shall identify in writing for each submittal all changes, deviations or substitutions from the requirements of the Contract Documents. The approval of any Contractor submittal shall not be deemed to authorize deviations, substitutions or changes in the requirements of the Contract Documents unless express written approval is obtained from Owner specifically authorizing such deviation, substitution or change. Further, Owner shall not make any change, deviation or substitution through the submittal process without specifically identifying and authorizing such deviation to Contractor. Owner shall be responsible for review and approval of submittals with reasonable promptness to avoid causing delay. Contractor shall perform all Work strictly in accordance with approved submittals. Owner's approval does not relieve Contractor from responsibility for Defective Work resulting from errors or omissions of any kind on the approved shop drawings.

5.10 SITE CONDITIONS If the conditions at the Worksite are (a) subsurface or other physical conditions which are materially different from those indicated in the Contract Documents, or (b) unusual or unknown physical conditions which are materially different from conditions ordinarily encountered and generally recognized as inherent in Work provided for in the Contract Documents, Contractor shall stop Work and give immediate written notice of the condition to Owner and the Architect/Engineer. Contractor shall not be required to perform any work relating to the unknown condition without the written mutual agreement of the Parties. Any change in the Contract Price and/or Contract Time as a result of the unknown condition shall be made by Change Order.

5.11 CUTTING, FITTING AND PATCHING Contractor shall perform cutting, fitting and patching necessary to coordinate the various parts of the Work and to prepare its Work for the work of Owner or others retained by Owner.

5.12 CLEANING UP Contractor shall regularly remove debris and waste materials at the Worksite resulting from the Work. Prior to discontinuing Work in an area, Contractor shall clean the area and remove all rubbish and its construction equipment, tools, machinery, waste and surplus materials. Contractor shall minimize and confine dust and debris resulting from construction activities. At the completion of the Work, Contractor shall remove from the Worksite all construction equipment, tools, surplus materials, waste materials and debris.

6. OWNER'S RESPONSIBILITIES Any information or services to be provided by Owner shall be provided in a timely manner so as not to delay the Work.

6.1 FINANCIAL INFORMATION Prior to commencement of the Work and thereafter at the written request of Contractor, Owner shall provide Contractor with evidence of Project financing. Evidence of such financing shall be a condition precedent to Contractor's commencing or continuing the Work. Contractor shall be notified prior to any material change in Project financing.

6.2 WORKSITE INFORMATION Owner shall provide at Owner's expense and with reasonable promptness the following, which Contractor shall be entitled to rely upon for its accuracy and completeness:

4

IMPORTANT: A vertical line in the margin indicates a change has been made to the original text. Prior to signing, recipients may wish to request from the party producing the document a "redlined" version indicating changes to the original text. Consultation with legal and insurance counsel and careful review of the entire document are strongly encouraged.
ConsensusDOCS 205 • STANDARD SHORT FORM AGREEMENT BETWEEN OWNER AND CONTRACTOR (Where the Contract Price Is a Lump Sum)
Copyright © 2007, ConsensusDOCS LLC; revised May 2009. YOU ARE ALLOWED TO USE THIS DOCUMENT FOR ONE CONTRACT ONLY. YOU MAY MAKE 9 COPIES OF THE COMPLETED DOCUMENT FOR DISTRIBUTION TO THE CONTRACT'S PARTIES. ANY OTHER USES, INCLUDING COPYING THE FORM DOCUMENT, ARE STRICTLY PROHIBITED.

6.2.1 information describing the physical characteristics of the site, including surveys, site evaluations, legal descriptions, data or drawings depicting existing conditions, subsurface and environmental studies, reports and investigations;

6.2.2 tests, inspections and other reports dealing with environmental matters, hazardous material and other existing conditions, including structural, mechanical and chemical tests, required by the Contract Documents or by law; and

6.2.3 any other information or services requested in writing by Contractor that are relevant to Contractor's performance of the Work and under Owner's control.

The information required by this Paragraph shall be provided in reasonable detail. Legal descriptions shall include easements, title restrictions, boundaries, and zoning restrictions. Worksite descriptions shall include existing buildings and other construction and all other pertinent site conditions. Adjacent property descriptions shall include structures, streets, sidewalks, allies, and other features relevant to the Work. Utility details shall include available services, lines at the Worksite and adjacent thereto and connection points. The information shall include public and private information, subsurface information, grades, contours, and elevations, drainage data, exact locations and dimensions, and benchmarks that can be used by Contractor in laying out the Work.

6.3 BUILDING PERMIT, FEES AND APPROVALS Except for those required of Contractor pursuant to this Agreement, Owner shall secure and pay for all other permits, approvals, easements, assessments and fees required for the development, construction, use or occupancy of permanent structures or for permanent changes in existing facilities, including the building permit.

6.4 ELECTRONIC DOCUMENTS If the Owner requires that the Owner, Architect/Engineer and Contractor exchange documents and data in electronic or digital form prior to any such exchange, the Owner, Architect/Engineer and Contractor shall agree on a written protocol governing all exchanges in ConsensusDOCS 200.2 or a separate Agreement.

7. SUBCONTRACTS Work not performed by Contractor with its own forces shall be performed by subcontractors. Contractor agrees to bind every subcontractor and material supplier (and require every subcontractor to so bind its subcontractors and material suppliers) to all the provisions of this Agreement and the Contract Documents as they apply to the subcontractor's and material supplier's portions of the Work.

8. CONTRACT TIME

8.1 DATE OF COMMENCEMENT The Date of Commencement is the date of this Agreement as first written on page one of this Agreement, unless otherwise set forth below: (Insert here any special provisions concerning notices to proceed and the Date of Commencement.)

8.2 TIME Substantial Completion of the Work shall be achieved in _____ (_____) Days from the Date of Commencement. Unless otherwise specified in the Certificate of Substantial Completion, the Work shall be finally complete within _____ (_____) Days after the date of Substantial Completion, subject to adjustments as provided for in the Contract Documents. Time limits stated above are of the essence of the Agreement.

9. SCHEDULE OF THE WORK Before submitting the first application for payment, Contractor shall submit, for review by the Architect/Engineer and approval by Owner, a Schedule of the Work that shall show the dates on which Contractor plans to begin and to complete various parts of the Work, including dates on which information and approvals are required from Owner.

10. DELAYS AND EXTENSIONS OF TIME

10.1   If the Contractor is delayed at any time in the commencement or progress of the Work by any cause beyond the control of the Contractor, the Contractor shall be entitled to an equitable extension of the Contract Time. Examples of causes beyond the control of the Contractor include, but are not limited to, the following: acts or omissions of the Owner, the Architect/Engineer or Others; changes in the Work or the sequencing of the Work ordered by the Owner, or arising from decisions of the Owner that impact the time of performance of the Work; transportation delays not reasonably foreseeable; labor disputes not involving the Contractor; general labor disputes impacting the Project but not specifically related to the Worksite; fire; terrorism, epidemics, adverse governmental actions, unavoidable accidents or circumstances; adverse weather conditions not reasonably anticipated; encountering Hazardous Materials; concealed or unknown conditions; delay authorized by the Owner pending dispute resolution. The Contractor shall process any requests for equitable extensions of Contract Time in accordance with the provisions of Paragraph 12.

10.2   In addition, if the Contractor incurs additional costs as a result of a delay that is caused by acts or omissions of the Owner, the Architect/Engineer or Others, changes in the Work or the sequencing of the Work ordered by the Owner, or arising from decisions of the Owner that impact the time of performance of the Work, encountering Hazardous Materials, or concealed or unknown conditions, delay authorized by the Owner pending dispute resolution, the Contractor shall be entitled to an equitable adjustment in the Contract Price subject to Paragraph 12.

10.3   In the event delays to the Work are encountered for any reason, Contractor shall provide prompt written notice to Owner of the cause of such delays after Contractor first recognizes the delay. Owner and Contractor agree to undertake reasonable steps to mitigate the effect of such delays.

10.4   NOTICE OF DELAY CLAIMS   If Contractor requests an equitable extension of Contract Time and/or an equitable adjustment in Contract Price as a result of a delay, Contractor shall give Owner written notice of the claim. If Contractor causes delay in the completion of the Work, Owner shall be entitled to recover its additional costs, subject to the mutual waiver of consequential damages herein.

11.   ALLOWANCES   All allowances stated in the Contract Documents shall be included in the Contract Price. While Owner may direct the amounts of, and particular material suppliers or subcontractors for, specific allowance items, if Contractor reasonably objects to a material supplier or subcontractor, it shall not be required to contract with them. Owner shall select allowance items in a timely manner so as not to delay the Work. Allowances shall include the costs of materials and equipment delivered to the Worksite less applicable trade discounts and including requisite taxes, unloading and handling at the Worksite, and labor and installation, unless specifically stated otherwise. Contractor's overhead and profit for the allowances shall be included in the Contract Price, but not in the allowances. The Contract Price shall be adjusted by Change Order to reflect the actual costs when they are greater than or less than the allowances.

12.   CHANGES

12.1   Contractor may request and/or Owner may order changes in the Work or the timing or sequencing of performance of the Work that impacts the Contract Price or the Contract Time. All such changes in the Work that affect Contract Time or Contract Price shall be formalized in a Change Order.

12.2   Owner and Contractor shall negotiate in good faith an appropriate adjustment to the Contract Price and/or the Contract Time and shall conclude these negotiations as expeditiously as possible. Acceptance of the Change Order and any adjustment in the Contract Price and/or Contract Time

6

shall not be unreasonably withheld.

12.3   COST OR CREDIT DETERMINATION

12.3.1   An increase or decrease in the Contract Price and/or the Contract Time resulting from a change in the Work shall be determined by one or more of the following methods:

12.3.1.1   unit prices set forth in this Agreement or as subsequently agreed;

12.3.1.2   a mutually accepted, itemized lump sum;

12.3.1.3   costs calculated on a basis agreed upon by the Owner and Contractor plus _____% overhead and _____% profit; or

12.3.1.4   by the method provided below:

12.4   UNIT PRICES   If unit prices are included in the Contract Documents or are subsequently agreed to by the Parties, but the character or quantity of such unit price items as originally contemplated is so different in a proposed Change Order that the original unit prices will cause substantial inequity to Owner or Contractor, such unit prices shall be equitably adjusted.

12.5   PERFORMANCE OF CHANGED WORK   Contractor shall not be obligated to perform Changed Work until a Change Order has been executed by Owner and Contractor.

13.   PAYMENT

13.1   SCHEDULE OF VALUES   Within twenty-one (21) Days from the date of execution of this Agreement, Contractor shall prepare and submit to Owner, and if directed, its Architect/Engineer, a schedule of values apportioned to the various divisions or phases of the Work. Each line item contained in the schedule of values shall be assigned a monetary price such that the total of all items shall equal the Contract Price.

13.2   PROGRESS PAYMENTS   Contractor shall submit to Owner and, if directed, its Architect/Engineer a monthly application for payment no later than the _____ Day of the calendar month for the preceding thirty (30) Days. Contractor's applications for payment shall be itemized and supported by Contractor's schedule of values and any other substantiating data as required by this Agreement. Payment applications shall include payment requests on account of properly authorized Change Orders. Owner shall pay the amount otherwise due on any payment application, less any amounts as set forth below, no later than twenty (20) Days after Contractor has submitted a complete and accurate payment application. Owner may deduct, from any progress payment, such amounts as may be retained pursuant to Paragraph 13.3.

13.3   RETAINAGE   From each progress payment made prior to Substantial Completion Owner may retain _____ percent (_____%) of the amount otherwise due after deduction of any amounts as provided in Paragraph 13.4 of this Agreement.

13.4   ADJUSTMENT OF CONTRACTOR'S PAYMENT APPLICATION   Owner may adjust or reject a payment application or nullify a previously approved payment application, in whole or in part, as may reasonably be necessary to protect Owner from loss or damage based upon the following, to the extent that Contractor is responsible for such under this Agreement:

13.4.1   Contractor's repeated failure to perform the Work as required by the Contract Documents;

7

IMPORTANT: A vertical line in the margin indicates a change has been made to the original text. Prior to signing, recipients may wish to request from the party producing the document a "redlined" version indicating changes to the original text. Consultation with legal and insurance counsel and careful review of the entire document are strongly encouraged.
ConsensusDOCS 205 • STANDARD SHORT FORM AGREEMENT BETWEEN OWNER AND CONTRACTOR (Where the Contract Price Is a Lump Sum) Copyright © 2007, ConsensusDOCS LLC; revised May 2009. YOU ARE ALLOWED TO USE THIS DOCUMENT FOR ONE CONTRACT ONLY. YOU MAY MAKE 9 COPIES OF THE COMPLETED DOCUMENT FOR DISTRIBUTION TO THE CONTRACT'S PARTIES. ANY OTHER USES, INCLUDING COPYING THE FORM DOCUMENT, ARE STRICTLY PROHIBITED.

13.4.2 loss or damage arising out of or relating to this Agreement and caused by Contractor to Owner or to others retained by Owner to whom the Owner may be liable;

13.4.3 Contractor's failure to properly pay Subcontractors for labor, materials or equipment furnished in connection with the Work following receipt of such payment from Owner;

13.4.4 Defective Work not corrected in a timely fashion;

13.4.5 reasonable evidence of delay in performance of the Work such that the Work will not be completed within the Contract Time, and

13.4.6 reasonable evidence demonstrating that the unpaid balance of the Contract Price is insufficient to fund the cost to complete the Work.

13.4.7 third party claims involving the Contractor or reasonable evidence demonstrating that third party claims are likely to be filed unless and until the Contractor furnishes the Owner with adequate security in the form of a surety bond, letter of credit or other collateral or commitment which are sufficient to discharge such claims if established.

No later than seven (7) Days after receipt of an application for payment, Owner shall give written notice to Contractor disapproving or nullifying it or a portion of it, specifying the reasons for the disapproval or nullification. When the above reasons for disapproving or nullifying an application for payment are removed, payment shall be made for the amounts previously withheld.

13.5 PAYMENT DELAY If for any reason not the fault of Contractor, Contractor does not receive a progress payment from Owner within seven (7) Days after the time such payment is due, Contractor, upon giving seven (7) Days' written notice to Owner, and without prejudice to and in addition to any other legal remedies, may stop Work until payment of the full amount owing to Contractor has been received. The Contract Price and Contract Time shall be equitably adjusted by Change Order for reasonable cost and delay resulting from shutdown, delay and start-up.

13.6 SUBSTANTIAL COMPLETION When Substantial Completion of the Work or a designated portion thereof is achieved, Contractor shall prepare a Certificate of Substantial Completion that shall establish the date of Substantial Completion, and the respective responsibilities of Owner and Contractor for interim items such as security, maintenance, utilities, insurance and damage to the Work, and fixing the time for completion of all items on the list accompanying the Certificate. The Certificate of Substantial Completion shall be submitted by Contractor to Owner for written acceptance of responsibilities assigned in the Certificate. Unless otherwise provided in the Certificate of Substantial Completion, warranties required by the Contract Documents shall commence on the date of Substantial Completion of the Work or a designated portion.

13.6.1 Upon acceptance by Owner of the Certificate of Substantial Completion, Owner shall pay to Contractor the remaining retainage held by Owner for the Work described in the Certificate of Substantial Completion less a sum equal to two hundred percent (200%) of the estimated cost of completing or correcting remaining items on that part of the Work, as agreed to by Owner and Contractor as necessary to achieve final completion. Uncompleted items shall be completed by Contractor in a mutually agreed time frame. Owner shall pay Contractor monthly the amount retained for unfinished items as each item is completed.

13.7 FINAL COMPLETION When final completion has been achieved, Contractor shall prepare for Owner's acceptance a final application for payment stating that to the best of Contractor's knowledge, and based on Owner's inspections, the Work has reached final completion in accordance with the Contract Documents.

8

IMPORTANT: A vertical line in the margin indicates a change has been made to the original text. Prior to signing, recipients may wish to request from the party producing the document a "redlined" version indicating changes to the original text. Consultation with legal and insurance counsel and careful review of the entire document are strongly encouraged.
ConsensusDOCS 205 • STANDARD SHORT FORM AGREEMENT BETWEEN OWNER AND CONTRACTOR (Where the Contract Price Is a Lump Sum) Copyright © 2007, ConsensusDOCS LLC; revised May 2009. YOU ARE ALLOWED TO USE THIS DOCUMENT FOR ONE CONTRACT ONLY. YOU MAY MAKE 9 COPIES OF THE COMPLETED DOCUMENT FOR DISTRIBUTION TO THE CONTRACT'S PARTIES. ANY OTHER USES, INCLUDING COPYING THE FORM DOCUMENT, ARE STRICTLY PROHIBITED.

13.7.1 Final payment of the balance of the Contract Price shall be made to Contractor within twenty (20) Days after Contractor has submitted to the Owner a complete and accurate application for final payment and the following submissions:

13.7.1.1 an affidavit declaring any indebtedness connected with the Work, e.g. payrolls or invoices for materials or equipment, to have been paid, satisfied or to be paid with the proceeds of final payment, so as not to encumber Owner's property;

13.7.1.2 as-built drawings, manuals, copies of warranties and all other close-out documents required by the Contract Documents;

13.7.1.3 release of any liens, conditioned on final payment being received;

13.7.1.4 consent of any surety, if applicable; and

13.7.1.5 a report of any accidents or injuries experienced by Contractor or its Subcontractors at the Worksite.

13.8 Claims not reserved in writing with the making of final payment shall be waived except for claims relating to liens or similar encumbrances, warranties, Defective Work and latent defects.

13.9 LATE PAYMENT Payments due but unpaid shall bear interest from the date payment is due at the statutory rate at the place of the Project.

14. INDEMNITY

14.1 To the fullest extent permitted by law, Contractor shall indemnify and hold harmless the Owner, Owner's officers, directors, members, consultants, agents and employees and the Architect/Engineer (the Indemnitees) from all claims for bodily injury and property damage, other than to the Work itself and other property insured under Paragraph 15.3, including reasonable attorneys' fees, costs and expenses, that may arise from the performance of the Work but only to the extent caused by the negligent acts or omissions of the Contractor, subcontractors or anyone employed directly or indirectly by any of them or by anyone for whose acts any of them may be liable. The Contractor shall be entitled to reimbursement of any defense costs paid above Contractor's percentage of liability for the underlying claim to the extent provided under Paragraph 14.2.

14.2 To the fullest extent permitted by law, Owner shall indemnify and hold harmless Contractor, its officers, directors or members, subcontractors or anyone employed directly or indirectly by any of them or anyone for whose acts any of them may be liable from all claims for bodily injury and property damage, other than property insured under Paragraph 15.3, including reasonable attorneys' fees, costs and expenses, that may arise from the performance of work by Owner, Architect/Engineer or others retained by Owner, but only to the extent caused by the negligent acts or omissions caused by the Owner, Architect/Engineer or others retained by Owner. The Owner shall be entitled to reimbursement of any defense costs paid above Owner's percentage of liability for the underlying claim to the extent provided under Paragraph 14.1.

14.3 NO LIMITATION ON LIABILITY In any and all claims against the Indemnitees by any employee of the Contractor, anyone directly or indirectly employed by the Contractor or anyone for whose acts the Contractor may be liable, the indemnification obligation shall not be limited in any way by any limitation on the amount or type of damages, compensation or benefits payable by or for the Contractor under Workers' Compensation acts, disability benefit acts or other employment benefit acts.

9

15. INSURANCE

15.1 Prior to the start of the Work, the Contractor shall procure and maintain in force Workers Compensation Insurance, Employers' Liability Insurance, Business Automobile Liability Insurance, and Commercial General Liability Insurance (CGL). The CGL policy shall include coverage for liability arising from premises, operations, independent contractors, products-completed operations, personal injury and advertising injury, contractual liability, and broad form property damage. If requested, the Contractor shall provide the Owner with certificates of the insurance coverage required. The Contractor's Employers' Liability, Business Automobile Liability, and Commercial General Liability policies, as required in this Paragraph 2, shall be written with at least the following limits of liability:

15.1.1   Employers' Liability Insurance

a. $_____

Bodily Injury by Accident

Each Accident

b. $_____

Bodily Injury by Disease

Policy Limit

c. $_____

Bodily Injury by Disease

Each Employee

15.1.2   Business Automobile Liability Insurance

a. $_____

Each Accident

15.1.3   Commercial General Liability Insurance

a. $_____

Each Occurrence

b. $_____

General Aggregate

c. $_____

Products/Completed

Operations Aggregate

d. $_____

Personal and Advertising

Injury Limit

10

**NOT FOR FURTHER REPRODUCTION
TO ORDER DOCUMENT, VISIT WWW.CONSENSUSDOCS.ORG**

15.2 Employers' Liability, Business Automobile Liability and Commercial General Liability coverage required under Paragraph 1 may be arranged under a single policy for the full limits required or by a combination of underlying policies with the balance provided by Excess or Umbrella Liability policies. The Contractor shall maintain in effect all insurance coverage required under Paragraph 15.1 with insurance companies lawfully authorized to do business in the jurisdiction in which the Project is located. If the Contractor fails to obtain or maintain any insurance coverage required under this Agreement, the Owner may purchase such coverage and charge the expense to the Contractor, or terminate this Agreement. The policies of insurance required under Subparagraph 15.1 shall contain a provision that the coverage afforded under the policies shall not be cancelled or allowed to expire until at least thirty (30) Days' prior written notice has been given to the Owner. The Contractor shall maintain completed operations liability insurance for one year after acceptance of the Work, Substantial Completion of the Project, or to the time required by the Contract Documents, whichever is longer. Prior to commencement of the Work, Contractor shall furnish the Owner with certificates evidencing the required coverage.

15.3 PROPERTY INSURANCE Before the start of Work, the Owner shall obtain and maintain Builder's Risk Policy upon the entire Project for the full cost of replacement at the time of loss. This insurance shall also name the Contractor, Subcontractors, Sub-subcontractors, Material Suppliers and Architect/Engineer as named insureds. This insurance shall be written as a Builder's Risk Policy or equivalent form to cover all risks of physical loss except those specifically excluded by the policy. The Owner shall be solely responsible for any deductible amounts or coinsurance penalties. This policy shall provide for a waiver of subrogation in favor of the Contractor, Subcontractors, Sub-subcontractors, Material Suppliers and Architect/Engineer. This insurance shall remain in effect until final payment has been made or until no person or entity other than the Owner has an insurable interest in the property to be covered by this insurance, whichever is sooner. Partial occupancy or use of the Work shall not commence until the Owner has secured the consent of the insurance company or companies providing the coverage required in this Paragraph. Prior to commencement of the Work, the Owner shall provide a copy of the property policy or policies obtained in compliance with this Paragraph.

15.3.1 If the Owner does not intend to purchase the property insurance required by this Agreement, including all of the coverages and deductibles described herein, the Owner shall give written notice to the Contractor and the Architect/Engineer before the Work is commenced. The Contractor may then provide insurance to protect its interests and the interests of the Subcontractors and Sub-subcontractors, including the coverage of deductibles. The cost of this insurance shall be charged to the Owner in a Change Order. The Owner shall be responsible for all of Contractor's costs reasonably attributed to the Owner's failure or neglect in purchasing or maintaining the coverage described above.

15.3.2 Owner and Contractor waive all rights against each other and their respective employees, agents, contractors, subcontractors and sub-subcontractors, and the Architect/Engineer for damages caused by risks covered by the property insurance except such rights as they may have to the proceeds of the insurance and such rights as the Contractor may have for the failure of the Owner to obtain and maintain property insurance in compliance with Subparagraph 15.2.

15.3.3 To the extent of the limits of Contractor's Commercial General Liability Insurance specified in Paragraph 15.1 or _____ Dollars ($_____) whichever is more, the Contractor shall indemnify and hold harmless the Owner against any and all liability, claims, demands, damages, losses and expenses, including attorneys' fees, in connection with or

11

arising out of any damage or alleged damage to any of Owner's existing adjacent property that may arise from the performance of the Work, to the extent caused by the negligent acts or omissions of the Contractor, Subcontractor or anyone employed directly or indirectly by any of them or by anyone for whose acts any of them may be liable.

15.4 OWNER'S INSURANCE The Owner may procure and maintain insurance against loss of use of the Owner's property caused by fire or other casualty loss. The Owner shall either self-insure or obtain and maintain its own liability insurance for protection against claims arising out of the performance of this Agreement, including without limitation, loss of use and claims, losses and expenses arising out of the Owner's errors or omissions.

15.5 ADDITIONAL LIABILITY COVERAGE Owner _____ shall/_____ shall not (indicate one) require Contractor to purchase and maintain liability coverage, primary to Owner's coverage under Subparagraph 15.4.

15.5.1 If required by Subparagraph 15.5. the additional liability coverage required of the Contractor shall be: [Designate Required Coverage]

_____ .1 ADDITIONAL INSURED. Owner shall be named as an additional insured on Contractor's Commercial General Liability Insurance specified, for operations and completed operations, but only with respect to liability for bodily injury, property damage or personal and advertising injury to the extent caused by the negligent acts or omissions of Contractor, or those acting on Contractor's behalf, in the performance of Contractor's Work for Owner at the Worksite.

_____ .2 OCP. Contractor shall provide an Owners' and Contractors' Protective Liability Insurance ("OCP") policy with limits equal to the limits on Commercial General Liability Insurance specified, or limits as otherwise required by Owner.

Any documented additional cost in the form of a surcharge associated with procuring the additional liability coverage in accordance with this Subparagraph shall be paid by the Owner directly or the costs may be reimbursed by Owner to Contractor by increasing the Contract Price to correspond to the actual cost required to purchase and maintain the additional liability coverage. Prior to commencement of the Work, Contractor shall obtain and furnish to the Owner a certificate evidencing that the additional liability coverages have been procured.

16. BONDS Performance and Payment Bonds ___ are/___ are not required of the Contractor. Such bonds shall be issued by a surety admitted in the State in which the Project is located and must be acceptable to Owner. Owner's acceptance shall not be withheld without reasonable cause. The penal sum of the Payment Bond shall equal the penal sum of the Performance Bond.

17. LIMITED MUTUAL WAIVER OF CONSEQUENTIAL DAMAGES Excluding losses covered by insurance required by the Contract Documents, the Owner and Contractor agree to waive all claims against each other for any consequential damages that may arise out of or relate to this Agreement, except for those specific items of damages excluded from this waiver as mutually agreed upon by the Parties and identified below. The Owner agrees to waive damages including but not limited to the Owner's loss of use of the Project, any rental expenses incurred, loss of income, profit or financing related to the Project, as well as the loss of business, loss of financing, principal office overhead and expenses, loss of profits not related to this Project, loss of reputation, or insolvency. The Contractor agrees to waive damages including but not limited to loss of business, loss of financing, principal office overhead and expenses, loss of profits not related to this Project, loss of bonding capacity, loss of reputation, or insolvency. The provisions of this Paragraph shall also apply to the termination of this Agreement and shall survive such termination.

The following items of damages are excluded from this mutual waiver:

17.1 The provisions of this Paragraph shall also apply to the termination of this Agreement and shall survive such termination. The Owner and the Contractor shall require similar waivers in contracts with Subcontractors and Others retained for the project.

18. RISK OF LOSS Except to the extent a loss is covered by applicable insurance, risk of loss and/or damage to the Work shall be upon the Contractor until the Date of Substantial Completion, unless otherwise agreed to by the Parties.

19. NOTICE TO CURE AND TERMINATION

19.1 NOTICE TO CURE A DEFAULT If Contractor persistently refuses or fails to supply enough qualified workers, proper materials, and/or equipment to maintain the approved Schedule of the Work in accordance with Article 9, or fails to make prompt payment to its workers, subcontractors or material suppliers, disregards laws, ordinances, rules, regulations or orders of any public authority having jurisdiction, or is otherwise guilty of a material breach of a provision of this Agreement, Contractor may be deemed in default. If Contractor fails within seven (7) business Days after written notification to commence and continue satisfactory correction of such default with diligence and promptness, then Owner shall give the Contractor a second written notice to correct the default within a three (3) business Day period. If the Contractor fails to promptly commence and continue satisfactory correction of the default following receipt of such second notice, the Owner, without prejudice to any other rights or remedies, shall have the right to take reasonable steps it deems necessary to correct deficiencies and charge the cost to Contractor who shall be liable for such payments including reasonable overhead, profit and attorneys' fees.

19.2 TERMINATION BY OWNER If, within seven (7) Days of receipt of a notice to cure pursuant to Paragraph 19.1, Contractor fails to commence and satisfactorily continue correction of the default set forth in the notice to cure, Owner may notify Contractor that it intends to terminate this Agreement for default absent appropriate corrective action within fourteen (14) additional Days. After the expiration of the additional fourteen (14) Day period, Owner may terminate this Agreement by written notice absent appropriate corrective action. Termination for default is in addition to any other remedies available to Owner under Paragraph 19.1. If Owner's costs arising out of Contractor's failure to cure, including the cost of completing the Work and reasonable attorney fees, exceed the unpaid Contract Price, Contractor shall be liable to Owner for such excess costs. If Owner's costs are less than the unpaid Contract Price, Owner shall pay the difference to Contractor. In the event Owner exercises its rights under this Paragraph, upon the request of Contractor, Owner shall furnish to Contractor a detailed accounting of the costs incurred by Owner.

19.2.1 The Owner shall make reasonable efforts to mitigate damages arising from the Contractor default and shall promptly invoice the Contractor for all amounts due pursuant to Paragraphs 19.1 and 19.2.

19.3 TERMINATION BY CONTRACTOR Upon seven (7) Days' written notice to Owner, Contractor may terminate this Agreement if the Work has been stopped for a thirty (30) Day period through no fault of Contractor for any of the following reasons:

.1 under court order or order of other governmental authorities having jurisdiction;

.2 as a result of the declaration of a national emergency or other governmental act during

13

which, through no act or fault of Contractor, materials are not available; or

19.4 In addition, upon seven (7) Days' written notice to Owner, Contractor may terminate the Agreement if Owner:

.1 fails to furnish reasonable evidence that sufficient funds are available and committed for the entire cost of the Project in accordance with Paragraph 6.1, or

.2 assigns this Agreement over Contractor's reasonable objection, or

.3 fails to pay Contractor in accordance with this Agreement and Contractor has complied with the notice provisions of Paragraph 13.5, or

.4 otherwise materially breaches this Agreement.

19.5 Upon termination by Contractor pursuant to this Agreement, Contractor shall be entitled to recover from Owner payment for all Work executed and for any proven loss, cost or expense in connection with the Work, including all demobilization costs plus reasonable overhead and profit.

19.6 OBLIGATIONS ARISING BEFORE TERMINATION Even after termination the provisions of this Agreement still apply to any Work performed, payments made, events occurring, costs charged or incurred or obligations arising before the termination date.

20. CLAIMS AND DISPUTE RESOLUTION

20.1 CLAIMS FOR ADDITIONAL COST OR TIME Except as provided in Paragraphs 10.3 and 10.4 for any claim for an increase in the Contract Price and/or the Contract Time, Contractor shall give Owner written notice of the claim within fourteen (14) Days after the occurrence giving rise to the claim or within fourteen (14) Days after Contractor first recognizes the condition giving rise to the claim, whichever is later. Except in an emergency, notice shall be given before proceeding with the Work. Any change in the Contract Price and/or the Contract Time resulting from such claim shall be authorized by Change Order.

20.2 WORK CONTINUANCE AND PAYMENT Unless otherwise agreed in writing, Contractor shall continue the Work and maintain the Schedule of the Work during any dispute resolution proceedings. If Contractor continues to perform, Owner shall continue to make payments in accordance with the Agreement.

20.3 INITIAL DISPUTE RESOLUTION PROCESSES If a dispute arises out of or relates to this Agreement or its breach, the Parties shall endeavor to settle the dispute first through direct discussions. If the dispute cannot be settled through direct discussions, the Parties shall endeavor to settle the dispute by mediation under the current Construction Industry Mediation Rules of the American Arbitration Association before recourse to any binding dispute resolution procedures.

20.4 BINDING DISPUTE RESOLUTION If the matter is unresolved after submission of the matter to mediation, the Parties shall submit the matter to the binding dispute resolution procedure designated herein (Designate only one):

_____ Arbitration using the current Construction Industry Arbitration Rules of the American Arbitration Association or the Parties may mutually agree to select another set of arbitration rules. The administration of the arbitration shall be as mutually agreed by the Parties.

_____ Litigation in either the state or federal court having jurisdiction of the matter in the location of the Project.

20.5 COST OF DISPUTE RESOLUTION The costs of any binding dispute resolution procedures shall be borne by the non-prevailing Party, as determined by the adjudicator of the dispute.

20.6 VENUE The venue of any binding dispute resolution procedure shall be the location of the Project, unless the Parties agree on a mutually convenient location.

21. ASSIGNMENT Neither Owner nor Contractor shall assign its interest in this Agreement without the written consent of the other except as to the assignment of proceeds. The terms and conditions of this Agreement shall be binding upon both Parties, their partners, successors, assigns and legal representatives. Neither Party to this Agreement shall assign the Agreement as a whole without written consent of the other.

22. GOVERNING LAW This Agreement shall be governed by the law in effect at the location of the Project.

23. JOINT DRAFTING The Parties expressly agree that this Agreement was jointly drafted, and that they both had opportunity to negotiate terms and to obtain assistance of counsel in reviewing terms prior to execution. This Agreement shall be construed neither against nor in favor of either Party, but shall be construed in a neutral manner.

OWNER: _____

BY: ....

PRINT NAME _____

PRINT TITLE _____

ATTEST: ....

CONTRACTOR: _____

BY: ....

PRINT NAME _____

PRINT TITLE _____

ATTEST: ....

15

Architect/Engineer: _____

Project or Designated Area Shall Include:

The Work under this Agreement has been reviewed and found to be substantially complete. The Date of Substantial Completion is hereby established as _____, which is also the date of commencement of warranties and guarantees required by the Contract Documents.

A list of items to be completed or corrected is appended hereto. Corrections or changes called for in this list will be made within _____ Days from the date of this Certificate. Signing of this Certificate of Substantial Completion by the Owner in no way alters the responsibility of the Contractor to complete all the Work in accordance with the Contract Documents, including untested or deferred Work.

The Contractor and Owner respectively, shall be responsible for security, maintenance, utilities, insurance and damage to the Work as follows:

The Owner accepts the Work or designated portion thereof as substantially complete and will assume full possession thereof at _____ (time) on _____ (date).

Contractor: ....

By: _____

Date: _____

Owner: ....

By: _____

Authorized Representative

Date: _____

2

Architect/Engineer: _____

Project or Designated Area Shall Include:

The Work under this Agreement has been reviewed and found to be complete in accordance with the Contract Documents. The Date of Final Completion is hereby established as _____. Signing of this Certificate of Final Completion by the Owner in no way alters the responsibility of the Contractor to complete all the work in accordance with the Contract Documents.

The Owner accepts the Work as complete and will assume full possession thereof at _____ (time) on _____ (date).

Contractor: ....

By: _____

Date: _____

Owner: ....

By: _____

Authorized Representative

Date: _____

Contractor and Subcontractor, for the following change(s) within the scope of the Subcontract Work:

The Contractor agrees to pay for all changes in the Subcontract Work performed by the Subcontractor under this Subcontract Change Order according to the terms of the Subcontract Agreement. The amount paid by the Contractor shall be full compensation for all work requested and for all effects of this change in the Subcontract Work. The change, if any, in the Subcontract Amount shall be computed according to one of the following methods.

    __ 1. Lump Sum of $_____

    __ 2. Costs Plus a Fee

    __ 3. Unit Price

    __ 4. Other

    __ 5. No Change

If Item 2, 3 or 4 is checked, the Subcontractor shall submit promptly to Contractor such itemized labor and material breakdowns as Contractor may require for Work performed or deleted from the Subcontract Agreement by this Subcontract Change Order. The Subcontractor shall include the amount of such change in its next application for payment in a separate line item.

The Subcontract Time, if affected by this Subcontract Change Order, is modified as follows:

    Add _____ Days OR deduct _____ Days.

Original Subcontract Amount: _____

Change in Subcontract Amount from previously approved Subcontract Change Orders: _____

Change in Subcontract Amount from this Subcontract Change Order: _____

Revised Subcontract Amount: _____

Subcontractor:

....

By: _____

Title: _____

Date: _____

Contractor:

....

2

NOT FOR FURTHER REPRODUCTION
TO ORDER DOCUMENT, VISIT WWW.CONSENSUSDOCS.ORG

By: _____

Title: _____

Date: _____

3

D. Experience Modification Worksheet

WORKERS COMPENSATION EXPERIENCE RATING

EFFECTIVE DATE

RISK IDENT. NO

STATE   ILLINOIS

1 CODE	2 ELR	3 D-RATI	4 PAYROLL	5 EXPECTED LOSSES	6 EXP PRIM LOSSES	7 CLAIM DATA	8 O IJ F	9 ACT INC LOSSES	10 ACT PRI LOSSES
CARRIER 14419			POLICY NO	WDV183808450		EFF-DATE	06/09/99	EXP-DATE	06/09/00
5437	487	18	150000	7305	1315	47800879	4 O	677922 #	5000
8742	022	21	45000	99	21	47802273	5 O	185444 #	5000
8810	014	24	32133	45	11	47802121	5 F	203329 #	5000
9807	ADDITIONAL		PREMIUM	(0)	(0)	49960188	6 F	418	418
POLICY-TOTAL			227133	(SUBJECT	PREMIUM =	15983	)	1067113	
CARRIER 10065			POLICY NO	3BG087822 00		EFF-DATE	06/09/00	EXP-DATE	06/09/01
5437	487	18	94600	4607	829	00214614	5 O	830	830
5606	132	17	70400	929	158	00214616	6 F	325	325
8742	022	21	33000	73	15				
8810	014	24	23564	33	8				
9807	ADDITIONAL		PREMIUM	(0)	(0)				
POLICY-TOTAL			221564	(SUBJECT	PREMIUM =	13137	)	1155	
CARRIER 15628			POLICY NO	WC134S333018011		EFF-DATE	06/10/01	EXP-DATE	06/10/02
5437	487	18	181634	8846	1592				
5606	132	17	71310	941	160				
8810	014	24	41052	57	14				
9807	ADDITIONAL		PREMIUM	(0)	(0)				
POLICY-TOTAL			293996	(SUBJECT	PREMIUM =	26943	)	0	

RATING REFLECTS A DECREASE OF 70% MEDICAL ONLY PRIMARY AND EXCESS LOSS
DOLLARS WHERE ERA IS APPLIED

```
****************************
****  REVISED RATING  ****
****************************
```

REVISED RATING TO INCLUDE UPDATED DATA FOR:

IL CORRECTION(S) (C-1) FOR POL #: WC134S333018011, EFF : 06/10/01

(ARAP) IF APPL : 1 36

(A)	(B)	(C) EXPECTED EXCESS (D-E)	(D)	(E)	(F) ACTUAL EXCESS (H-I)	(G)	(H)	(I)
009		18812	22935	4123	472500	16250	488553	16053

* Total by Policy Year of all cases $2,000 or less.
# Limited loss.
C Catastrophic loss.

		(11) PRIMARY LOSSES	(12) STABILIZING VALUE	(13) RATABLE EXCESS	(14) TOTALS	
		(I)	(C) X (1-W) + (G)	(A) X (F)	(JI)	
ACTUAL		16053	33369	42525	91947	(15) EXP.MOD.
		(E)		(A) X (C)	(K)	(JI / (K)
EXPECTED		4123	33369	1693	39185	2 35

PAGE NUMBER   1

DATE

E. Environmental Regulation, Sustainability, and Construction Management

Environmentalism—the idea that every man-made physical alteration to nature affects the entire planet—has century-old roots. Legal and regulatory management of these effects was added starting in the 1960s, followed by voluntary efforts to define and encourage "sustainability" in the 1990s. Since these forces are still changing, their origins and present status will be discussed to understand trends and emerging developments. This chapter does not seek to provide a detailed explanation of the features and merits of environmentalism and sustainability, but rather focuses on the impacts on and opportunities for construction management.

Environmental beliefs and values

Philosophers have postulated for hundreds of years that undeveloped land represents a virtuous desirable natural order and that man in this primitive state is naturally good. Industrialization, which was spearheaded by Northern Europeans, corrupted this natural goodness and is the source of many problems. So, environmentalists value undeveloped land (open space) and higher densities for surrounding buildings. Slogans such as " the space between buildings is the space between people" illustrate these values.

Frequent themes are:

Walking, bicycles, and public transportation are favored over cars.

Energy and water use must be minimized.

Resources should not be exhausted, so renewable materials (e.g., can be grown within 10 years) and renewable energy (e.g., wind, solar, wave, but not hydropower) are favored.

Local materials and native plants are favored.

Reuse of existing building components and recycling are favored.

Microclimates, such as heat islands, should be managed.

Open space should be maintained.

Indoor air quality improvement and occupant control are favored.

Construction managers who build on open space are placed on the bad side of the environmental ledger. Although this is not always explicitly stated, it is an undercurrent in both attitudes and many regulations.

Regulation Can Limit Possible Uses and Increase Costs

Private property can become partially government property

Restrictions and mandates for the "public good" restrict private property rights.

Land-use planning, zoning ordinances, and building codes have long placed restrictions on building setbacks, height, and use to regulate fire safety, traffic congestion, and offensive noise and odors. But the belief that any development on private property has an impact on the entire planet can justify far expanded government regulations.

For example, it has long been accepted that property owners can allow the natural storm water flow over their land, but cannot develop the land in a way that makes the flow worse for the downstream neighbor. Yet, many regulations now require temporary or permanent retention of surface water on a property in the form of detention or retention ponds, storage tanks, and permeable paving surfaces.

"Stakeholders" rights without ownership or responsibility

The concept of "stakeholders" assumes that distant non-owners are affected by a property's development and therefore have the right to influence this development—effectively granting an implied public right to private property. This assumed right is used to justify further regulation. Restrictions or prohibition of use to provide community open space, or development limitations to protect a plant or animal can restrict or eliminate development possibilities. Demands for off-site improvements for the public good, such as parks or bicycle trails, can further restrict economic development.

Private property can be confiscated or rendered economically useless

In Kelo vs. the City of New London (Connecticut), the city government believed demolition of existing houses and sales of the land to a developer would yield higher tax revenues. The city implemented this eminent domain transfer, litigation ensued, and the U.S. Supreme Court ultimately upheld the city's action. (The houses were demolished, but, due to an economic downturn, the developer was unable to perform as intended and none of the anticipated revenue was received.)

Confiscation is not the only way to reduce or eliminate property value. Some North Carolina oceanfront property setbacks were increased to "protect" the beach, but the zoning ordinance then rendered the remaining lot sizes unbuildable, eliminating the lots' economic value. Impact fees designed to provide a "public good" will similarly reduce property value.

Regulators and regulations have large impacts

Regulations and regulators were discussed in more detail in the previous chapter on laws, regulations codes, and standards. The environmental regulators are the Federal EPA(Environmental Protection Agency), State EPAs, State Fire Marshals, and OSHA (Occupation and Health Act), and after September 11, 2001, the Army Corps of Engineers became associated with the Department of Homeland Security. The Corp can now influence developments adjacent to navigable waterways and all streams and rivers feeding into these waterways. This then includes virtually every moving water body including small streams one can hop across without getting wet.

These regulators, coupled with local zoning regulation, can make development of wetlands and any area that may have an "endangered" plant or animal an expensive decade-long permitting process with no guarantee of success. A construction manager significantly involved in preconstruction services may participate (in a minor role—engineers and lawyers play a larger part) for fees in this process.

Regulators have defined "hazardous substances" (e.g., asbestos, lead, mold, PCBs, and petroleum) and regulate testing and remediation. Larger sites that have multiple hazardous chemicals called "brownfields" are further regulated. Attempts have been made to declare silica (the most abundant mineral in the earth's crust), carbon dioxide (which we all exhale and plants respirate), and fly ash (a by-product of coal combustion used as a concrete additive) as hazardous substances. Environmental remediation increases analysis, professional services, testing, fees, and costly disposal. Construction managers typically avoid remediation entirely unless properly licensed, insured, and trained for the task, but must include appropriate times in the project schedule for performance by others.

Regulations can increase construction site solid waste disposal effort and cost, including segregation of construction materials for recycling. This can involve additional labor for sorting, and additional waste handling equipment, such as chutes and storage containers, with the associated on-site space allowed. The cost of solid waste disposal varies radically by area of the country. Some areas can haul a few minutes to a local dump, but others such as Florida where high ground water limits suitable dump sites—making haul time long and tip fees (fees to dump a load) high—become a large project expense that must be included in project cost planning.

Owners May Seek "Sustainable" Environmental Performance

In the United States, the Green Building Council was founded in 1993 and developed LEED (Leadership in Energy and Environmental Design), a scoring system to measure sustainablity. Many similar organizations were founded in countries throughout the world. The Green Building Council develops standards by consensus—utilizing the inputs of many committees populated by building practitioners—such as architects and engineers, material suppliers, equipment manufacturers, and developers—but few construction managers.

The values of the Green Building Council

The Green Building Council values the concept of environmentalism and the image it provides its proponents. Specific goals and cost-effectiveness are sought when consistent with these values.

LEED scoring and construction management

The USGBC (U.S. Green Building Council) developed and uses a LEED scoring system that has a maximum of 100 points plus 10 bonus points to determine a development's rating.

Platinum	80 and above
Gold	60–79 points
Silver	50–59 points
Certified	40–49 points

Bonus points

Innovation in design	6 points possible
Regional priority	4 points possible

There are scoring systems for each project category, such a Shell and Core, Residential, and Adaptive Reuse. The impact of the New Construction and Major Renovations scoring system that applies to many of the construction managers' project types is discussed below.

LEED scoring for New Construction and Major Renovation

Sustainable Sites		26 Possible Points
Prerequisite 1	Construction Activity Pollution Prevention	Required
Credit 1	Site Selection	1
Credit 2	Development Density and Community Connectivity	5
Credit 3	Brownfield Redevelopment	1
Credit 4.1	Alternative Transportation—Public Transportation Access	6
Credit 4.2	Alternative Transportation—Bicycle Storage and Changing Rooms	1
Credit 4.3	Alternative Transportation—Low Emitting and Fuel-Efficient Vehicles	3
Credit 4.4	Alternative Transportation—Parking Capacity	2
Credit 5.1	Site Development—Protect or Restore Habitat	1
Credit 5.2	Site Development—Maximize Open Space	1
Credit 6.1	Storm Water Design—Quantity Control	1
Credit 6.2	Storm Water Design—Quality Control	1

Credit 7.1	Heat Island Effect—Non-roof	1
Credit 7.2	Heat Island Effect—Roof	1
Credit 8	Light Pollution Reduction	1

Construction management impact and involvement

This scoring focuses first on real estate site selection and concept design decisions and then on storm water, heat island, and light pollution management. Lump sum hard bid contractors have no input in these decisions. The construction manager's preconstruction assistance with site selection focuses on soil conditions and the logistics of transportation and material storage and availability of needed skilled labor. The construction manager adds little value and provides minimal input for this LEED category, but should understand the concepts well enough to offer value engineering suggestions consistent with these goals.

Many owners already own their project site, and other owners, such as manufacturers, need access to highway, rail, and water transportation, as well as proximity to their business partners, material vendors, and workers. Other owners, such as warehouses, also require low-cost land. These considerations may dictate a site that has a low LEED score—and a platinum or gold rating may become unachievable.

Water Efficiency		10 Possible Points
Prerequisite 1	Water Use Reduction	Required
Credit 1	Water-Efficient Landscaping	2–4
Credit 2	Innovative Wastewater Technologies	2
Credit 3	Water Use Reduction	2–4

Construction management impact and involvement

The scoring focuses on water use reduction for the interior water using fixtures and landscaping and wastewater management. Again, the construction manager knowledgeable about these considerations can assist with some value engineering suggestions, but this impact is usually minor.

Energy and Atmosphere		35 Possible Points
Prerequisite 1	Fundamental Commissioning of Building Energy Systems	Required
Prerequisite 2	Minimum Energy Performance	Required
Prerequisite 3	Fundamental Refrigerant Management	Required
Credit 1	Optimize Energy Performance	1–19
Credit 2	On-site Renewable Energy	1–7
Credit 3	Enhanced Commissioning	2
Credit 4	Enhanced Refrigerant Management	2
Credit 5	Measurement and verification	3
Credit 6	Green Power	2

Construction management impact and involvement

Energy management, the largest score in this category, has long been a focus of construction management value engineering. The construction managers, assisted by mechanical contractors, can bring their long-developed capabilities to the LEED process. Similarly, refrigeration management has developed and continues to develop as a standard operating construction procedure. Alternative energy sources of green power (which involve mechanical and electrical engineering) can also be addressed when economically viable.

Commissioning by parties outside the construction firm that is a required part of this category reverses decades of quality improvement gains and compromises organizational efficiency. Projects have always been commissioned, but LEED adds another party to the process. Traditionally, the installing contractor commissioned, tested, adjusted, and balanced their installed work to confirm and demonstrate specification conformance. Under the LEED system, a separate commissioning consultant, reporting directly to the owner, is required.

LEED guidelines permit the architect or construction manager to hire this consultant for smaller projects, but prohibit the construction manager from hiring the commissioning consultant for larger projects. And the bar for commissioning consultant experience is low—experience commissioning only two previous projects is needed.

Adding a commissioning consultant to the project team severely compromises the quality process. The quality process, discussed extensively in the earlier quality chapter, requires building quality into the process not catching and correcting defects as an end-of-project inspection activity. The quality process holds that those closest to the work know it best—and placing them in self-control is essential for quality. And the tradesman (who are closest to the work), who are experienced and proud of their work, will frequently detect clues of future problems, such as vibration or noise that are not detected by formal commissioning tests. Since they installed the work and are most familiar with the minute details, they may know where to find the defect and may voluntarily correct the problem when noticed—even when not required by contract. This benefit of trade skills and motivation is lost with a commissioning consultant.

The injection of the commissioning consultant reporting directly to the owner creates a matrix management organizational structure that is more costly and inefficient—and the lines and quantity of communication increase. The construction managers and their mechanical electrical subcontractors must perform as specified by their contracts and must answer to the commissioning consultant through the owner—but there is little incentive and no mandate to do it well. Also, model contracts are not designed for this multiple reporting relationship.

Materials and Resources		14 Possible Points
Prerequisite 1	Storage and Collection of Recyclables	Required
Credit 1.1	Building Reuse—Maintain Existing Walls, Floors, and Roof	1–3
Credit 1.2	Building Reuse—Maintain Existing Interior Nonstructural Elements	1
Credit 2	Construction Waste Management	1–2
Credit 3	Material Reuse	1–2
Credit 4	Recycle Content	1–2
Credit 5	Regional Materials	1–2
Credit 6	Rapidly Renewable Materials	1
Credit 7	Certified Wood	1

Construction management impact and involvement

Building reuse is a design consideration, but can have cost and scheduling impacts. Revealed unfavorable concealed conditions can increase costs and delay the schedule. The construction manager's input on constructability can avoid these problems and minimize cost increases—a hugely valuable contribution.

The construction manager may have some value engineering input on materials, and the management of construction waste must be planned as an additional project cost.

Indoor Environmental Quality		15 Possible Points
Prerequisite 1	Minimum Indoor Air Quality Performance	Required
Prerequisite 2	Environmental Tobacco Smoke (ETS) Control	Required
Credit 1	Outdoor Air Delivery Monitoring	1
Credit 2	Increased Ventilation	1
Credit 3.1	Construction Indoor Air Quality Management Plan–During Construction	1
Credit 3.2	Construction Indoor Air Quality Management Plan–Before Occupancy	1
Credit 4.1	Low-Emitting Materials—Adhesives and Sealants	1
Credit 4.2	Low-Emitting Materials—Paints and Coatings	1
Credit 4.3	Low-Emitting Materials—Flooring Systems	1
Credit 4.4	Low-Emitting Materials—Composite Wood and Agrifiber Products	1
Credit 5	Indoor Chemical and Pollutant Source Control	1
Credit 6.1	Controllability of Systems—Lighting	1
Credit 6.2	Controllability of Systems—Thermal Comfort	1
Credit 7.1	Thermal Comfort—Design	1
Credit 7.2	Thermal Comfort—Verification	1
Credit 8.1	Daylight and Views—Daylight	1
Credit 8.2	Daylight and Views—Views	1

Construction management impact and involvement

The first component of indoor air quality is the out-gassing of materials such as adhesives, sealants, paints, calking, and flooring systems. Out-gassing is first controlled by initial selection of materials, followed by increasing the amount and duration of ventilation during construction and before occupancy. The construction manager's awareness of materials for value engineering is helpful. And additional time for longer preoccupancy ventilation must be scheduled.

The next components are the amount, quality, and control of mechanically provided ventilation—assisted by natural ventilation. Additional attention is given to occupant controls of the ventilation, heat and air conditioning, and lighting. These are just slightly different focuses of the established mechanical, electrical, and lighting principles familiar to the construction manager—so do not change the manager's traditional value engineering and quality assurance roles.

Air quality during construction and before occupancy must be given additional consideration. This can require very significant amounts of additional air filtration (e.g., filters at each return grille) for which the HVAC system was not designed or capable of handling well—often increasing static pressure increases beyond design specifications. And longer airing out time must be included in the project schedule.

Innovation in Design		6 Possible Points
Credit 1	Innovation in Design	1–5
Credit 2	LEED Accredited Professional	1

Construction management impact and involvement

The construction manager has no input or involvement with this category.

Regional Priority		4 Possible Points
Credit 1	Regional Priority	1–4

Construction management impact and involvement

The Green Building Council establishes priorities based on the ZIP code of the project, and points are granted for achievement of these priorities. The construction manager has no input or involvement with this category.

The Construction Manager's Threats and Opportunities from LEED

Sales opportunities—more effort means more cost and profit

Owners may seek a LEED certification for their values and image enhancement. Construction managers who are least familiar with the process and can provide the benefits listed above may have a sales advantage. Also, much of the LEED process requires additional documentation, certification, meetings, and reviews that increase the amount and cost of construction management services required. And sustainability also has higher construction costs, which increases fees and profit.

But a drawback, as discussed in commissioning above, is that the construction manager's project leadership role is diminished.

Risk management, warrantees, and contracts

As environmental awareness heightens, so does the need to clarify and appropriately transfer project environmental risks away from the construction manager. New sustainable materials, such as agrifibers and bamboo, have been rushed to market to gain LEED points. As longer term performance has become known, many have been found to perform below expectation or failed completely. Clarification of responsibility for warranty of these untested products needs special attention in contract negotiation.

Definition of the scope of work by plans and specifications or by performance standards has always been sensitive—with the clarity of plans and specifications overwhelmingly favored by the construction manager. Commissioning, which focuses on achievement of specified performance standards, must be clarified in the contract negotiation stage—so the CM is not liable if the work was installed as designed but does not perform as anticipated.

Accurate definition of the amount of regulatory and impact fees at the start of the project has become increasingly difficult or impossible. These fees should be handled either by total exclusion (fees to be paid by owner) or by inclusion as an allowance to be later verified by actual expenditures.

Cost–benefit analysis and value engineering

LEED construction usually increases construction costs, so preconstruction cost–benefit analysis and value engineering become more challenging. This is compounded since the project will incur hard costs for the public's benefit, but the public will never return money to the project. The project has all the cost, and someone else has all the benefits.

Further, some potential benefits, such as increased worker productivity produced by improved indoor air quality, are not measured at all by the usual business management and accounting systems. Projected benefits based on untested assumptions are then used—so the cost is measurable but the benefit is assumed. And green power such as on-site wind or solar power generation will, with current technology and utility rates, never break even.

The construction manager preparing budgets offering value engineering suggestions with cost–benefit analyses should focus on the items that can have a demonstrable cost payback—such as the cost of more energy-efficient mechanical equipment versus the reduction in utility costs.

Future impact of environmentalism on construction management

The implied public right to private property and associated regulation and impact fees now continue to accelerate. But knowing the origin of these trends may aid understanding if the trend later reverses.

LEED is a costly luxury. Developing countries may now feel that "it's a good idea but we don't have enough money to undertake it now", and may be unreceptive or hostile to pressures to achieve sustainability. And a severe prolonged economic downturn in the developed countries may compel cost reductions that make LEED activity less desirable—so construction managers may be wise to hedge their career or company focus on LEED.

Environmental regulations are causing regional development shifts in the United States. For example, the difficult power plant permitting in some areas of the country that can take 10 or more years has caused new power plant development to focus on the southern United States: South Carolina, Georgia, Alabama, Mississippi, and Texas. These states now have power plants under permit and design development, but the northeast and Midwest have none.

Power plants provide present construction work. And competitive energy cost is a business advantage that will promote commercial, industrial, and residential development in these areas for decades—producing more and diverse construction opportunities. A 20-year energy head start in these regions may provide career-long improved construction management employment opportunities.

Summary

Environmentalism and environmental regulation affect the project scope and usually increase both project cost and schedule. Sustainability has similar impacts, but the construction manager can minimize these impacts by value engineering and constructability advice.

Environmental regulation and sustainability also increase project management services and fees, and project cost and overhead and profit. But contract negotiation must manage the risk of new materials and performance standards—usually transferring most environmental and performance risk to others.

Environmental regulation is prevalent and sustainability fashionable in the developed world—but these are costly luxuries. Continuation of this popularity and transfer to the developing world are trends that must be watched to determine the probable location of future construction work and jobs.

F. PMI Knowledge Areas and Process Groups in Construction Management

Over the last 60 years, construction management has developed into an organized discipline with significant management capabilities. During this time, the PMI (Project Management Institute) developed a more generalized approach for most project types in most industries, and later added a construction extension. The PMP (Project Management Professional) certification conferred by the PMI is becoming a needed credential for construction managers in the Middle East, South America, and South East Asia. And the GSA (General Services Administration) of the U.S. government has identified the PMP as screening criteria to evaluate potential construction managers. Yet, more widespread adoption of the PMI methodology has lagged. This text makes this adoption more accessible.

Contractor selection was once almost exclusively based on price, and competition was frequently intense, with a fraction of a percent separating the winner from losers. Contractors developed very robust estimating capabilities, and larger contractors had estimating departments with full-time professional estimators. Even in project management delivery systems with significant preconstruction services, price is still an award criteria—such as early determination of the GMP (guaranteed maximum price).

More sophisticated contractors have developed competent scheduling and schedule management capabilities. Although these contractors well know the impact of time on cost, communicating this link to owners remains a management challenge.

Contractors have other significant strengths as well. The specification organization provided by the Construction Specification Institute is excellent and widely accepted. This shared structure makes cost estimating, scheduling, and communication of work breakdown structures and work packages clear and efficient—an advantage equaled in few other industries. Project monitoring and cost control are also highly developed.

But construction managers are not as strong in other areas, such as risk management, human resources, and communication. And integration of all these knowledge and management areas needs improvement. The PMI knowledge areas and processes are strong where the construction industry is weak. This text seeks to bring these benefits to construction management in a way that can be selectively adopted.

Construction is a highly fragmented industry. All players in construction management have small market share. And all need many subcontractors and vendors, and some of these may have larger global sales than the construction management firm. No one can immediately mandate a sweeping industry practice change.

This text seeks to include all the PMI knowledge areas, but organized in the format used and accepted in construction today. The relation between chapters in this text and knowledge areas is shown below.

This book's chapter order and the PMI equivalent knowledge areas:

		Construction Project Management	Project Management Institute PMBOK®
		Chapters	**Knowledge areas, processes** (Including construction extension)
		The Construction Industry—a Culture and a Business	
		Project players and construction management processes	
	1.1	The personnel and companies required for a construction project	9 Project human resource management
	1.2	The builders—construction managers, general contractors, subcontractors, and vendors	9 Project human resource management

1.3	Project management, the construction project life cycle and chronology	2	Project management processes, life cycle
	The Construction Business and Regulatory Framework		
1.4	Accounting (financial)—a management tool and required report card	15	Project financial management
1.5	Finance—the time value of money affects many project decisions	15	Project financial management
1.6	Insurance—a legal requirement, a huge project cost, and a risk management tool	11	Project risk management
1.7	Laws, regulations, codes, and standards	5	Project scope management
	Winning the Job, Starting the Project *Planning, costing, and initiation*		
	Project Scope evaluation, definition, planning *Finding a feasible and worthwhile project*		
2.1	A workable purpose must be defined first	4	Project integration management
2.2	A qualitative project understanding and definition of feasible limits come next	4	Project integration management
2.3	Risks must be evaluated and responses planned and managed	11	Project risk management
2.4	The integrated project scope and approach must be defined and accepted	4	Project integration management
	Costing—finding feasible and needed costs		
2.5	Estimating project costs to determine and confirm the scope and approach	7	Project cost management
2.6	Estimating to achieve target project costs	7	Project cost management
	Time planning and scheduling integrates with scope and cost planning		
2.7	Time is continuous and has costs and impacts	6	Project time management
2.8	Scheduling and time planning also determines and confirms the scope and approach	6	Project time management
	Project delivery methods and bidding and "buying the job"		
2.9	Construction project delivery methods continue to change	12	Project procurement management
2.10	Negotiating, bidding, and buying the job	12	Project procurement management
	Building the Project *Execution, control, completion*		
	People—Their nature, organization and management		
3.1	Human nature and the capacity, and bias of people and companies must be recognized	9	Project human resource management
3.2	Human resource organization and management	9	Project human resource management
	Communication and documentation are essential management tools		
3.3	Communication starts with correct observation	10	Project communication management
3.4	Organization of observations requires organizational structure	5	Project scope management
3.5	Managing information, documentation, and communication	10	Project communication management
	Monitoring and controlling the project for quality and profit		

		Construction Project Management— A Managerial Approach	Project management Institute
3.6		Cost control is crucial for cost management and productivity improvement	8 Project quality management
3.7		Cost accounting seeks real-time information and improvement	7 Project cost management
3.8		Schedule implementation and management are integrated with cost management	6 Project time management
3.9		Precision takes time and money and can impact scope	8 Project quality management
3.10		Quality management achieves targeted performance	8 Project quality management
	Risk management is a tool that affects project planning and execution		
3.11		Safety starts with management planning and continues with labor execution	13 Project safety management
3.12		Claim management also starts in planning and continues in execution	16 Project Claim Management
	Project completion and closeout—a key last step and a crucial next step		
3.13		Project closeout—completion, documentation, lessons learned, and sales	4 Project integration management
	Appendices		
		Environmental regulation, sustainability, and construction management	14 Project environmental management

The PMI knowledge areas order and this book's equivalent chapters:

		Construction Project Management— A Managerial Approach	Project management Institute
		Chapters	**Knowledge areas, processes** (chapters including construction extension)
1.3		Project management, the construction project life cycle and chronology	2 Project management processes, life cycle
2.1		A workable purpose must be defined first	4 Project integration management
2.2		A qualitative project understanding and definition of feasible limits come next	
2.4		The integrated project scope and approach must be defined and accepted	
3.13		Project closeout—completion, documentation, lessons learned, and sales	
1.7		Laws, regulations, codes, and standards	5 Project scope management
3.4		Organization of observations requires organizational structure	
2.7		Time is continuous and has costs and impacts	6 Project time management
2.8		Scheduling and time planning also determines and confirms the scope and approach	
3.8		Schedule implementation and management are integrated with cost management	
2.5		Estimating project costs to determine and confirm the scope and approach	7 Project cost management
2.6		Estimating to achieve target project costs	
3.7		Cost accounting seeks real-time information and improvement	
3.6		Cost control is crucial for cost management and productivity improvement	8 Project quality management

3.9	Precision takes time and money and can impact scope	
3.10	Quality management achieves targeted performance	
1.1	The personnel and companies required for a construction project	9 Project human resource management
1.2	The builders—construction managers, general contractors, subcontractors, and vendors	
3.1	Human nature and the capacity, and bias of people and companies must be recognized	
3.2	Human resource organization and management	
3.3	Communication starts with correct observation	10 Project communication management
3.5	Managing information, documentation, and communication	
1.6	Insurance—a legal requirement, a huge project cost, and a risk management tool	11 Project risk management
2.3	Risks must be evaluated and responses planned and managed	
2.10	Negotiating, bidding, and buying the job	12 Project procurement management
2.9	Project delivery methods continue to change	
3.11	Safety starts with management planning and continues with labor execution	13 Project safety management
Appendix	Environmental regulation, sustainability, and construction management	14 Project environmental management
1.4	Accounting (financial)—A management tool and required report card	15 Project financial management
1.5	Finance—The time value of money affects many project decisions	
3.12	Claim management also starts in planning and continues in execution	16 Project claim management

The PMI initiating and planning processes are found in Part II. The executing and monitoring and control processes are found in Part III, and closing process is found in Chapter 3.13.

Construction people speak plainly and directly, and the language in this text is the language of construction. The more formalized PMI terms were minimized, but the concepts remain.

G. Industry and Trade Associations

American Concrete Institute (ACI)
38800 Country Club Drive
Farmington Hills, MI 48331
248-848-3700
www.concrete.org

American Institute of Architects (AIA)
1735 New York Avenue, NW
Washington, DC 20006-5292
202-626-7300
www.aia.com

American Institute of Constructors (AIC)
400 North Washington Street
Alexandria, VA 22314
703-683-4999
www.aicnet.org

American Institute of Steel Construction (AISC)
One East Wacker Drive, Suite 700
Chicago IL 60601-1802
312-670-2400
www.aisc.org

American Iron and Steel Institute (AISI)
1140 Connecticut Avenue, NW, Suite 705
Washington, DC 20036
202-452-7100
www.steel.org

American National Standards Institute (ANSI)
1819 L Street, NW, 6th Floor
Washington, DC 20036
202-293-8020
www.ansi.org

American Society for Testing and Materials (ASTM)
100 Barr Harbor Drive
West Conshohocken, PA 19428-2959
610-832-9500
www.astm.com

American Society of Civil Engineers (ASCE)
1801 Alexander Bell Drive
Reston, VA 20191-4400
800-548-2723
www.asce.com

American Society of Heating, Refrigeration and Air-Conditioning Engineers (ASHRAE)
1791 Tullie Circle, NE
Atlanta, GA 30329
800-527-4723
www.ashrae.org

American Society of Professional Estimators (ASPE)
2525 Perimeter Place Drive, Suite 103
Nashville, TN 37214
615-316-9200
www.aspenational.org

American Subcontractors Association (ASA)
1004 Duke Street
Alexandria, VA 22314-3450
703-684-3450
www.asaonline.com

Architectural Woodworking Institute (AWI)
46179 Westlake Drive, Suite 120
Potomac Falls, VA 20165
571-323-3636
www.awinet.org

Asphalt Institute

2696 Research Park Drive

Lexington, KY 40511-8480

859-288-4960

www.asphaltinstitute.org

Associated Builders and Contractors (ABC)

4250 North Fairfax Drive, 9th Floor

Arlington, VA 22203-1607

703-812-2000

www.abc.org

Associated General Contractors of America (AGC)

2300 Wilson Blvd, Suite 400

Arlington, VA 22201

703-548-2118

www.agc.org

Building Owners and Managers Association International (BOMA)

1101 15th Street, NW, Suite 800

Washington, DC 20005

202-408-2662

www.boma.com

Carrier Corporation

One Carrier Place

Farmington, CT 06032

800-674-3000

www.carrier.com

Construction Industry Institute (CII)

3925 West Braker Lane

Austin, TX 78759-5316

512-232-3000

www.construction-institute.org

Construction Management Association of America (CMAA)

7926 Jones Branch Drive, Suite 800

McLean, VA 22102-3303

703-356-2622

www.cmaanet.org

Construction Specifications Institute (CSI)

99 Canal Center Plaza, Suite 300

Alexandria, VA 22314

800-689-2999

www.csinet.org

Design-Build Institute of America (DBIA)

1100 H Street, NW, Suite 500

Washington, DC 20005-5476

202-682-0100

www.dbia.org

Illuminating Engineering Society (IES)

120 Wall Street, Floor 17

New York, NY 10005-4001

212-248-5000

www.ies.org

International Organization of Standardization (ISO)

1, ch. De la Voie-Creuse

Case postal 56

CH-1211 Geneva 20

Switzerland

+41-22-749-01-11

www.iso.org

Masonry Institute of America (MIA)

22815 Frampton Avenue

Torrance, CA 90501-5034

800-221-4000

www.masonryinstitute.org

Mechanical Contractors Association of America (MCAA)

1385 Picard Drive

Rockville, MD 20850

301-869-5800

www.mcaa.org

National Association of Home Builders (NAHB)

1201 15th Street, NW

Washington, DC 20005

800-368-5242

www.nahb.org

National Electrical Contractors Association (NECA)

3 Bethesda Metro Center, Suite 1100

Bethesda, MD 20814

301-657-3110

www.necanet.org

National Fire Protection Agency (NFPA)

1 Battery Park

Quincy, MA 02169-7471

617-770-3000

www.nfpa.com

National Institute of Building Sciences (NIBS)

1090 Vermont Avenue NW, Suite 700

Washington, DC 20005

202-289-7800

www.nibs.org

National Roofing Contractors Association (NRCA)

10255 West Higgins Road, Suite 600

Rosemont, IL 60018-5607

847-299-9070

www.nrca.net

Portland Cement Association (PCA)

5420 Old Orchard Road

Skokie, IL 60077

847-966-6200

www.cement.org

Project Management Institute (PMI)

14 Campus Boulevard

Newton Square, PA 19073-3299

610-356-4600

www.pmi.org

Sheet Metal and Air Conditioning Contractors' National Association (SMACNA)

4201 Lafayette Center Drive

Chantilly, VA 20151-1209

703-803-2980

www.smacna.org

Trane (an Ingersoll-Rand Company)

One Centennial Avenue

Piscataway, NJ 08854

732-652-7000

www.trane.com

US Green Building Council (USGBC)

1015 18th Street NW, Suite 508

Washington, DC 20036

202-828-7422

www.usgbc.org

Underwriters Laboratories (UL)

333 Pfingsten Road

Northbrook, IL 60062

847-272-8800

www.ul.com

United States Gypsum Corporation (USG)

550 West Adams Street

Chicago, IL 60661-3676

312-436-4000

www.usg.com

York International Corporation (a Johnson Controls Company)

631 South Richland Avenue

York, PA 17403

717-771-7890

www.york.com

Index